Edexcel IGCSE
Further Pure Mathematics

Student Book

Greg Attwood

K Pledger, D Wilkins, A Macpherson, B Moran, J Petran, G Staley

A PEARSON COMPANY

Published by Pearson Education Limited, a company incorporated in England and Wales, having its registered office at Edinburgh Gate, Harlow, Essex, CM20 2JE. Registered company number: 872828.

www.pearsonschoolsandfecolleges.co.uk

Edexcel is a registered trademark of Edexcel Limited

Text © Greg Attwood, Keith Pledger, David Wilkins, Alistair Macpherson, Bronwen Moran, Joseph Petran and Geoff Staley 2010

First published 2010

14 13 12 11 10
10 9 8 7 6 5 4 3 2 1

ISBN 978 0 435044 14 5

Edited by Deborah Dobson and Maggie Rumble
Designed by Richard Ponsford and Creative Monkey
Typeset by Techset
Original illustrations © Pearson Education Ltd 2010
Illustrated by Techset
Cover design by Creative Monkey
Cover photo © Ian Cartwright / Imagestate
Printed by Multivista Global Ltd

Acknowledgements
The author and publisher would like to thank the following individuals and organisations for permission to reproduce photographs:
p.37 Photodisc. Jules Frazier; p.68 Annie Reynolds. Photolink. Photodisc; p.73 Pearson Education Ltd. Gareth Boden; p.75 Comstock Images p.82 Lawrence Manning. Corbis; p.85 Pearson Education Ltd. Lord and Leverett; p.87 Photodisc. Steve Cole; p.96 Photodisc. Alex L. Fradk p.202 TongRo Image Stock. Alamy.

All other images © Pearson Education Ltd 2010.

Every effort has been made to contact copyright holders of material reproduced in this book. Any omissions will be rectified in subsequent printings if notice is given to the publishers.

Websites
The websites used in this book were correct and up to date at the time of publication. It is essential for tutors to preview each website before using it in class so as to ensure that the URL is still accurate, relevant and appropriate. We suggest that tutors bookmark useful websites an consider enabling students to access them through the school/college intranet.

Disclaimer
This material has been published on behalf of Edexcel and offers high-quality support for the delivery of Edexcel qualifications.

This does not mean that the material is essential to achieve any Edexcel qualification, nor does it mean that it is the only suitable material available to support any Edexcel qualification. Edexcel material will not be used verbatim in setting any Edexcel examination or assessment Any resource lists produced by Edexcel shall include this and other appropriate resources.

Copies of official specifications for all Edexcel qualifications may be found on the Edexcel website: www.edexcel.com.

Contents

About this book

This book has several features to help you with IGCSE Further Pure Mathematics.

Clear diagrams
Graphs and technial diagrams support the text to illustrate a formula or pose a question for you to answer.

Hints boxes
These either provide help on how to tackle a question, or informtion relating to the topic

Chapter summaries
The key points are summarised at the end of every chapter. Check you understand them all fully before moving on. The summaries are also useful for revision.

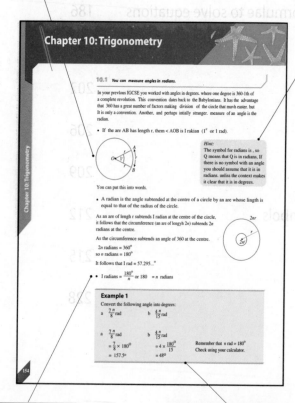

Chapter 10: Trigonometry

10.1 *You can measure angles in radians.*

In your previous IGCSE you worked with angles in degrees, where one degree is 360-1th of a complete revolution. This convention dates back to the Babylonians. It has the advantage that 360 has a great number of factors making division of the circle that muvh easter. but It is only a convention. Another, and perhaps intially stranger, measure of an angle is the radian.

• If the arc AB has length r, them < AOB is 1 rakian (1° or 1 rad).

Hint:
The symbol for radians is , so Q means that Q is in radians, If there is no symbol with an angle you should assume that it is in radians, unliss the context makes it clear that it is in degrees.

You can put this into words.

• A radian is the angle subtended at the centre of a circle by an arc whose lingth is equal to that of the radius of the circle.

As an arc of lengh r subtends I radian at the centre of the circle, it follows that the circumference (an arc of lengyh 2π) subtends 2π radians at the centre.

As the circumference subtends an angle of 360 at the centre.

2π radians = 360°
so π radians = 180°

It follows that I rad = 57.295...°

• I radians = $\frac{180^o}{\pi}$ or 180 = π radians

Example 1
Convert the following angle into degrees:

a $\frac{7\pi}{8}$ rad   b $\frac{4\pi}{15}$ rad

a $\frac{7\pi}{8}$ rad

$= \frac{7}{8} \times 180^O$

$= 157.5^O$

b $\frac{4\pi}{15}$ rad

$= 4 \times \frac{180^O}{15}$

$= 48^O$

Remember that π rad = 180°
Check using your calculator.

Mathematical formulae
All the formulae needed for the IGCSE examinations have been covered.

Worked examples
when a new topic is introduced, worked examples take a typical question and show you step - by-step how to answer it.

Chapter 10: Summary

1. The sine rule is
$\frac{a}{\sin A} = \frac{b}{\sin B} = \frac{c}{\sin C}$ or $\frac{\sin A}{a} = \frac{\sin B}{b} = \frac{\sin C}{c}$

2. The cosine rule is
$a^2 = b^2 + c^2 - 2bc \cos A$ or $b^2 = a^2 + c^2 - 2ac \cos B$
or $c^2 = a^2 + b^2 - 2ab \cos C$

3. You can find an unknown angle using a rearranged form of the cosine rule.
$\cos A = \frac{b^2 + c^2 - a^2}{2bc}$ or $\cos B = \frac{a^2 + c^2 - b^2}{2ac}$ or $\cos C = \frac{a^2 + b^2 - c^2}{2ab}$

4. You can find the area of a triangle using the formula
area = $\frac{1}{2} ab \sin C$
if you know the length of two sides a and b and the value of the angle C between them

5. 1 radian = $\frac{180^o}{\pi}$

6. The length of an arc of a circle is $l = r\theta$

7. The area of a sector is $A = \frac{1}{2}r^2\theta$

8. The addition (or compound angle) formulae are
• $\sin(A + B) = \sin A \cos B + \cos A \sin B$ $\sin(A - B) = \sin A \cos B - \cos A \sin B$
• $\cos(A + B) = \cos A \cos B - \sin A \sin B$ $\cos(A - B) = \cos A \cos B + \sin A \sin B$
• $\tan(A + B) = \frac{\tan A + \tan B}{1 - \tan A \tan B}$ $\tan(A - B) = \frac{\tan A - \tan B}{1 + \tan A \tan B}$

9. $\tan\theta = \frac{\sin\theta}{\cos\theta}$ (providing $\cos\theta \neq 0$, when tan θ is not defined)

10. $\sin^2\theta + \cos^2\theta = 1$

11. A first solution of the equation sin $\alpha = k$ is your calculator value. $\alpha = \sin^{-1} k$. A second solution is $(180° - \alpha)$, or $(\pi - \alpha)$ if you are working in radians. Other solutions are found by adding or subtracting multiples of 360° or 2π radians.

12. A first solution of the equation cos $\alpha = k$ is your calculator value of $\alpha = \cos^{-1} k$. A second solution is $(360° - \alpha)$, or $(2\pi - \alpha)$ if you are working in radians. Other solutions are found by adding or subtracting multiples of 360° or 2π radians.

13. A first solution of the equation tan $\alpha = k$ is your calculator value of $\alpha = \tan^{-1} k$. A second solution is $(180° + \alpha)$ or $(\pi + \alpha)$ if you are working in radians. Other solutions are found by adding or subtracting multiples of 360° or 2π radians.

1.1 You can simplify expressions by using rules of indices

$a^m \times a^n = a^{m+n}$

$a^m \div a^n = a^{m-n}$

$(a^m)^n = a^{mn}$

$a^{-m} = \dfrac{1}{a^m}$

$a^{\frac{1}{m}} = \sqrt[m]{a}$ **Hint:** The mth root of a.

$a^{\frac{n}{m}} = \sqrt[m]{a^n}$

Example 1

Simplify these expressions:

a $x^2 \times x^5$ **b** $2r^2 \times 3r^3$ **c** $b^4 \div b^4$

d $6x^{-3} \div 3x^{-5}$ **e** $(a^3)^2 \times 2a^2$ **f** $(3x^2)^3 \div x^4$

---

a $x^2 \times x^5$
$= x^{2+5}$ Use the rule $a^m \times a^n = a^{m+n}$ to simplify the index.
$= x^7$

b $2r^2 \times 3r^3$ Rewrite the expression with the numbers together and
$= 2 \times 3 \times r^2 \times r^3$ the r terms together.
$= 6 \times r^{2+3}$ $2 \times 3 = 6$
$= 6r^5$ $r^2 \times r^3 = r^{2+3}$

c $b^4 \div b^4$ Use the rule $a^m \times a^n = a^{m+n}$ to simplify the index.
$= b^{4-4}$
$= b^0 = 1$ Use the rule $a^m \div a^n = a^{m-n}$

d $6x^{-3} \div 3x^{-5}$
$= 6 \div 3 \times x^{-3} \div x^{-5}$ $x^{-3} \div x^{-5} = x^{-3--5} = x^2$
$= 2 \times x^2$
$= 2x^2$

e $(a^3)^2 \times 2a^2$ Use the rule $(a^m)^n = a^{mn}$ to simplify the index.
$= a^6 \times 2a^2$ $a^6 \times 2a^2 = 1 \times 2 \times a^6 \times a^2 = 2 \times a^{6+2}$
$= 2 \times a^6 \times a^2$
$= 2 \times a^{6+2}$
$= 2a^8$

f $(3x^2)^3 \div x^4$ Use the rule $(a^m)^n = a^{mn}$ to simplify the index.
$= 27x^6 \div x^4$
$= 27 \times x^6 \div x^4$
$= 27 \times x^{6-4}$
$= 27x^2$

Example 2

Simplify:

a $x^4 \div x^{-3}$ **b** $x^{\frac{1}{2}} \times x^{\frac{3}{2}}$ **c** $(x^3)^{\frac{2}{3}}$ **d** $2x^{1.5} \div 4x^{-0.25}$

a $x^4 \div x^{-3}$

$= x^{4--3}$ Use the rule $a^m \div a^n = a^{m-n}$.

$= x^7$ Remember $-(-) = +$.

b $x^{\frac{1}{2}} \times x^{\frac{3}{2}}$ —— This could also be written as $\sqrt{x}$.

$= x^{\frac{1}{2}+\frac{3}{2}}$ Use the rule $a^m \times a^n = a^{m+n}$.

$= x^2$

c $(x^3)^{\frac{2}{3}}$ Use the rule $(a^m)^n = a^{mn}$.

$= x^{3 \times \frac{2}{3}}$

$= x^2$

d $2x^{1.5} \div 4x^{-0.25}$ Use the rule $a^m \div a^n = a^{m-n}$.

$= \frac{1}{2}x^{1.5--0.25}$ $2 \div 4 = \frac{1}{2}$

$= \frac{1}{2}x^{1.75}$ $1.5 - -0.25 = 1.75$

Example 3

Evaluate:

a $9^{\frac{1}{2}}$ **b** $64^{\frac{1}{3}}$ **c** $49^{\frac{3}{2}}$ **d** $25^{-\frac{3}{2}}$

a $9^{\frac{1}{2}}$

$= \sqrt{9}$ Using $a^{\frac{1}{m}} = \sqrt[m]{a}$.

Both 3 and -3 are square roots of 9.

$= \pm 3$ $\sqrt{9}$ strictly means $+3$ and $\pm\sqrt{9} = \pm 3$ but always check if the negative square root is a required answer.

b $64^{\frac{1}{3}}$

$= \sqrt[3]{64}$ This means the cube root of 64.

$= 4$ As $4 \times 4 \times 4 = 64$.

c $49^{\frac{2}{3}}$

$= (\sqrt{49})^3$ Using $a^{\frac{n}{m}} = \sqrt[m]{a^n}$.

$= \pm 343$ This means the square root of 49, cubed.

d $25^{-\frac{3}{2}}$

$= \frac{1}{25^{\frac{3}{2}}}$ Using $a^{-m} = \frac{1}{a^m}$.

$= \frac{1}{(\pm\sqrt{25})^3}$ $\sqrt{25} = \pm 5$

$= \frac{1}{(\pm 5)^3}$

$= \pm \frac{1}{215}$

Exercise 1A

Simplify these expressions:

1 **a** $x^3 \times x^4$ **b** $2x^3 \times 3x^2$

    c $4p^3 \div 2p$ **d** $3x^{-4} \div x^{-2}$

    e $k^3 \div k^{-2}$ **f** $(y^2)^5$

    g $10x^5 \div 2x^{-3}$ **h** $(p^3)^2 \div p^4$

    i $(2a^3)^2 \div 2a^3$ **j** $8p^{-4} \div 4p^3$

    k $2a^{-4} \times 3a^{-5}$ **l** $21a^3b^2 \div 7ab^4$

    m $9x^2 \times 3(x^2)^3$ **n** $3x^3 \times 2x^2 \times 4x^6$

    o $7a^4 \times (3a^4)^2$ **p** $(4y^3)^3 \div 2y^3$

    q $2a^3 \div 3a^2 \times 6a^5$ **r** $3a^4 \times 2a^5 \times a^3$

2 Simplify:

    a $x^3 \div x^{-2}$ **b** $x^5 \div x^7$ **c** $x^{\frac{3}{2}} \times x^{\frac{5}{2}}$

    d $(x^2)^{\frac{3}{2}}$ **e** $(x^3)^{\frac{5}{3}}$ **f** $3x^{0.5} \times 4x^{-0.5}$

    g $9x^{\frac{2}{3}} \div 3x^{\frac{1}{6}}$ **h** $5x^{1\frac{2}{5}} \div x^{\frac{2}{5}}$ **i** $3x^4 \times 2x^{-5}$

3 Evaluate:

    a $25^{\frac{1}{2}}$ **b** $81^{\frac{1}{2}}$ **c** $27^{\frac{1}{3}}$

    d 4^{-2} **e** $9^{-\frac{1}{2}}$ **f** $(-5)^{-3}$

    g $\left(\frac{3}{4}\right)^0$ **h** $1296^{\frac{1}{4}}$ **i** $\left(1\frac{9}{16}\right)^{\frac{3}{2}}$

    j $\left(\frac{27}{8}\right)^{\frac{2}{3}}$ **k** $\left(\frac{6}{5}\right)^{-1}$ **l** $\left(\frac{343}{512}\right)^{-\frac{2}{3}}$

1.2 *You can write a number exactly using surds, e.g.* $\sqrt{2}$, $\sqrt{3}$ -5, $\sqrt{19}$. *You cannot evaluate surds exactly because they give never-ending, non-repeating decimal fractions,*
e.g. $\sqrt{2}$ = 1.414213 562...
The square root of a prime number is a surd.

- **You can manipulate surds using these rules:**

$$\sqrt{(ab)} = \sqrt{a} \times \sqrt{b}$$

$$\sqrt{\frac{a}{b}} = \frac{\sqrt{a}}{\sqrt{b}}$$

- **You can rationalise the denominator of** $\dfrac{1}{\sqrt{a}}$ **by multiplying the top and bottom by** $\sqrt{a}$.

Example 4

Simplify:

a $\sqrt{12}$ **b** $\dfrac{\sqrt{20}}{2}$ **c** $5\sqrt{6} - 2\sqrt{24} + \sqrt{294}$

a $\sqrt{12}$

$= \sqrt{(4 \times 3)}$

$= \sqrt{4} \times \sqrt{3}$ Use the rule $\sqrt{ab} = \sqrt{a} \times \sqrt{b}$.

$= 2\sqrt{3}$ $\sqrt{4} = 2$

b $\dfrac{\sqrt{20}}{2}$ $\sqrt{20} = \sqrt{4} \times \sqrt{5}$

$= \dfrac{\sqrt{4} \times \sqrt{5}}{2}$ $\sqrt{4} = 2$

$= \dfrac{2 \times \sqrt{5}}{2}$ Cancel by 2.

$= \sqrt{5}$

c $5\sqrt{6} - 2\sqrt{24} + \sqrt{294}$

$= 5\sqrt{6} - 2\sqrt{6} \times \sqrt{4} + \sqrt{6} \times \sqrt{49}$ $\sqrt{6}$ is a common factor.

$= \sqrt{6}(5 - 2\sqrt{4} + \sqrt{49})$ Work out the square roots $\sqrt{4}$ and $\sqrt{49}$.

$= 6(5 - 2 \times 2 + 7)$ $5 - 4 + 7 = 8$

$= \sqrt{6}(8)$

$= 8\sqrt{6}$

Example 5

Rationalise the denominator of:

a $\dfrac{1}{\sqrt{3}}$ **b** $\dfrac{12}{\sqrt{2}}$

a $\dfrac{1}{\sqrt{3}}$

$= \dfrac{1 \times \sqrt{3}}{\sqrt{3} \times \sqrt{3}}$ Multiply the top and bottom by $\sqrt{3}$.

$= \dfrac{\sqrt{3}}{3}$ $\sqrt{3} \times \sqrt{3} = (\sqrt{3})^2 = 3$

b $\dfrac{12}{\sqrt{2}} = \dfrac{12}{\sqrt{2}} \times \dfrac{\sqrt{2}}{\sqrt{2}}$ Multiply the top and bottom by $\sqrt{2}$.

$= \dfrac{12\sqrt{2}}{2}$ Remember $\sqrt{2} \times \sqrt{2} = 2$

$= 6\sqrt{2}$ Simplify your answer

Exercise 1B

Simplify:

1 $\sqrt{28}$ **2** $\sqrt{72}$ **3** $\sqrt{50}$

4 $\sqrt{32}$ **5** $\sqrt{90}$ **6** $\dfrac{\sqrt{12}}{2}$

7 $\dfrac{\sqrt{27}}{3}$ **8** $\sqrt{20} + \sqrt{80}$ **9** $\sqrt{200} + \sqrt{18} - \sqrt{72}$

10 $\sqrt{175} + \sqrt{63} + 2\sqrt{28}$ **11** $1\sqrt{28} - 2\sqrt{63} + \sqrt{7}$ **12** $\sqrt{80} - 2\sqrt{20} + 3\sqrt{45}$

13 $3\sqrt{80} - 2\sqrt{20} + 5\sqrt{45}$ **14** $\dfrac{\sqrt{44}}{\sqrt{11}}$ **15** $\sqrt{12} + 3\sqrt{48} + \sqrt{75}$

16 $\dfrac{1}{\sqrt{5}}$ **17** $\dfrac{1}{\sqrt{11}}$ **18** $\dfrac{1}{\sqrt{2}}$

19 $\dfrac{\sqrt{3}}{\sqrt{15}}$ **20** $\dfrac{\sqrt{12}}{\sqrt{48}}$ **21** $\dfrac{\sqrt{5}}{\sqrt{80}}$

22 $\dfrac{\sqrt{12}}{\sqrt{156}}$ **23** $\dfrac{\sqrt{7}}{\sqrt{63}}$

1.3 You need to know how to write an expression as a logarithm

- $\log_a n = x$ **means that** $a^x = n$, **where** a **is called the base of the logarithm.**

In the IGCSE the base of the logarithm will always be a positive integer greater than 1.

Example 6

Write as a logarithm $2^5 = 32$.

Here $a = 2, x = 5, n = 32$.

$2^5 = 32$ — Base

So $\log_2 32 = 5$ — Logarithm

     In words, you would say '2 to the power 5 equals 32'.

In words, you would say 'the logarithm of 32, to base 2, is 5'.

Example 7

Rewrite as a logarithm:

a $10^3 = 1000$ **b** $5^4 = 625$ **c** $2^{10} = 1024$

a $\log_{10} 1000 = 3$

b $\log_5 625 = 4$

c $\log_2 1024 = 10$

- $\log_a 1 = 0$ Because $a^0 = 1$.

- $\log_a a = 1$ Because $a^1 = a$.

Example 8

Find the value of

a $\log_3 81$ b $\log_4 0.25$ c $\log_a (a^5)$

a $\log_3 81 = 4$ Because $3^4 = 81$.

b $\log_4 0.25 = -1$ Because $4^{-1} = \frac{1}{4} = 0.25$.

c $\log_a (a^5) = 5$ Because $a^5 = a^5$!

You can use the $\boxed{\log}$ key on a calculator to calculate logarithms to base 10

Example 9

Find the value of x for which $10^x = 500$.

$$10^x = 500$$

So $\log_{10} 500 = x$ Since $10^2 = 100$ and $10^3 = 1000$, x must be somewhere between 2 and 3.

$$x = \log_{10} 500$$

$$= 2.70 \text{ (to 3 s.f.)}$$ The log (or lg) button on your calculator gives values of logs to base 10.

Exercise 1C

1   Rewrite as a logarithm:

   a $4^4 = 256$ b $3^{-2} = \frac{1}{9}$

   c $10^6 = 1\,000\,000$ d $11^1 = 11$

2   Rewrite using a power:

   a $\log_2 16 = 4$ b $\log_5 25 = 2$ c $\log_9 3 = \frac{1}{2}$

   d $\log_5 0.2 = -1$ e $\log_{10} 100\,000 = 5$

3   Find the value of:

   a $\log_2 8$ b $\log_5 25$ c $\log_{10} 10\,000\,000$

   d $\log_{12} 12$ e $\log_3 729$ f $\log_{10} \sqrt{10}$

   g $\log_4 (0.25)$ h $\log_a (a^{10})$

4   Find the value of x for which:

   a $\log_5 x = 4$ b $\log_x 81 = 2$

   c $\log_7 x = 1$ d $\log_x (2x) = 2$

5 Find from your calculator the value to 3 s.f. of:

 a $\log_{10} 20$ **b** $\log_{10} 4$

 c $\log_{10} 7000$ **d** $\log_{10} 0.786$

6 Find from your calculator the value to 3 s.f. of:

 a $\log_{10} 11$ **b** $\log_{10} 35.3$

 c $\log_{10} 0.3$ **d** $\log_{10} 999$

1.4 *You need to know the laws of logarithms*

Suppose that $\log_a x = b$ and $\log_a y = c$

Rewriting with powers: $a^b = x$ and $a^c = y$

Multiplying: $xy = a^b \times a^c = a^{b+c}$ (see section 1.1)

          $xy = a^{b+c}$

Rewriting as a logarithm: $\log_a xy = b + c$

- $\log_a xy = \log_a x + \log_a y$ **(the multiplication law)**

It can also be shown that:

- $\log_a \left(\dfrac{x}{y}\right) = \log_a x - \log_a y$ **(the division law)**   Remember: $\dfrac{a^b}{a^c} = a^b \div a^c = a^{b-c}$

- $\log_a (x)^k = k \log_a x$ **(the power law)**   Remember: $(a^b)^k = a^{bk}$

Note: You need to learn and remember the above three laws of logarithms.

Since $\left(\dfrac{1}{x}\right) = x^{-1}$, the power rule shows that $\log_a \left(\dfrac{1}{x}\right) = \log_a (x^{-1}) = -\log_a x$.

- $\log_a \left(\dfrac{1}{x}\right) = -\log_a x$

And from the previous section

- $\log_a a = 1$ **(since $a^1 = 1$)**
- $\log_a 1 = 0$ **(since $a^0 = 1$)**

Example 10

Write as a single logarithm:

 a $\log_3 6 + \log_3 7$ **b** $\log_2 15 - \log_2 3$

 c $2 \log_5 3 + 3 \log_5 2$ **d** $\log_{10} 3 - 4 \log_{10} \left(\tfrac{1}{2}\right)$

 a $\log_3 (6 \times 7)$ Use the multiplication law.
   $= \log_3 42$

 b $\log_2 (15 \div 3)$ Use the division law.
   $= \log_2 5$

 c $2 \log_5 3 = \log_5 (3^2) = \log_5 9$ First apply the power law to both parts of
   $3 \log_5 2 = \log_5 (2^3) = \log_5 8$ the expression.
   $\log_5 9 + \log_5 8 = \log_5 72$ Then use the multiplication law.

 d $4 \log_{10}\left(\tfrac{1}{2}\right) = \log_{10}\left(\tfrac{1}{2}\right)^4 = \log_{10}\left(\tfrac{1}{16}\right)$ Use the power first.

   $\log_{10} 3 - \log_{10}\left(\tfrac{1}{16}\right) = \log_{10}\left(3 \div \tfrac{1}{16}\right)$

       $= \log_{10} 48$ Then use the division law.

Example 11

Write in terms of $\log_a x$, $\log_a y$ and $\log_a z$

a $\log_a (x^2 y z^3)$ **b** $\log_a \left(\dfrac{x}{y^3}\right)$ **c** $\log_a \left(\dfrac{x\sqrt{y}}{z}\right)$ **d** $\log_a \left(\dfrac{x}{a^4}\right)$

a $\log_a (x^2 y z^3)$

$\quad = \log_a (x^2) + \log_a y + \log_a (z^3)$

$\quad = 2\log_a x + \log_a y + 3\log_a z$

b $\log_a \left(\dfrac{x}{y^3}\right)$

$\quad = \log_a x - \log_a (y^3)$

$\quad = \log_a x - 3\log_a y$

c $\log_a \left(\dfrac{x\sqrt{y}}{z}\right)$

$\quad = \log_a (x\sqrt{y}) - \log_a z$

$\quad = \log_a x + \log_a \sqrt{y} - \log_a z$

$\quad = \log_a x + \tfrac{1}{2}\log_a y - \log_a z$ Use the power law $\left(\sqrt{y} = y^{\frac{1}{2}}\right)$.

d $\log_a \left(\dfrac{x}{a^4}\right)$

$\quad = \log_a x - \log_a (a^4)$

$\quad = \log_a x - 4\log_a a$

$\quad = \log_a x - 4$ $\log_a a = 1.$

Exercise 1D

1 Write as a single logarithm:

  a $\log_2 7 + \log_2 3$ **b** $\log_2 36 - \log_2 4$

  c $3\log_5 2 + \log_5 10$ **d** $2\log_6 8 - 4\log_6 3$

  e $\log_{10} 5 + \log_{10} 6 - \log_{10} \left(\tfrac{1}{4}\right)$

2 Write as a single logarithm, then simplify your answer:

  a $\log_2 40 - \log_2 5$ **b** $\log_6 4 + \log_6 9$

  c $2\log_{12} 3 + 4\log_{12} 2$ **d** $\log_8 25 + \log_8 10 - 3\log_8 5$

  e $2\log_{10} 20 - (\log_{10} 5 + \log_{10} 8)$

3 Write in terms of $\log_a x$, $\log_a y$ and $\log_a z$:

  a $\log_a (x^3 y^4 z)$ **b** $\log_a \left(\dfrac{x^5}{y^2}\right)$ **c** $\log_a (a^2 x^2)$

  d $\log_a \left(\dfrac{x\sqrt{y}}{z}\right)$ **b** $\log_a \sqrt{ax}$

Working in base a, suppose that: $\qquad\qquad \log_a x = m$

Writing this as a power: $\qquad\qquad\qquad a^m = x$

Taking logs to a different base b: $\qquad \log_b (a^m) = \log_b x$

Using the power law: $\qquad\qquad m \log_b a = \log_b x$

Writing m as $\log_a x$: $\qquad\qquad \log_b x = \log_a x \times \log_b a$

This can be written as:

- $\log_a x = \dfrac{\log_b x}{\log_b a}$

This is the change of base rule for logarithms.

Using this rule, notice in particular that $\log_a b = \dfrac{\log_b b}{\log_b a}$, but $\log_b b = 1$, so:

- $\log_a b = \dfrac{1}{\log_b a}$

Example 12

Solve the following equations, giving your answers to 3 significant figures.

a $3^x = 20$ $\qquad\qquad$ **b** $8^x = 11$ $\qquad\qquad$ **c** $10^x = 0.7$

a $3^x = 20 \implies x = \log_3 20$ $\qquad$ Use the definition of logarithms from section 1.3.

By change of base formula, changing to base 10

$\qquad$ Some calculators can evaluate $\log_3 20$. If your calculator does not have this facility, you can use the change of base formula and use base 10

$\log_3 20 = \dfrac{\log_{10} 20}{\log_{10} 3}$

$\qquad$ The log button on your calculator uses $\log_{10}$. Use this to find $\log_{10} 20$ and $\log_{10} 3$.

$\log_3 20 = \dfrac{1.3010...}{0.4771...}$

$\qquad\quad = 2.73$ $\qquad$ Give answer to 3 sf.

b $8^x = 11 \implies x = \log_8 11$ $\qquad$ Use the definition from section 1.3.

Changing to base 10

$\log_8 11 = \dfrac{\log_{10} 11}{\log_{10} 8}$ $\qquad$ Evaluate using calculator and give answer to 3 sf.

$\qquad\quad = 1.15$

c $10^x = 0.7 \implies x = \log_{10} 0.7$ $\qquad$ This can be found directly using the log button on

$\qquad\qquad\qquad = -0.155$ $\qquad$ a calculator.

NB A logarithm can give a negative answer:

$\log_b x < 0$ when $0 < x < 1$

Example 13

Solve the equation $\log_5 x + 6\log_x 5 = 5$:

$$\log_5 x + \frac{6}{\log_5 x} = 5 \qquad \text{Use change of base rule (special case).}$$

Let $\log_5 x = y$

$$y + \frac{6}{y} = 5$$
$$y^2 + 6 = 5y \qquad \text{Multiply by } y.$$
$$y^2 - 5y + 6 = 0$$
$$(y-3)(y-2) = 0$$

So $y = 3$ or $y = 2$

$\log_5 x = 3$ or $\log_5 x = 2$

$x = 5^3$ or $x = 5^2$ \qquad Write as powers.

$x = 125$ or $x = 25$

Exercise 1E

1 Find, to 3 decimal places:

   a $\log_7 120$ **b** $\log_3 45$ **c** $\log_2 19$

   d $\log_{11} 3$ **e** $\log_6 4$

2 Solve, giving your answer to 3 significant figures:

   a $8^x = 14$ **b** $9^x = 99$ **c** $12^x = 6$

3 Solve, giving your answer to 3 significant figures:

   a $2^x = 75$ **b** $3^x = 10$

   c $5^x = 2$ **d** $4^{2x} = 100$

4 Solve, giving your answer to 3 significant figures:

   a $\log_2 x = 8 + 9\log_x 2$ **b** $\log_4 x + 2\log_x 4 + 3 = 0$ **c** $\log_2 x + \log_4 x = 2$

1.6 You need to be familiar with the functions $y = a^x$ and $y = \log_b x$ and to know the shapes of their graphs

As an example, look at a table of values for $y = 2^x$:

x	-3	-2	-1	0	1	2	3
y	$\frac{1}{8}$	$\frac{1}{4}$	$\frac{1}{2}$	1	2	4	8

Note that

$$2^0 = 1 \text{ (in fact } a^0 = 1 \text{ always if } a > 0)$$

and $\quad 2^{-3} = \dfrac{1}{2^3} = \dfrac{1}{8}$ (a negative index implies the 'reciprocal' of a positive index)

Hint:
A function that involves a variable power such as x is called an exponential function.

10

The graph of $y = 2^x$ looks like this:

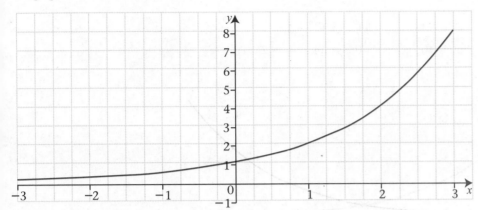

Other graphs of the type $y = a^x$ are of a similar shape, always passing through $(0, 1)$.

Now look at the table of values of $y = \log_2 x$:

x	$\frac{1}{8}$	$\frac{1}{4}$	$\frac{1}{2}$	1	2	4	8
y	-3	-2	-1	0	1	2	3

You should note that the values for x and y have swapped around.
This means that the shape of the curve is simply a reflection in the line $y = x$.

The graph of $y = \log_b x$ will have a similar shape and it will always pass through $(1, 0)$ since $\log_b 1 = 0$ for every value of b.

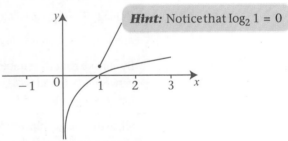

Hint: Notice that $\log_2 1 = 0$

Hint: The y axis is an asymptote to the curve.

Example 14

a On the same axes sketch the graphs of $y = 3^x$ $y = 2^x$ and $y = 1.5^x$

b On another set of axes sketch the graphs of $y = \left(\frac{1}{2}\right)^x$ and $y = 2^x$.

a For all the three graphs, $y = 1$ when $x = 0$. $a^0 = 1$

When $x > 0$, $3^x > 2^x > 1.5^x$

When $x < 0$, $3^x < 2^x < 1.5^x$

Work out the relative positions of the three graphs

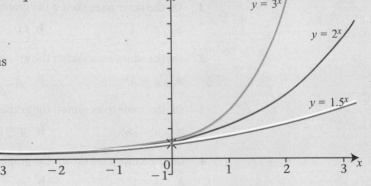

b $\frac{1}{2} = 2^{-1}$

So $y = \left(\frac{1}{2}\right)^x$ is the same as $y = (2^{-1})^x = 2^{-x}$. $(a^m)^n = a^{mn}$

So the graph of $y = \left(\frac{1}{2}\right)^x$ is a reflection in the y-axis of the graph of $y = 2^x$.

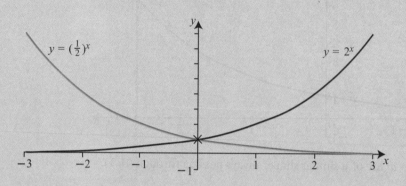

Example 15

On the same axes, sketch the graphs of $y = \log_2 x$ and $y = \log_5 x$.

For both graphs $y = 0$ when $x = 1$.   Since $\log_b 1 = 0$ for every value of b

But $\log_2 2 = 1$ so $y = \log_2 x$ passes through $(2, 1)$

and $\log_5 5 = 1$ so $y = \log_5 x$ passes through $(5, 1)$.

By considering the shape of the graphs
between $y = 0$ and $y = 1$, you can see that
$\log_2 x > \log_5 x$ for $x > 1$.

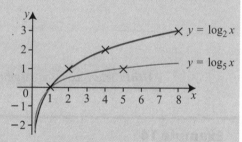

Since the log graphs are reflections of the
exponential graphs then from Example 14
you can see that the reverse will apply the
other side of $(1, 0)$. So $\log_2 x < \log_5 x$ for $x < 1$.

Exercise 1F

1 On the same axes sketch the graphs of

    a $y = 4^x$ **b** $y = 6^x$ **c** $y = \left(\frac{1}{4}\right)^x$

2 On the same axes sketch the graphs of

    a $y = 3^x$.   **b** $y = \log_3 x$ **c** $y = \left(\frac{1}{3}\right)^x$

3 On the same axes sketch the graphs of

    a $y = \log_4 x$ **b** $y = \log_6 x$

4 On the same axes sketch the graphs of

    a $y = 1^x$ **b** $y = \log_3 x$

    c Write down the coordinates of the point of intersection of these two graphs.

Exercise 1G

1   Simplify:

    a $y^3 \times y^5$ **b** $3x^2 \times 2x^5$

    c $(4x^2)^3 \div 2x^5$ **d** $4b^2 \times 3b^3 \times b^4$

2   Simplify:

    a $9x^3 \div 3x^{-3}$ **b** $(4^{\frac{3}{2}})^{\frac{1}{3}}$

    a $3x^{-2} \times 2x^4$ **d** $3x^{\frac{1}{3}} \div 6x^{\frac{2}{3}}$

3   Evaluate:

    a $\left(\dfrac{8}{27}\right)^{\frac{2}{3}}$ **d** $\left(\dfrac{225}{289}\right)^{\frac{2}{3}}$

4   Simplify:

    a $\dfrac{3}{\sqrt{63}}$ **b** $\sqrt{20} + 2\sqrt{45} - \sqrt{80}$

5   Rationalise:

    a $\dfrac{1}{\sqrt{3}}$ **b** $\dfrac{15}{\sqrt{5}}$

6   **a**   Express $\log_a (p^2 q)$ in terms of $\log_a p$ and $\log_a q$.

    b   Given that $\log_a (pq) = 5$ and $\log_a (p^2 q) = 9$, find the values of $\log_a p$ and $\log_a q$.

7   Solve the following equations giving your answers to 3 significant figures:

    a $5^x = 80$ **b** $7^x = 123$

8   **a**   Given that $\log_3 x = 2$, determine the value of x.

    b   Calculate the value of y for which $2\log_3 y - \log_3 (y + 4) = 2$.

    c   Calculate the values of z for which $\log_3 z = 4\log_z 3$.

9   Find the values of x for which $\log_3 x - 2\log_x 3 = 1$.

10   Solve the equation

    $\log_3 (2 - 3x) = \log_9 (6x^2 - 19x + 2)$.

Logarithms

1 You can simplify expressions by using rules of indices (powers).

$$a^m \times a^n = a^{m+n}$$

$$a^m \div a^n = a^{m-n}$$

$$a^{-m} = \frac{1}{a^m}$$

$$a^{\frac{1}{m}} = \sqrt[m]{a}$$

$$a^{\frac{n}{m}} = \sqrt[m]{a^n}$$

$$(a^m)^n = a^{mn}$$

$$a^0 = 1$$

2 You can manipulate surds using the rules:

$$\sqrt{ab} = \sqrt{a} \times \sqrt{b}$$

$$\sqrt{\frac{a}{b}} = \frac{\sqrt{a}}{\sqrt{b}}$$

3 The rule to rationalise surds is:

Fractions in the form $\frac{1}{\sqrt{a}}$, multiply the top and bottom by $\sqrt{a}$.

4 $\log_a n = x$ means that $a^x = n$, where a is called the base of the logarithm.

5 $\log_a 1 = 0$

$\log_a a = 1$

6 $\log_{10} x$ is sometimes written as $\log x$.

7 The laws of logarithms are

$\log_a xy = \log_a x + \log_a y$ (the multiplication law)

$\log_a \left(\frac{x}{y}\right) = \log_a x - \log_a y$ (the division law)

$\log_a (x)^k = k \log_a x$ (the power law)

8 From the power law,

$\log_a \left(\frac{1}{x}\right) = -\log_a x$

9 The change of base rule for logarithms can be written as $\log_a x = \dfrac{\log_b x}{\log_b a}$

10 From the change of base rule, $\log_a b = \dfrac{1}{\log_b a}$

2.1 You can factorise quadratic expressions

- A quadratic expression has the form $ax^2 + bx + c$, where a, b, c are constants and $a \neq 0$.

Example 1

Factorise:

a $6x^2 + 9x$ **b** $x^2 - 5x - 6$ **c** $x^2 + 6x + 8$

d $6x^2 - 11x - 10$ **e** $x^2 - 25$ **f** $4x^2 - 9y^2$

a $6x^2 + 9x$
$= 3x(2x + 3)$

3 and x are common factors of $6x^2$ and $9x$.
So take $3x$ outside the bracket.

b $x^2 - 5x - 6$
$ac = -6$
So $x^2 - 5x + 6 = x^2 + x - 6x - 6$
$= x(x + 1) - 6(x + 1)$
$= (x + 1)(x - 6)$

Here $a = 1$, $b = -5$ and $c = -6$.
You need to find two brackets that multiply together to give $x^2 - 5x - 6$. So:
① Work out ac.
② Work out the two factors of ac which add that give you b.
   -6 and $+1 = -5$
③ Rewrite the bx term using these two factors.
④ Factorise first two terms and last two terms.
⑤ $x + 1$ is a factor of both terms, so take that outside the bracket. This is now completely factorised.

c $x^2 + 6x + 8$
$= x^2 + 2x + 4x + 8$
$= x(x + 2) + 4(x + 2)$
$= (x + 2)(x + 4)$

Since $ac = 8$ and $2 + 4 = 6 = b$, factorise.
$x + 2$ is a factor so you can factorise into 2 brackets.

d $6x^2 - 11x - 10$
$= 6x^2 - 15x + 4x - 10$
$= 3x(2x - 5) + 2(2x - 5)$
$= (2x - 5)(3x + 2)$

$ac = -60$ and $4 - 15 = -11 = b$.
Factorise.
Factorise $(2x - 5)$.

e $x^2 - 25$
$= x^2 - 5^2$
$= (x + 5)(x - 5)$

This is called the difference of two squares as the two terms are x^2 and 5^2.
The two x terms, $5x$ and $-5x$, cancel each other out.

f $4x^2 - 9y^2$
$= 2^2 x^2 - 3^2 y^2$
$= (2x + 3y)(2x - 3y)$

This is the same as $(2x)^2 - (3y)^2$.

Exercise 2A

Factorise:

1 $x^2 + 4x$

2 $2x^2 + 6x$

3 $x^2 + 11x + 24$

4 $x^2 + 8x + 12$

5 $x^2 + 3x - 40$

6 $x^2 - 8x + 12$

7 $x^2 + 5x + 6$

8 $x^2 - 2x - 24$

9 $x^2 - 3x - 10$

10 $x^2 + x - 20$

11 $2x^2 + 5x + 2$

12 $3x^2 + 10x - 8$

13 $5x^2 - 16x + 3$

14 $6x^2 - 8x - 8$

15 $2x^2 + 7x - 15$

16 $2x^4 + 14x^2 + 24$

17 $x^2 - 4$

18 $x^2 - 49$

19 $4x^2 - 25$

20 $9x^2 - 25y^2$

21 $36x^2 - 4$

22 $2x^2 - 50$

23 $6x^2 - 10x + 4$

24 $15x^2 + 42x - 9$

> **Hints:**
> Question 14 – Take 2 out as a common factor first.
> Question 16 – let $y = x^2$.

2.2 *You can write quadratic expressions in another form by completing the square.*

$$x^2 + 2bx + b^2 = (x + b)^2$$
$$x^2 - 2bx + b^2 = (x - b)^2$$

> These are e both perfect squares.

To complete the square of the function $x^2 + 2bx$ you need a further term b^2. So the completed square form is

$$x^2 + 2bx = (x + b)^2 - b^2$$

Similarly

$$x^2 - 2bx = (x - b)^2 - b^2$$

Example 2

Complete the square for the expression $x^2 + 8x$

$x^2 + 8x$ $2b = 8$, so $b = 4$
$= (x + 4)^2 - 4^2$
$= (x + 4)^2 - 16$

In general

- **Completing the square:** $x^2 + bx = \left(x + \dfrac{b}{2}\right)^2 - \left(\dfrac{b}{2}\right)^2$

Example 3

Complete the square for the expressions

a $x^2 + 12x$ **b** $2x^2 - 10x$

a $x^2 + 12x$ $2b = 12$, so $b = 6$
    $= (x + 6)^2 - 6^2$
    $= (x + 6)^2 - 36$

b $2x^2 - 10x$ Here the coefficient of x^2 is 2.
    $= 2(x^2 - 5x)$ So take out the coefficient of x^2.
    $= 2\left[\left(x - \frac{5}{2}\right)^2 - \left(\frac{5}{2}\right)^2\right]$ Complete the square on $(x^2 - 5x)$.
    $= 2\left(x - \frac{5}{2}\right)^2 - \frac{25}{2}$ Use $b = -5$.

Exercise 2B

Complete the square for the expressions:

1 $x^2 + 4x$ **2** $x^2 - 6x$ **3** $x^2 - 16x$ **4** $x^2 + x$

5 $x^2 - 14x$ **6** $2x^2 + 16x$ **7** $3x^2 - 24x$ **8** $2x^2 - 4x$

9 $5x^2 + 20x$ **10** $2x^2 - 5x$ **11** $3x^2 + 9x$ **12** $3x^2 - x$

2.3   *You can solve quadratic equations*

Quadratic equations can have two solutions or roots. (In some cases the two roots are equal.)
To solve a quadratic equation put it in the form $ax^2 + bx + c = 0$.

Example 4

Solve the equation $x^2 = 9x$

           $x^2 = 9x$
       $x^2 - 9x = 0$ Rearrange in the form $ax^2 + bx + c = 0$.
      $x(x - 9) = 0$ Factorise by x.
Then either $x = 0$ Then either part of the product could be zero.
  or $x - 9 = 0 \Rightarrow x = 9$

So $x = 0$ or $x = 9$ are the two solutions   A quadratic equation has two solutions
of the equation $x^2 = 9x$.   (roots). In some cases the two roots are equal.

Example 5

Solve the equation $x^2 - 2x - 15 = 0$

    $x^2 - 2x - 15 = 0$
   $(x + 3)(x - 5) = 0$ Factorise.
Then either $x + 3 = 0 \Rightarrow x = -3$
or $x - 5 = 0 \Rightarrow x = 5$

The solutions are $x = -3$ or $x = 5$.

Example 6

Solve the equation $6x^2 + 13x - 5 = 0$

$$6x^2 + 13x - 5 = 0$$
$$(3x - 1)(2x + 5) = 0$$ Factorise.

Then either $3x - 1 = 0 \Rightarrow x = \frac{1}{3}$

or $\quad\quad 2x + 5 = 0 \Rightarrow x = -\frac{5}{2}$

The solutions can be fractions or any other type of number.

The solutions are $x = \frac{1}{3}$ or $x = -\frac{5}{2}$.

Example 7

Solve the equation $x^2 - 5x + 18 = 2 + 3x$

$$x^2 - 5x + 18 = 2 + 3x$$
$$x^2 - 8x + 16 = 0$$ Rearrange in the form $ax^2 + bx + c = 0$.
$$(x - 4)(x - 4) = 0$$ Factorise.

Then either $x - 4 = 0 \Rightarrow x = 4$

or $\quad\quad x - 4 = 0 \Rightarrow x = 4$ Here $x = 4$ is the only solution, i.e. the

$\Rightarrow \quad\quad\quad x = 4$ two roots are equal.

Example 8

Solve the equation $(2x - 3)^2 = 25$

$$(2x - 3)^2 = 25$$
$$2x - 3 = \pm 5$$ This is a special case.
$$2x = 3 \pm 5$$ Take the square root of both sides.

Then either $2x = 3 + 5 \Rightarrow x = 4$ Remember $\sqrt{25} = +5$ or -5.

or $\quad\quad 2x = 3 - 5 \Rightarrow x = -1$ Add 3 to both sides.

The solutions are $x = 4$ or $x = -1$.

Example 9

Solve the equation $(x - 3)^2 = 7$

$$(x - 3)^2 = 7$$
$$x - 3 = \pm\sqrt{7}$$ Square root. (If you do not have a
$$x = +3 \pm\sqrt{7}$$ calculator, leave this in surd form.)

Then either $x = 3 + \sqrt{7}$

or $\quad\quad x = 3 - \sqrt{7}$

The solutions are $x = 3 + \sqrt{7}$ or $x = 3 - \sqrt{7}$.

Example 10

Solve the equation $x^2 + 8x + 10 = 0$ by completing the square.

$$x^2 + 8x + 10 = 0$$ Check coefficient of $x^2 = 1$.
$$x^2 + 8x = -10$$ Subtract 10 to get LHS in the form $ax^2 + b$.
$$(x + 4)^2 - 4^2 = -10$$ Complete the square for $(x^2 + 8x)$.
$$(x + 4)^2 = -10 + 16$$ Add 4^2 to both sides.
$$(x + 4)^2 = 6$$
$$(x + 4) = \pm\sqrt{6}$$ Square root both sides.
$$x = -4 \pm\sqrt{6}$$ Subtract 4 from both sides.

Then the solutions (roots) of Leave your answer in surd form as

$x^2 + 8x + 10 = 0$ are either this is a non-calculator question.

$x = -4 + \sqrt{6}$ or $x = -4 - \sqrt{6}$.

Example 11

Solve the equation $2x^2 - 8x + 7 = 0$.

$2x^2 - 8x + 7 = 0$ The coefficient of $x^2 = 2$.

$x^2 - 4x + \frac{7}{2} = 0$ So divide by 2.

$x^2 - 4x = -\frac{7}{2}$ Subtract $\frac{7}{2}$ from both sides.

$(x - 2)^2 - (2)^2 = -\frac{7}{2}$ Complete the square for $x^2 - 4x$.

$(x - 2)^2 = -\frac{7}{2} + 4$ Add $(2)^2$ to both sides.

$(x - 2)^2 = \frac{1}{2}$ Combine the RHS.

$x - 2 = \pm\sqrt{\frac{1}{2}}$ Square root both sides.

$x = 2 \pm \frac{1}{\sqrt{2}}$ Add 2 to both sides.

So the roots are either

$x = 2 + \dfrac{1}{\sqrt{2}}$

or $x = 2 - \dfrac{1}{\sqrt{2}}$

Exercise 2C

Solve the following equations:

1   $x^2 = 4x$ 2 $x^2 = 25x$

3   $3x^2 = 6x$ 4 $5x^2 = 30x$

5   $x^2 + 3x + 2 = 0$ 6 $x^2 + 5x + 4 = 0$

7   $x^2 + 7x + 10 = 0$ 8 $x^2 - x - 6 = 0$

9   $x^2 - 8x + 15 = 0$ 10 $x^2 - 9x + 20 = 0$

11   $x^2 - 5x - 6 = 0$ 12 $x^2 - 4x - 12 = 0$

13   $2x^2 + 7x + 3 = 0$ 14 $6x^2 - 7x - 3 = 0$

15   $6x^2 - 5x - 6 = 0$ 16 $4x^2 - 16x + 15 = 0$

17   $3x^2 + 5x = 2$ 18 $(2x - 3)^2 = 9$

19   $(x - 7)^2 = 36$ 20 $2x^2 = 8$

21   $3x^2 = 5$ 22 $(x - 3)^2 = 13$

23   $(3x - 1)^2 = 11$ 24 $5x^2 - 10x^2 = -7 + x + x^2$

25   $6x^2 - 7 = 11x$ 26 $4x^2 + 17x = 6x - 2x^2$

Solve these quadratic equations by completing the square (remember to leave your answer in surd form):

27   $x^2 + 6x + 1 = 0$ 28 $x^2 + 12x + 3 = 0$

29   $x^2 - 10x = 5$ 30 $x^2 + 4x - 2 = 0$

31   $x^2 - 3x - 5 = 0$ 32 $2x^2 - 7 = 4x$

33   $4x^2 - x = 8$ 34 $10 = 3x - x^2$

35   $15 - 6x - 2x^2 = 0$ 36 $5x^2 + 8x - 2 = 0$

2.4 *You can solve quadratic equations* $ax^2 + bx + c = 0$ *by using the formula*

$$x = \frac{-b \pm \sqrt{(b^2 - 4ac)}}{2a}$$

Example 12

Show that the solutions of $ax^2 + bx + c = 0$ are

$$x = \frac{-b \pm \sqrt{(b^2 - 4ac)}}{2a}$$ To do this complete the square.

$$x^2 + \frac{b}{a}x + \frac{c}{a} = 0$$ The coefficient x^2 is a so divide by a.

$$x^2 + \frac{b}{a}x = -\frac{c}{a}$$ Subtract $\frac{c}{a}$ from both sides.

$$\left(x + \frac{b}{2a}\right)^2 - \frac{b^2}{4a^2} = -\frac{c}{a}$$ Complete the square.

$$\left(x + \frac{b}{2a}\right)^2 = \frac{b^2}{4a^2} - \frac{c}{a}$$ Add $\frac{b^2}{4a^2}$ to both sides.

$$\left(x + \frac{b}{2a}\right)^2 = \frac{b^2 - 4ac}{4a^2}$$ Combine the RHS.

$$x + \frac{b}{2a} = \frac{\pm\sqrt{(b^2 - 4ac)}}{2a}$$ Square root.

Thus $$x = \frac{-b \pm \sqrt{(b^2 - 4ac)}}{2a}$$ Subtract —$2ba$— from both sides.

Example 13

Solve $4x^2 - 3x - 2 = 0$ by using the formula.

$$x = \frac{-(-3) \pm \sqrt{[(-3)^2 - 4(4)(-2)]}}{2 \times 4}$$ Use $x = \dfrac{-b \pm \sqrt{(b^2 - 4ac)}}{2a}$

where $a = 4, b = -3, c = -2$.

$$x = \frac{+3 \pm \sqrt{(9 + 32)}}{8}$$ $-4 \times 4 \times -2 = +32$

$$x = \frac{+3 \pm \sqrt{41}}{8}$$

Then $x = \dfrac{+3 + \sqrt{41}}{8}$ or 1.18

or $x = \dfrac{+3 - \sqrt{41}}{8}$ or -0.425 Leave your answer in surd form.

The part of the formula $b^2 - 4ac$ is called the **discriminant**.
The discriminant can be used to identify whether the roots of a particular equation are equal and real, unequal and real or not real.

The discriminant of the equation $ax^2 + bx + c = 0$ is $b^2 - 4ac$
- **If $b^2 - 4ac > 0$ the roots of the equation are real and unequal**
- **If $b^2 - 4ac = 0$ the roots of the equations are real and equal**
- **If $b^2 - 4ac < 0$ there are no real roots of the equation**

Example 14

Calculate the discriminant of each of the following equations and, where possible, find the root(s) to 3 significant figures.

(a) $2x^2 - 3x + 5 = 0$ **(b)** $3x^2 - x - 1 = 0$ **(c)** $4x^2 - 12x + 9 = 0$

(a) $2x^2 - 3x + 5 = 0$

$a = 2,\ b = -3,\ c = 5$ Identify values for a, b and c.

$b^2 - 4ac = (-3)^2 - 4 \times 2 \times 5 = 9 - 40 = -31$ Evaluate $b^2 - 4ac$ remembering that $(-3)^2 = +9$

So there are no real roots

(b) $3x^2 - x - 1 = 0$

$a = 3,\ b = -1,\ c = -1$ Identify the values for a, b and c and calculate the discriminant

$b^2 - 4ac = (-1)^2 - 4 \times 3 \times (-1)$

$\qquad = 1 + 12 = 13$

So there are two unequal real roots

Roots are: $x = \dfrac{-(-1) \pm \sqrt{13}}{2 \times 3}$ Use the formula to find the solutions

$\qquad x = 0.768,\ -0.434$

(c) $4x^2 - 12x + 9 = 0$

Discriminant $= (-12)^2 - 4 \times 4 \times 9$ Calculate the discriminant

$\qquad = 144 - 144$

$\qquad = 0$

So the roots are real and equal

$\qquad x = \dfrac{-(-12)}{2 \times 4}$ Using the formula

$\qquad x = \dfrac{3}{2}$ When the discriminant $= 0$ you can always factorise so in this case:
$4x^2 - 12x + 9 = (2x - 3)^2 = 0$
giving $x = \dfrac{3}{2}$

Exercise 2D

In questions $1 - 8$ use the discriminant to determine whether the following equations have no real roots, equal roots or unequal roots.

Where possible find the root(s) to 3 significant figures.

1 $x^2 - 2x + 1 = 0$ **2** $x^2 - 2x - 1 = 0$

3 $x^2 - 3x - 2 = 0$ **4** $x^2 - 3x + 4 = 0$

5 $2x^2 + x - 2 = 0$ **6** $3x^2 - x + 3 = 0$

7 $3x^2 = 7 - x$ **8** $2x^2 = x + 4$

In questions 9-18 solve the equations by using the formula and give your answers correct to 3 significant figures.

9 $x^2 + 3x + 1 = 0$ **10** $x^2 - 3x - 2 = 0$

11 $x^2 + 6x + 6 = 0$ **12** $x^2 - 5x - 2 = 0$

13 $3x^2 + 10x - 2 = 0$ **14** $4x^2 - 4x - 1 = 0$

15 $7x^2 + 9x + 1 = 0$ **16** $5x^2 + 4x - 3 = 0$

17 $4x^2 - 7x = 2$ **18** $11x^2 + 2x - 7 = 0$

2.5 *You can use functions of the roots of a quadratic equation*

The quadratic equation $ax^2 + bx + c = 0$ can be written as

$$x^2 + \frac{b}{a}x + \frac{c}{a} = 0 \quad \text{or} \quad x^2 + px + q = 0$$

If the roots of $x^2 + px + q = 0$ are α and β then

$$x^2 + px + q = (x - \alpha)(x - \beta)$$

so $x^2 + px + q = x^2 - \alpha x - \beta x + \alpha\beta$

i.e. $x^2 + px + q = x^2 - (\alpha + \beta)x + \alpha\beta$

Comparing coefficients $p = -(\alpha + \beta)$
and $q = \alpha\beta$

So for a quadratic equation with coefficient of $x^2 = 1$ and with roots α and β

Sum of roots $= \alpha + \beta = -$ the coefficient of x

and   Product of roots $= \alpha\beta = $ the constant term

So for the equation $ax^2 + bx + c = 0$

- **sum of roots $= \alpha + \beta = -\dfrac{b}{a}$**

- **product of roots $= \alpha\beta = \dfrac{c}{a}$**

These results can also be used to find the equation of a quadratic equation given its roots.

Example 15

The roots of the equation $3x^2 + x - 6 = 0$ are α and β.

a Find an expression for $\alpha + \beta$ and an expression for $\alpha\beta$.

b Hence find an expression for $\alpha^2 + \beta^2$ and an expression for $\alpha^2\beta^2$.

c Find a quadratic equation with roots α^2 and β^2.

a $3x^2 + x - 6 = 0$ Divide by 3 to obtain a quadratic equation with
      $\Rightarrow x^2 + \frac{1}{3}x - 2 = 0$ coefficient of $x^2 = 1$

      Sum of roots, $\alpha + \beta = -\frac{1}{3}$ The sum of the roots $= -$ the coefficient of x

      Product of roots, $\alpha\beta = -2$ and the product of the roots $=$ the constant term

b $(\alpha + \beta)^2 = \alpha^2 + 2\alpha\beta + \beta^2$

so $\alpha^2 + \beta^2 = (\alpha + \beta)^2 - 2\alpha\beta$

i.e. $\alpha^2 + \beta^2 = \left(-\frac{1}{3}\right)^2 - 2(-2)$

$\quad 4\frac{1}{9} \quad$ or $\quad \frac{37}{9}$

$\alpha^2\beta^2 = (\alpha\beta)^2 = (-2)^2 = 4$

This sort of manipulation is often useful in questions of this type.

Use values from part **a**.

c Let the equation be $x^2 + px + q = 0$

$p = -(\alpha^2 + \beta^2) = -\frac{37}{9}$

$q = \alpha^2\beta^2 = 4$

Use $p = -$ sum of roots and

$q = $ product of the roots.

So equation is: $x^2 - \frac{37}{9}x + 4 = 0$

or $\qquad 9x^2 - 37x + 36 = 0$

You can simplify the equation so that the coefficients are all integers.

Notice that this question can be answered *without* finding the values of α and β, indeed sometimes α and β may not even be real numbers.

Example 16

The roots of the equation $x^2 - 3x - 2 = 0$ are α and β.
Without finding the value of α or the value of β, find equations with roots

a $\quad 3\alpha, 3\beta \qquad$ **b** $\quad \dfrac{1}{\alpha}, \dfrac{1}{\beta} \qquad$ **c** $\quad \alpha^2, \beta^2$

If α and β are the roots of $x^2 - 3x - 2 = 0$

then $\quad \alpha + \beta = 3$

$\qquad \alpha\beta = -2$

Use the formulae for sum of roots and product of roots.

a If roots are 3α and 3β then

Sum of roots $= 3(\alpha + \beta) = 3 \times 3 = 9$

Product of roots $= 3\alpha \times 3\beta = 9\alpha\beta = -18$

Equation is: $x^2 - 9x - 18 = 0$

Using $\alpha + \beta = 3$

$\qquad \alpha\beta = -2$

Coefficient of x is $-$ (sum of roots) and product of the roots is the constant term.

b If roots are $\dfrac{1}{\alpha}, \dfrac{1}{\beta}$ then

Sum of roots $= \dfrac{1}{\alpha} + \dfrac{1}{\beta} = \dfrac{\beta + \alpha}{\alpha\beta}$

$\qquad\qquad = \dfrac{3}{-2} \quad$ or $\quad -1.5$

Using $\alpha + \beta = 3$

$\qquad \alpha\beta = -2$

Product of roots $= \dfrac{1}{\alpha} \times \dfrac{1}{\beta} = \dfrac{1}{\alpha\beta}$

$\qquad\qquad\quad = \dfrac{1}{-2} \quad$ or $\quad -0.5$

Equation is: $x^2 + \frac{3}{2}x - \frac{1}{2} = 0$

or $\qquad 2x^2 + 3x - 1 = 0$

Coefficient of x is $-$(sum of roots) and product of the roots is the constant term.

c If the roots are α^2, β^2 then

Sum of roots $= \alpha^2 + \beta^2 = (\alpha + \beta)^2 - 2\alpha\beta$

$\qquad\qquad = 3^2 - 2(-2) = 13$

Notice the manipulation as used in Example 15.

Product of roots $= \alpha^2\beta^2 = (\alpha\beta)^2 = (-2)^2 = 4$

Equation is: $x^2 - 13x + 4 = 0$

Exercise 2E

1 The roots of the equation $x^2 + 5x + 2 = 0$ are α and β, find an equation whose roots are
  a $2\alpha + 1$ and $2\beta + 1$ **b** $\alpha\beta$ and $\alpha^2\beta^2$

2 The roots of the equation $x^2 + 6x + 1 = 0$ are α and β, find an equation whose roots are
  a $\alpha + 3$ and $\beta + 3$ **b** $\dfrac{\alpha}{\beta}$ and $\dfrac{\beta}{\alpha}$

3 The roots of the equation $x^2 - x + 3 = 0$ are α and β, find an equation whose roots are
  a $\alpha + 2$ and $\beta + 2$ **b** α^2 and β^2

4 The roots of the equation $x^2 + x - 1 = 0$ are α and β, find an equation whose roots are
  a $\dfrac{1}{\alpha}$ and $\dfrac{1}{\beta}$ **b** $\dfrac{\alpha}{\alpha + \beta}$ and $\dfrac{\beta}{\alpha + \beta}$

Mixed Exercise 2F

1 Factorise these expressions completely:
  a $3x^2 + 4x$ **b** $4y^2 + 10y$
  c $x^2 + xy + xy^2$ **d** $8xy^2 + 10x^2y$

2 Factorise:
  a $x^2 + 3x + 2$ **b** $3x^2 + 6x$ **c** $x^2 - 2x - 35$
  d $2x^2 - x - 3$ **e** $5x^2 - 13x - 6$ **f** $6 - 5x - x^2$

3 Solve the following equations:
  a $y^2 + 3y + 2 = 0$ **b** $3x^2 + 13x - 10 = 0$
  c $5x^2 - 10x = 4x + 3$ **d** $(2x - 5)^2 = 7$

4 Solve the following equations by:
  i completing the square   **ii** using the formula.
  a $x^2 + 5x + 2 = 0$ **b** $x^2 - 4x - 3 = 0$
  c $5x^2 + 3x - 1 = 0$ **d** $3x^2 - 5x = 4$

5 Given that for all values of x:
$3x^2 + 12x + 5 = p(x + q)^2 + r$
  a find the values of p, q and r **b** solve the equation $3x^2 + 12x + 5 = 0$.

6 Find the values of k for which $x^2 + kx + 4 = 0$ has equal roots.

7 Find the values of k for which $kx^2 + 8x + k = 0$ has equal roots.

8 Given that α and β $(\alpha > \beta)$ are the roots of the equation $2x^2 - 7x + 3 = 0$, find the exact value of
  a $\alpha^2 + \beta^2$ **b** $\alpha - \beta$ **c** $\alpha^3 - \beta^3$

Hint:
$\alpha^3 - \beta^3 =$
$(\alpha - \beta)(\alpha^2 + \alpha\beta + \beta^2)$

9 The equation $x^2 - 2tx + t = 0$, where t is a positive constant, has roots α and β.
  a Find, in terms of t, $\alpha\beta$ and $\alpha^2 + \beta^2$
  Given that $\alpha - \beta = 24$, find
  b the value of t,
  c an equation with roots $\dfrac{\alpha}{\beta}$ and $\dfrac{\beta}{\alpha}$.

1 $x^2 - y^2 = (x - y)(x + y)$

This is called the difference of two squares.

2 The general form of a quadratic equation is

$0 = ax^2 + bx + c$ where a, b, c are constants and $a \neq 0$.

3 Quadratic equations can be solved by:

- factorisation
- completing the square:

$$x^2 + bx = \left(x + \frac{b}{2}\right)^2 - \left(\frac{b}{2}\right)^2$$

- using the formula

$$x = \frac{-b \pm \sqrt{(b^2 - 4ac)}}{2a}$$

4 A quadratic equation has two solutions, which may be equal, or there may be no real solutions.

5 The **discriminant** of the quadratic expression

$ax^2 + bx + c$ is $b^2 - 4ac$

6 If α and β are the roots of the equation $ax^2 + bx + c = 0$

- $\alpha + \beta = -\dfrac{b}{a}$
- $\alpha\beta = \dfrac{c}{a}$

Example 1

Divide $x^3 + 2x^2 - 17x + 6$ by $(x - 3)$.

1

$$
\begin{array}{r}
x^2 \\
x - 3 \overline{\smash{)}x^3 + 2x^2 - 17x + 6} \\
\underline{x^3 - 3x^2} \\
5x^2 - 17x
\end{array}
$$

Start by dividing the first term of the polynomial by x, so that $x^3 \div x = x^2$.

Next multiply $(x - 3)$ by x^2, so that $x^2 \times (x - 3) = x^3 - 3x^2$.

Now subtract, so that $(x^3 + 2x^2) - (x^3 - 3x^2) = 5x^2$.

Finally copy $-17x$.

2

$$
\begin{array}{r}
x^2 + 5x \\
x - 3 \overline{\smash{)}x^3 + 2x^2 - 17x + 6} \\
\underline{x^3 - 3x^2} \\
5x^2 - 17x \\
\underline{5x^2 - 15x} \\
-2x + 6
\end{array}
$$

Repeat the method. Divide $5x^2$ by x, so that $5x^2 \div x = 5x$.

Multiply $(x - 3)$ by $5x$, so that $5x \times (x - 3) = 5x^2 - 15x$.

Subtract, so that $(5x^2 - 17x) - (5x^2 - 15x) = -2x$.

Copy 6.

3

$$
\begin{array}{r}
x^2 + 5x - 2 \\
x - 3 \overline{\smash{)}x^3 + 2x^2 - 17x + 6} \\
\underline{x^3 - 3x^2} \\
5x^2 - 17x \\
\underline{5x^2 - 15x} \\
-2x + 6 \\
\underline{-2x + 6} \\
0
\end{array}
$$

Repeat the method. Divide $-2x$ by x, so that $-2x \div x = -2$.

Multiply $(x - 3)$ by -2, so that $-2 \times (x - 3) = -2x + 6$.

Subtract, so that $(-2x + 6) - (-2x + 6) = 0$.

No numbers left to copy, so you have finished.

So $x^3 + 2x^2 - 17x + 6 \div (x - 3) = x^2 + 5x - 2$.

This is called the quotient.

Example 2

Divide $4x^3 + x^2 - 11x + 6$ by $4x - 3$

1

$$
\begin{array}{r}
x^2 \\
4x - 3 \overline{\smash{)}4x^3 + x^2 - 11x + 6} \\
\underline{4x^3 - 3x^2} \\
4x^2 - 11x + 6
\end{array}
$$

Divide $4x$ into $4x^3$ to get x^2

Then multiply $x^2(4x - 3)$

Subtract, remembering that $x^2 - -3x^2 = +4x^2$

2
$$4x - 3 \overline{)4x^3 + x^2 - 11x + 6} \qquad \overset{x^2 + x}{}$$

Repeat method.
Divide $4x^2$ by $4x$ to get x.

$$\underline{4x^3 - 3x^2}$$
$$4x^2 - 11x + 6$$
$$\underline{4x^2 - 3x}$$

Multiply $x(4x - 3)$ and subtract

$$-8x + 6$$

3
$$4x - 3 \overline{)4x^3 + x^2 - 11x + 6} \qquad \overset{x^2 + x - 2}{}$$

Finally divide $-8x$ by $4x$ to get -2

$$\underline{4x^3 - 3x^2}$$
$$4x^2 - 11x + 6$$
$$\underline{4x^2 - 3x}$$
$$-8x + 6$$
$$\underline{-8x + 6}$$

Multiply $-2(4x - 3)$ and subtract to get 0

$$0$$

so $4x^3 + x^2 - 11x + 6 = (4x - 3)(x^2 + x - 2)$

Exercise 3A

1   Divide:
   a $x^3 + 6x^2 + 8x + 3$ by $(x + 1)$ **b** $x^3 + 7x^2 - 3x - 54$ by $(x + 6)$
   c $x^3 - x^2 + x + 14$ by $(x + 2)$ **d** $x^3 - 5x^2 + 8x - 4$ by $(x - 2)$
   e $x^3 - 8x^2 + 13x + 10$ by $(x - 5)$

2   Divide:
   a $6x^3 + 27x^2 + 14x + 8$ by $(x + 4)$ **b** $3x^3 - 10x^2 - 10x + 8$ by $(x - 4)$
   c $2x^3 + 4x^2 - 9x - 9$ by $(x + 3)$ **d** $-3x^3 + 2x^2 - 2x - 7$ by $(x + 1)$
   e $-5x^3 - 27x^2 + 23x + 30$ by $(x + 6)$

3   Divide
   a $2x^3 + 5x^2 - 5x + 1$ by $(2x - 1)$ **b** $3x^3 + 2x^2 - 3x - 2$ by $(3x + 2)$
   c $6x^3 + x^2 - 7x + 2$ by $(3x - 1)$ **d** $4x^3 + 4x^2 + 5x + 12$ by $(2x + 3)$
   e $2x^3 + 7x^2 + 7x + 2$ by $(2x + 1)$

3.2   *You can factorise a polynomial by using the factor theorem:*
If f(x) is a polynomial and f(p) = 0, then x − p is a factor of f(x).

Example 3

Show that $(x - 2)$ is a factor of $x^3 + x^2 - 4x - 4$ by the factor theorem

$f(x) = x^3 + x^2 - 4x - 4$ Write the polynomial as a function.

$f(2) = (2)^3 + (2)^2 - 4(2) - 4$ Substitute $x = 2$ into the polynomial.

$\qquad = 8 + 4 - 8 - 4$ Use the factor theorem:

$\qquad = 0$ If $f(p) = 0$, then $x - p$ is a factor of $f(x)$.

Here $p = 2$. so $(x - 2)$ is a factor of $x^3 + x^2 - 4x - 4$.

So $(x - 2)$ is a factor of $x^3 + x^2 - 4x - 4$.

Example 4

Factorise $2x^3 + x^2 - 18x - 9$.

$f(x) = 2x^3 + x^2 - 18x - 9$

Write the polynomial as a function.

$f(-1) = 2(-1)^3 + (-1)^2 - 18(-1) - 9 = 8$
$f(1) = 2(1)^3 + (1)^2 - 18(1) - 9 = -24$
$f(2) = 2(2)^3 + (2)^2 - 18(2) - 9 = -25$
$f(3) = 2(3)^3 + (3)^2 - 18(3) - 9 = 0$

Try values of x, e.g. $-1, 1, 2, 3, \ldots$ until you find $f(p) = 0$.

$f(3) = 0$.

So $(x - 3)$ is a factor of $2x^3 + x^2 - 18x - 9$.

Use the factor theorem:
If $f(p) = 0$, then $x - p$ is a factor of $f(x)$.
Here $p = 3$.

$$
\begin{array}{r}
2x^2 + 7x + 3 \\
x - 3 \overline{) 2x^3 + x^2 - 18x - 9} \\
\underline{2x^3 - 6x^2} \\
7x^2 - 18x \\
\underline{7x^2 - 21x} \\
3x - 9 \\
\underline{3x - 9} \\
0
\end{array}
$$

Divide $2x^3 + x^2 - 18x - 9$ by $(x - 3)$.

You can check your division here:
$(x - 3)$ is a factor of $2x^3 + x^2 - 18x - 9$,
so the remainder must $= 0$.

$2x^3 + x^2 - 18x - 9 = (x - 3)(2x^2 + 7x + 3)$ $2x^2 + 7x + 3$ can also be factorised.
$ = (x - 3)(2x + 1)(x + 3)$

Example 5

Given that $(x + 1)$ is a factor of $4x^4 - 3x^2 + a$, find the value of a.

$f(x) = 4x^4 - 3x^2 + a$

Write the polynominal as a function.

$f(-1) = 0$

Use the factor theorem the other way around:

$4(-1)^4 - 3(-1)^2 + a = 0$

$x - p$ is a factor of $f(x)$, so $f(p) = 0$

$4 - 3 + a = 0$

Here $p = -1$.

$a = -1$

Substitute $x = -1$ and solve the equation for a.
Remember $(-1)^4 = 1$.

Exercise 3B

1 Use the factor theorem to show that:
   a $(x - 1)$ is a factor of $4x^3 - 3x^2 - 1$
   b $(x + 3)$ is a factor of $5x^4 - 45x^2 - 6x - 18$
   c $(x - 4)$ is a factor of $-3x^3 + 13x^2 - 6x + 8$

2 Show that $(x - 1)$ is a factor of $x^3 + 6x^2 + 5x - 12$ and hence factorise the expression completely.

3 Show that $(x + 1)$ is a factor of $x^3 + 3x^2 - 33x - 35$ and hence factorise the expression completely.

4 Show that $(x - 5)$ is a factor of $x^3 - 7x^2 + 2x + 40$ and hence factorise the expression completely.

5 Show that $(x - 2)$ is a factor of $2x^3 + 3x^2 - 18x + 8$ and hence factorise the expression completely.

6 Each of these expressions has a factor $(x \pm p)$. Find a value of p and hence factorise the expression completely.
   a $x^3 - 10x^2 + 19x + 30$ **b** $x^3 + x^2 - 4x - 4$ **c** $x^3 - 4x^2 - 11x + 30$

7 Factorise:
   a $2x^3 + 5x^2 - 4x - 3$ **b** $2x^3 - 17x^2 + 38x - 15$
   c $3x^3 + 8x^2 + 3x - 2$ **d** $6x^3 + 11x^2 - 3x - 2$
   e $4x^3 - 12x^2 - 7x + 30$

8 Given that $(x - 1)$ is a factor of $5x^3 - 9x^2 + 2x + a$ find the value of a.

9 Given that $(x + 3)$ is a factor of $6x^3 - bx^2 + 18$ find the value of b.

10 Given that $(x - 1)$ and $(x + 1)$ are factors of $px^3 + qx^2 - 3x - 7$ find the values of p and q.

> **Hint for question 10:**
> Solve simultaneous equations.

3.3 *You can find the remainder when a polynomial is divided by $(ax - b)$ by using the remainder theorem:*
If a polynomial $f(x)$ is divided by $(ax - b)$ then the remainder is $f\left(\dfrac{b}{a}\right)$.

Example 6

Find the remainder when $x^3 - 20x + 3$ is divided by $(x - 4)$ using:
a algebraic division   **b** the remainder theorem

a
$$\begin{array}{r} x^2 + 4x - 4 \\ x - 4 \overline{) x^3 + 0x^2 - 20x + 3} \\ \underline{x^3 - 4x^2} \\ 4x^2 - 20x \\ \underline{4x^2 - 16x} \\ -4x + 3 \\ \underline{-4x + 16} \\ -13 \end{array}$$

Divide $x^3 - 20x + 3$ by $(x - 4)$.

Remember to use $0x^2$.

The remainder is -13.

b $f(x) = x^3 - 20x + 3$

Write the polynomial as a function.

Use the remainder theorem: If $f(x)$ is divided by $(ax - b)$, then the remainder is $f\left(\dfrac{b}{a}\right)$.

$f(4) = (4)^3 - 20(4) + 3$
   $= 64 - 80 + 3$
   $= -13$

Compare $(x - 4)$ to $(ax - b)$, so $a = 1, b = 4$ and the remainder is $f\left(\dfrac{4}{1}\right)$, i.e. $f(4)$.
Substitute $x = 4$.

The remainder is -13.
So we could write

$$\frac{x^3 - 20x + 3}{x - 4} = x^2 + 4x - 4 + \frac{-13}{x - 4}$$

or $x^3 - 20x + 3 = (x - 4)(x^2 + 4x - 4) - 13$ This -13 is called the **remainder**
   This $x^2 + 4x - 4$ is called the **quotient**

Example 7

When $8x^4 - 4x^3 + ax^2 - 1$ is divided by $(2x + 1)$ the remainder is 3. Find the value of a.

$$f(x) = 8x^4 - 4x^3 + ax^2 - 1$$

$f\left(-\frac{1}{2}\right) = 3$	Use the remainder theorem: If $f(x)$ is divided by $(ax - b)$, then the remainder is $f\left(\frac{b}{a}\right)$.
$8\left(-\frac{1}{2}\right)^4 - 4\left(-\frac{1}{2}\right)^3 + a\left(-\frac{1}{2}\right)^2 - 1 = 3$	Compare $(2x + 1)$ to $(ax - b)$, so $a = 2$, $b = -1$ and the remainder is $f\left(-\frac{1}{2}\right)$.
$8\left(\frac{1}{16}\right) - 4\left(-\frac{1}{8}\right) + a\left(\frac{1}{4}\right) - 1 = 3$	
$\frac{1}{2} + \frac{1}{2} + \frac{1}{4}a - 1 = 3$	Using the fact that the remainder is 3, substitute $x = -\frac{1}{2}$ and solve the equation for a.
$\frac{1}{4}a = 3$	
$a = 12$	$\left(-\frac{1}{2}\right)^3 = -\frac{1}{2} \times -\frac{1}{2} \times -\frac{1}{2} = -\frac{1}{8}$

Exercise 3C

1 Find the remainder when:

    a $4x^3 - 5x^2 + 7x + 1$ is divided by $(x - 2)$

    b $2x^5 - 32x^3 + x - 10$ is divided by $(x - 4)$

    c $-2x^3 + 6x^2 + 5x - 3$ is divided by $(x + 1)$

    d $7x^3 + 6x^2 - 45x + 1$ is divided by $(x + 3)$

2 When $2x^3 - 3x^2 - 2x + a$ is divided by $(x - 1)$ the remainder is 24. Find the value of a.

3 When $-3x^3 + 4x^2 + bx + 6$ is divided by $(x + 2)$ the remainder is 10. Find the value of b.

4 When $16x^3 - 32x^2 + cx - 8$ is divided by $(2x - 1)$ the remainder is 1. Find the value of c.

5 Show that $(2x - 1)$ is a factor of $2x^3 + 17x^2 + 31x - 20$.

6 $f(x) = x^2 + 3x + q$. Given $f(2) = 3$, find $f(-2)$.

> **Hint for question 6:**
> First find q.

7 $g(x) = x^3 + ax^2 + 3x + 6$. Given $g(-1) = 2$, find the remainder when $g(x)$ is divided by $(3x - 2)$.

8 The expression $2x^3 - x^2 + ax + b$ gives a remainder 14 when divided by $(x - 2)$ and a remainder -86 when divided by $(x + 3)$. Find the values of a and b.

9 The expression $3x^3 + 2x^2 - px + q$ is divisible by $(x - 1)$ but leaves a remainder of 10 when divided by $(x + 1)$.
Find the values of a and b.

> **Hint for question 9:**
> Solve simultaneous equations.

3.4 You can use the substitution method to solve simultaneous equations where one equation is linear and the other is quadratic.

Example 8

Solve the equations:

a $x + 2y = 3$
    $x^2 + 3xy = 10$

b $3x - 2y = 1$
    $x^2 + y^2 = 25$

a $x = 3 - 2y$ ⟶ Rearrange the linear equation to get $x = \ldots$ or $y = \ldots$ (here $x = \ldots$).

$(3 - 2y)^2 + 3y(3 - 2y) = 10$ ⟶ Substitute this into the quadratic equation (here in place of x).

$9 - 12y + 4y^2 + 9y - 6y^2 = 10$

$-2y^2 - 3y - 1 = 0$

$-2y^2 + 3y + 1 = 0$

$(2y + 1)(y + 1) = 0$

$(3 - 2y)^2$ means $(3 - 2y)(3 - 2y)$ (see Chapter 2).

Solve for y using factorisation.

$y = \frac{1}{2}$ or $y = -1$

So $x = 4$ or $x = 5$ ⟶ Find the corresponding x-values by substituting the y-values into $x = 3 - 2y$.

Solutions are $x = 4$, $y = -\frac{1}{2}$
and $x = 5$, $y = -1$

There are two solution pairs. The graph of the linear equation (straight line) would intersect the graph of the quadratic (curve) at two points.

b $3x - 2y = 1$

$2y = 3x - 1$

$y = \frac{3x - 1}{2}$ ⟶ Find $y = \ldots$ from linear equation.

$x^2 + \left(\frac{3x - 1}{2}\right)^2 = 25$ ⟶ Substitute $y = \frac{3x - 1}{2}$ into the quadratic equation to form an equation in x.

$x^2 + \left(\frac{9x^2 - 6x + 1}{4}\right) = 25$ ⟶ Now multiply by 4.

$4x^2 + 9x^2 - 6x + 1 = 100$

$13x^2 - 6x - 99 = 0$

$(13x + 33)(x - 3) = 0$ ⟶ Solve for x.

$x = -\frac{33}{13}$ or $x = 3$

$y = -\frac{56}{13}$ or $y = 4$ ⟶ Substitute x-values into $y = \frac{3x - 1}{2}$.

Solutions are $x = 3$, $y = 4$
and $x = -\frac{3}{13}$, $y = -\frac{56}{13}$

Exercise 3D

1 Solve the simultaneous equations:

    a $x + y = 11$
         $xy = 30$

    b $2x + y = 1$
         $x^2 + y^2 = 1$

    c $y = 3x$
         $2y^2 - xy = 15$

    d $x + y = 9$
         $x^2 - 3xy + 2y^2 = 0$

    e $3a + b = 8$
         $3a^2 + b^2 = 28$

    f $2u + v = 7$
         $uv = 6$

2 Find the coordinates of the points at which the line with equation $y = x - 4$ intersects the curve with equation $y^2 = 2x^2 - 17$.

3 Find the coordinates of the points at which the line with equation $y = 3x - 1$ intersects the curve with equation $y^2 - xy = 15$.

4 Solve the simultaneous equations:

    a $3x + 2y = 7$
         $x^2 + y = 8$

    b $2x + 2y = 7$
         $x^2 - 4y^2 = 8$

5 Solve the simultaneous equations, giving your answers in their simplest surd form:

    a $x - y = 6$
         $xy = 4$

    b $2x + 3y = 13$
         $x^2 + y^2 = 78$

3.5 *You can solve linear inequalities using similar methods to those for solving linear equations.*

- **When you multiply or divide an inequality by a negative number, you need to reverse the inequality sign.**

Example 9

Find the set of values of x for which:

    a $2x - 5 < 7$
    b $5x + 9 \geqslant x + 20$
    c $12 - 3x < 27$
    d $3(x - 5) > 5 - 2(x - 8)$

    a $2x - 5 < 7$

           $2x < 12$ Add 5 to both sides.

            $x < 6$ Divide both sides by 2.

    b $5x + 9 \geqslant x + 20$

        $4x + 9 \geqslant 20$ Subtract x from both sides.

           $4x \geqslant 11$ Subtract 9 from both sides.

           $x \geqslant 2.75$ Divide both sides by 4.

    c $12 - 3x < 27$ For **c**, two approaches are shown:

         $-3x < 15$ Subtract 12 from both sides.

           $x > -5$ Divide both sides by -3. (You therefore need to turn round the inequality sign.)

       $12 - 3x < 27$

          $12 < 27 + 3x$ Add $3x$ to both sides.

         $-15 < 3x$ Subtract 27 from both sides.

          $-5 < x$ Divide both sides by 3.

           $x > -5$ Rewrite with x on LHS.

d $3(x - 5) > 5 - 2(x - 8)$

$\qquad 3x - 15 > 5 - 2x + 16 \qquad$ Multiply out (note: $-2 \times -8 = +16$).

$\qquad\quad 5x > 5 + 16 + 15 \qquad$ Add 15 to both sides.

$\qquad\quad 5x > 36$

$\qquad\qquad x > 7.2 \qquad\qquad$ Divide both sides by 5.

Example 10

Find the set of values of x for which:

$\qquad x - 5 > 1 - x$ and $15 - 3x > 5 + 2x$

$\begin{array}{ll} x - 5 > 1 - x & \qquad 15 - 3x > 5 + 2x \\ 2x - 5 > 1 & \qquad 10 - 3x > 2x \\ \quad 2x > 6 & \qquad\quad 10 > 5x \\ \quad\; x > 3 & \qquad\qquad 2 > x \\ & \qquad\qquad\; x < 2 \end{array}$

Draw a number line. Note that there is no overlap between the two sets of values.

So there are no values of x for which both inequalities are true together.

Exercise 3E

1 Find the set of values of x for which:

a	$2x - 3 < 5$	**b**	$5x + 4 \geqslant 39$
c	$6x - 3 > 2x + 7$	**d**	$5x + 6 \leqslant -12 - x$
e	$15 - x > 4$	**f**	$21 - 2x > 8 + 3x$
g	$1 + x < 25 + 3x$	**h**	$7x - 7 < 7 - 7x$
i	$5 - 0.5x \geqslant 1$	**j**	$5x + 4 > 12 - 2x$

2 Find the set of values of x for which:

a	$2(x - 3) \geqslant 0$	**b**	$8(1 - x) > x - 1$
c	$3(x + 7) \leqslant 8 - x$	**d**	$2(x - 3) - (x + 12) < 0$
e	$1 + 11(2 - x) < 10(x - 4)$	**f**	$2(x - 5) \geqslant 3(4 - x)$
g	$12x - 3(x - 3) < 45$	**h**	$x - 2(5 + 2x) < 11$
i	$x(x - 4) \geqslant x^2 + 2$	**j**	$x(5 - x) \geqslant 3 + x - x^2$

3 Find the set of values of x for which:

a $3(x - 2) > x - 4$ and $4x + 12 > 2x + 17$

b $2x - 5 < x - 1$ and $7(x + 1) > 23 - x$

c $2x - 3 > 2$ and $3(x + 2) < 12 + x$

d $15 - x < 2(11 - x)$ and $5(3x - 1) > 12x + 19$

e $3x + 8 \leqslant 20$ and $2(3x - 7) \geqslant x + 6$

3.6 *To solve a quadratic inequality you*
- *solve the corresponding quadratic equation, then*
- *sketch the graph of the quadratic function, then*
- *use your sketch to find the required set of values.*

Example 11

Find the set of values of x for which $x^2 - 4x - 5 < 0$ and draw a sketch to show this.

$x^2 - 4x - 5 = 0$ Quadratic equation.

$(x + 1)(x - 5) = 0$ Factorise (or use the quadratic formula). (See Section 2.4.)

$x = -1$ or $x = 5$ -1 and 5 are called critical values.

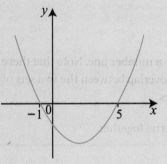

Your sketch does not need to be accurate. All you really need to know is that the graph is '∪-shaped' and crosses the x-axis at -1 and 5.

$x^2 - 4x - 5 < 0$ ($y < 0$) for the part of the graph below the x-axis, as shown by the paler part in the rough sketch.

So the required set of values is $-1 < x < 5$.

Example 12

Find the set of values of x for which $3 - 5x - 2x^2 < 0$ and sketch the graph of $y = 3 - 5x - 2x^2$.

$3 - 5x - 2x^2 = 0$ Quadratic equation.

$2x^2 + 5x - 3 = 0$ Multiply by -1 (so it's easier to factorise).

$(2x - 1)(x + 3) = 0$

$x = \frac{1}{2}$ or $x = -3$ $\frac{1}{2}$ and -3 are the critical values.

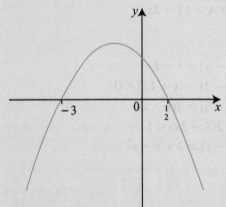

Since the coefficient of x^2 is negative, the graph is 'upside-down ∪-shaped' and crosses the x-axis at -3 and $\frac{1}{2}$.

$3 - 5x - 2x^2 < 0$ ($y < 0$) for the outer parts of the graph, below the x-axis, as shown by the paler parts in the rough sketch.

So the required set of values is $x < -3$ or $x > \frac{1}{2}$.

You may have to rearrange the quadratic inequality to get all the terms 'on one side' before you can solve it, as shown in the next example.

Example 13

Find the set of values of x for which $12 + 4x > x^2$.

1. $12 + 4x > x^2$

$12 + 4x - x^2 > 0$

$x^2 - 4x - 12 = 0$

$(x + 2)(x - 6) = 0$

$x = -2$ or $x = 6$

There are two possible approaches depending on which side of the inequality sign you put the expression.

Sketch of $y = 12 + 4x - x^2$

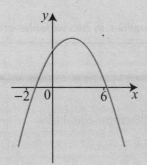

$12 + 4x - x^2 > 0$

Solution: $-2 < x < 6$

2. $12 + 4x > x^2$

$0 > x^2 - 4x - 12$

$x^2 - 4x - 12 < 0$

$x^2 - 4x - 12 = 0$

$(x + 2)(x - 6) = 0$

$x = -2$ or $x = 6$

Sketch of $y = x^2 - 4x - 12$

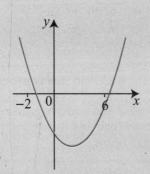

$x^2 - 4x - 12 < 0$

Solution: $-2 < x < 6$

Exercise 3F

1 Find the set of values of x for which:

  a $x^2 - 11x + 24 < 0$ **b** $12 - x - x^2 > 0$ **c** $x^2 - 3x - 10 > 0$

  d $x^2 + 7x + 12 \geqslant 0$ **e** $7 + 13x - 2x^2 > 0$ **f** $10 + x - 2x^2 < 0$

  g $4x^2 - 8x + 3 \leqslant 0$ **h** $-2 + 7x - 3x^2 < 0$ **i** $x^2 - 9 < 0$

  j $6x^2 + 11x - 10 > 0$ **k** $x^2 - 5x > 0$ **l** $2x^2 + 3x \leqslant 0$

2 Find the set of values of x for which:

  a $x^2 < 10 - 3x$ **b** $11 < x^2 + 10$

  c $x(3 - 2x) > 1$ **d** $x(x + 11) < 3(1 - x^2)$

3.7 *You can represent linear inequalities in two variables graphically*

Example 14

Find the region satisfied by the following inequalities

$$y \geqslant 0, \quad y - x < 1, \quad x + y \leqslant 3$$

First draw some axes and the lines
$y = 0, y - x = 1$ and $x + y = 3$

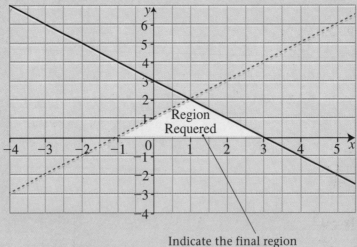

There is a convention that if the inequality is $<$ or $>$ the line is dotted. If the inequality is $\leqslant$ or $\geqslant$ the line is solid.

Region Requered

Pick a point, $(0,0)$ is usually easy to use, and determine whether your point satisfies each inequality. Shade out the unwanted region.

Indicate the final region

The following example illustrates a problem in **linear programming**

Example 15

A manufacturer makes two types of chair and the cost of materials and hours of labour for each chair are given in the table below.

	Materials	Labour
Chair A	£5	2 hours
Chair B	£7	1.5 hours

The manufacturer has a budget of £140 and 42 hours of labour available.

Find the maximum number of chairs that can be made and how many of each type.

Let x = number of chair A First formulate some inequalities
    y = number of chair B

Clearly $x > 0$ and $y > 0$

Cost of materials

    $5x + 7y \leqslant 140$ Using the budget of £140

Time in labour

    $2x + 1.5y \leqslant 42$ Since only 42 hours of labour is available

Now draw the lines on a graph

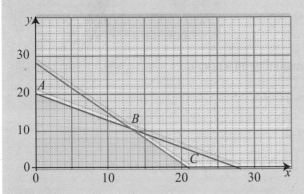

Any value in the unshaded region could be manufactured.
But the maximum value will be close to one of the vertices of the regions marked
A, B and C.

Point C (21 chairs) is better than point A (20 chairs) so compare C and B.

The point B is the intersection of the two lines i.e (13, 10.7).

The point (13, 10) (= 23 chairs) satisfies both inequalities since
Materials cost : £65 + £70 = £135
Labour: 26 + 15 = 41 hours

So the maximum number of chairs is 23,   Check that final position satisfies both
13 of type A and 10 of type B inequalities.

Exercise 3G

For Questions 1-8, describe the **unshaded** region in the graph.

1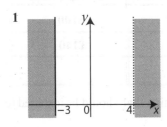

2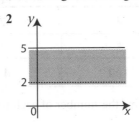

3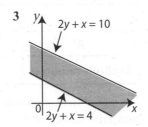

4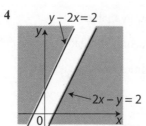

5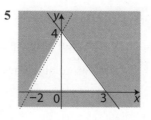

6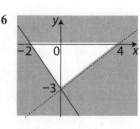

7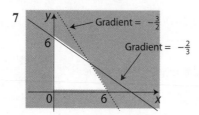

8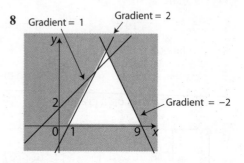

For Questions 9–12, illustrate each inequality on a graph.

9 $y \geq 2x$, $x + 2y \leq 4$ and $y + 2x > 1$

10 $2y > x$, $y + 2x \leq 4$ and $y > 2x + 2$

11 $x \geq 0$, $y > 0$, $y < \dfrac{x}{2} + 4$ and $y \leq 6 - 2x$

12 $x > 0$, $y \geq 0$, $3x + 4y \leq 12$ and $5x + 2y \leq 10$

13 A club hires a minibus for a pantomime trip.
The number of passengers must be no more than 14 and the cost of hiring the minibus is £72. The club advertises the trip at £8 for children and £12 for adults but insists that there should be more children than adults and at least two adults.

   a Write down some inequalities and represent these graphically to describe the constraints on this trip.

   b Find the smallest-sized group the club can take and still cover the cost of the trip.

       Any money raised over £72 will be used to buy refreshments in the interval.

   c Find the maximum amount that could be available for refreshments and state how many children and adults will be on the trip.

14 The table below gives details of some new machines being installed in a factory and the weekly profit from each machine.

Machine	Floor area (m²)	No. of operators	Weekly profit
A	4	2	£100
B	5	3	£140
Available resources	100	40	

Use a graphical approach to find the number of each machine that should be installed to maximise weekly profit.

15 A manufacturer makes two kinds of ornament. The machine time and craftsman's time along with the profit for each ornament are shown in the table below.

	Machine Time (h)	Craftsman's Time (h)	Profit
Ornament A	3	1.5	£12
Ornament B	2	2.5	£15
Timeavailable	48	45	

The manufacturer wishes to maximise profit.
Use a graphical approach to find the number of each type of ornament that should be made.

Mixed Exercise 3H

1 Solve the simultaneous equations:
$$x + 2y = 3$$
$$x^2 - 4y^2 = -33$$

2 Show that the elimination of x from the simultaneous equations
$$x - 2y = 1$$
$$3xy - y^2 = 8$$
produces the equation
$$5y^2 + 3y - 8 = 0.$$
Solve this quadratic equation and hence find the pairs (x, y) for which the simultaneous equations are satisfied.
© Edexcel Limited

3 Solve the simultaneous equations:
$$x + 2y = 3$$
$$x^2 - 2y + 4y^2 = 18$$
© Edexcel Limited

4 a Solve the inequality $3x - 8 > x + 13$.

  b Solve the inequality $x^2 - 5x - 14 > 0$.
© Edexcel Limited

5 Find the set of values of x for which $(x - 1)(x - 4) < 2(x - 4)$.

6 Find the set of values of x for which:

  a $6x - 7 < 2x + 3$

  b $2x^2 - 11x + 5 < 0$

  c both $6x - 7 < 2x + 3$ and $2x^2 - 11x + 5 < 0$.
© Edexcel Limited

7 Find algebraically the set of values of x for which $(2x - 3)(x + 2) > 3(x - 2)$.
© Edexcel Limited

8 Show that $(x - 3)$ is a factor of $2x^3 - 2x^2 - 17x + 15$. Hence express $2x^3 - 2x^2 - 17x + 15$ in the form $(x - 3)(Ax^2 + Bx + C)$, where the values A, B and C are to be found.

9 Show that $(x - 2)$ is a factor of $x^3 + 4x^2 - 3x - 18$. Hence express $x^3 + 4x^2 - 3x - 18$ in the form $(x - 2)(px + q)^2$, where the values p and q are to be found.

10 Factorise completely $2x^3 + 3x^2 - 18x + 8$.

11 Find the value of k if $(x - 2)$ is a factor of $x^3 - 3x^2 + kx - 10$.

12 Find the remainder when $16x^5 - 20x^4 + 8$ is divided by $(2x - 1)$.

Chapter 3: Identities and inequalities

13 $f(x) = 2x^2 + px + q$. Given that $f(-3) = 0$, and $f(4) = 21$:

   a find the value of p and q

   b factorise $f(x)$

14 $h(x) = x^3 + 4x^2 + rx + s$. Given $h(-1) = 0$, and $h(2) = 30$:

   a find the value of r and s

   b find the remainder when $h(x)$ is divided by $(3x - 1)$

15 $g(x) = 2x^3 + 9x^2 - 6x - 5$.

   a Factorise $g(x)$

   b Solve $g(x) = 0$

16 The remainder obtained when $x^3 - 5x^2 + px + 6$ is divided by $(x + 2)$ is equal to the remainder obtained when the same expression is divided by $(x - 3)$.
Find the value of p.

17 The remainder obtained when $x^3 + dx^2 - 5x + 6$ is divided by $(x - 1)$ is twice the remainder obtained when the same expression is divided by $(x + 1)$.
Find the value of d.

18 **a** Show that $(x - 2)$ is a factor of $f(x) = x^3 + x^2 - 5x - 2$.

   b Hence, or otherwise, find the exact solutions of the equation $f(x) = 0$.   © Edexcel Limited

19 Given that -1 is a root of the equation $2x^3 - 5x^2 - 4x + 3$, find the two positive roots.   © Edexcel Limited

20 Write down the four pairs of inequalities that describe the regions A, B, C and D.

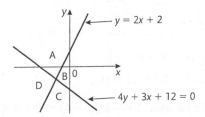

21 Write down the inequalities that define the unshaded region marked A on the graph.

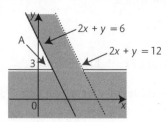

22 Illustrate the region that satisfies the inequalities $y \leqslant \dfrac{x}{2} + 3$, $y > 3x - 4$ and $y + 2x + 4 > 0$.

1   If f(x) is a polynomial and f(a) = 0, then ($x - a$) is a factor of f(x).

2   If f(x) is a polynomial and f$\left(\dfrac{b}{a}\right)$ = 0, then ($ax - b$) is a factor of f(x).

3   If a polynomial f(x) is divided by ($ax - b$) then the remainder is f$\left(\dfrac{b}{a}\right)$.

4   When you multiply or divide an inequality by a negative number, you need to reverse the inequality sign.

5   To solve a quadratic inequality you
   • solve the corresponding quadratic equation, then
   • sketch the graph of the quadratic function, then
   • use your sketch to find the required set of values.

You can sketch cubic curves of the form y = ax³ + bx² + cx + d.

Example 1

Sketch the curve with the equation $y = (x - 2)(x - 1)(x + 1)$

$0 = (x - 2)(x - 1)(x + 1)$

So $x = 2$ or $x = 1$ or $x = -1$

So the curve crosses the x-axis at $(2, 0) (1, 0)$ and $(-1, 0)$.

When $x = 0, y = -2 \times -1 \times 1 = 2$

So the curve crosses the y-axis at $(0, 2)$.

Put $y = 0$ and solve for x to find the roots (the points where the curve crosses the x-axis).

Put $x = 0$ to find where the curve crosses the y-axis.

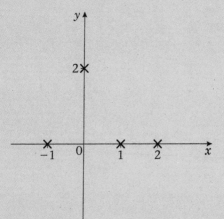

When x is large and positive, y is large and positive.
When x is large and negative, y is large and negative.

Check what happens to y for large positive and negative values of x.

You can write this as
$x \to \infty, y \to \infty$
$x \to -\infty, y \to -\infty$

$x \to \infty, y \to \infty$

This is called a maximum point because the gradient changes from +ve to 0 to −ve.

This is called a minimum point because the gradient changes from −ve to 0 to +ve.

$x \to -\infty, y \to -\infty$

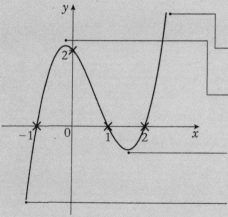

In your exam you will not be expected to work out the coordinates of the maximum or minimum points without further work, but you should mark points where the curve meets the axes.

Example 2

Sketch the curves with the following equations and show the points where they cross the coordinate axes.

a $y = (x - 2)(1 - x)(1 + x)$

b $y = x(x + 1)(x + 2)$

a $0 = (x - 2)(1 - x)(1 + x)$

So $x = 2, x = 1$ or $x = -1$ ·Put $y = 0$ and solve for x.

So the curve crosses the x-axis at $(2, 0), (1, 0)$ and $(-1, 0)$.

When $x = 0, y = -2 \times 1 \times 1 = -2$ Find the value of y when $x = 0$.

So the curve crosses the y-axis at $(0, -2)$.

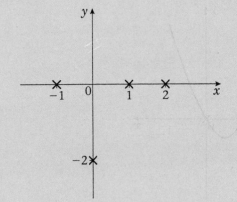

$x \to \infty, y \to -\infty$ Check what happens to y for large.

$x \to -\infty, y \to \infty$ positive and negative values of x

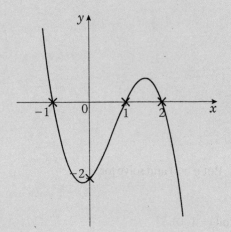

Notice that this curve is a reflection in the x-axis of the curve in Example 1.

b $y = x(x + 1)(x + 2)$

   $0 = x(x + 1)(x + 2)$ Put $y = 0$ and solve for x.

   So $x = 0$, $x = -1$ or $x = -2$

So the curve crosses the x-axis at $(0, 0)$, $(-1, 0)$ and $(-2, 0)$.

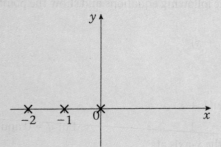

$x \rightarrow \infty, y \rightarrow \infty$ Check what happens to y for large positive
$x \rightarrow -\infty, y \rightarrow -\infty$ and negative values of x.

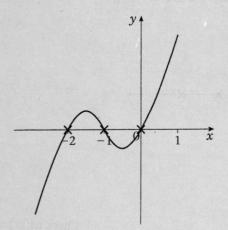

Example 3

Sketch the following curves.

a $y = (x - 1)^2(x + 1)$

b $y = x^3 - 2x^2 - 3x$

a $y = (x - 1)^2 (x + 1)$

   $0 = (x - 1)^2 (x + 1)$ Put $y = 0$ and solve for x.

   So $x = 1$ or $x = -1$.

So the curve crosses the x-axis at $(1, 0)$ and $(-1, 0)$.

When $x = 0$, $y = (-1)^2 \times 1 = 1$ Find the value of y when $x = 0$.

So the curve crosses the y-axis at $(0, 1)$.

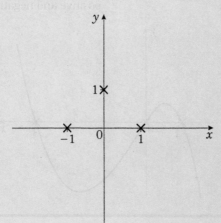

$x \rightarrow \infty, y \rightarrow \infty$

$x \rightarrow -\infty, y \rightarrow -\infty$

Check what happens to y for large positive and negative values of x.

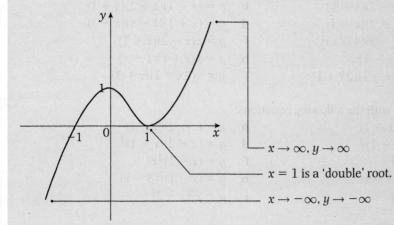

$x \rightarrow \infty, y \rightarrow \infty$

$x = 1$ is a 'double' root.

$x \rightarrow -\infty, y \rightarrow -\infty$

b $y = x^3 - 2x^2 - 3x$

$= x(x^2 - 2x - 3)$

$= x(x - 3)(x + 1)$

First factorise.

$0 = x(x - 3)(x + 1)$

So $x = 0$, $x = 3$ or $x = -1$

So the curve crosses the x-axis at $(0, 0)$, $(3, 0)$ and $(-1, 0)$.

So the curve crosses the y-axis at $(0, 0)$.

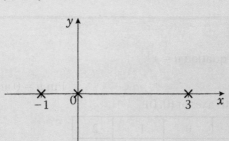

$x \to \infty, y \to \infty$

$x \to -\infty, y \to -\infty$

Check what happens to y for large positive and negative values of x.

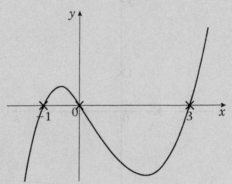

Exercise 4A

1 Sketch the following curves and indicate clearly the points of intersection with the axes:

a $y = (x - 3)(x - 2)(x + 1)$ **b** $y = (x - 1)(x + 2)(x + 3)$

c $y = (x + 1)(x + 2)(x + 3)$ **d** $y = (x + 1)(1 - x)(x + 3)$

e $y = (x - 2)(x - 3)(4 - x)$ **f** $y = x(x - 2)(x + 1)$

g $y = x(x + 1)(x - 1)$ **h** $y = x(x + 1)(1 - x)$

i $y = (x - 2)(2x - 1)(2x + 1)$ **j** $y = x(2x - 1)(x + 3)$

2 Sketch the curves with the following equations:

a $y = (x + 1)^2(x - 1)$ **b** $y = (x + 2)(x - 1)^2$

c $y = (2 - x)(x + 1)^2$ **d** $y = (x - 2)(x + 1)^2$

e $y = x^2(x + 2)$ **f** $y = (x - 1)^2 x$

g $y = (1 - x)^2(3 + x)$ **h** $y = (x - 1)^2(3 - x)$

i $y = x^2(2 - x)$ **j** $y = x^2(x - 2)$

3 Factorise the following equations and then sketch the curves:

a $y = x^3 + x^2 - 2x$ **b** $y = x^3 + 5x^2 + 4x$

c $y = x^3 + 2x^2 + x$ **d** $y = 3x + 2x^2 - x^3$

e $y = x^3 - x^2$ **f** $y = x - x^3$

g $y = 12x^3 - 3x$ **h** $y = x^3 - x^2 - 2x$

i $y = x^3 - 9x$ **j** $y = x^3 - 9x^2$

4.2 *You need to be able to sketch and interpret graphs of cubic functions of the form $y = x^3$*

Example 4

Sketch the curve with equation $y = x^3$.

$0 = x^3$ Put $y = 0$ and solve for x.

So the curve crosses both axes at $(0, 0)$.

x	-2	-1	0	1	2
$y = x^3$	-8	-1	0	1	8

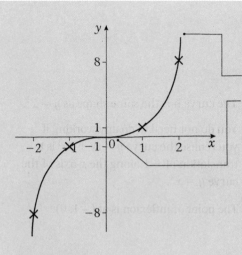

As the curve passes the axes at only one point, find its shape by plotting a few points.

Notice that as x increases, y increases rapidly.

The curve is 'flat' at $(0, 0)$. This point is called a point of inflexion. The gradient is positive just before $(0, 0)$ and positive just after $(0, 0)$.

Notice that the shape of this curve is the same as the curve with equation $y = (x + 1)^3$, which is shown in Example 5.

Example 5

Sketch the curve with equations:

a $y = -x^3$

b $y = (x + 1)^3$

c $y = (3 - x)^3$

Show their positions relative to the curve with equation $y = x^3$.

a $y = -x^3$

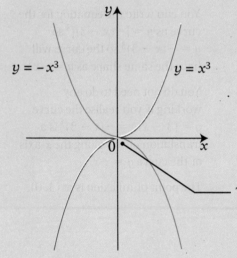

You do not need to plot any points. It is quicker if you realise the curve $y = 2x^3$ is a reflection in the x-axis of the curve $y = x^3$. You can check this by looking at the values used to sketch $y = x^3$. So, for example, $x = 2$ will now correspond to $y = -8$ on the curve $y = 2x^3$.

The curve is still flat at $(0, 0)$.

b $y = (x + 1)^3$

$0 = (x + 1)^3$ Put $y = 0$ to find where the curve crosses the x-axis.

So $x = -1$

So the curve crosses the x-axis at $(-1, 0)$.

When $x = 0$, $y = 1^3 = 1$ Put $x = 0$ to find where the curve crosses the y-axis.

So the curve crosses the y-axis at $(0, 1)$.

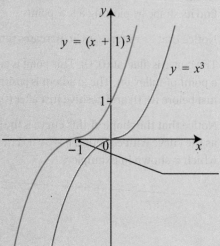

The curve has the same shape as $y = x^3$.

You do not need to do any working if you realise the curve $y = (x + 1)^3$ is a translation of -1 along the x-axis of the curve $y = x^3$.

The point of inflexion is at $(-1, 0)$.

c $y = (3 - x)^3$

$0 = (3 - x)^3$ Put $y = 0$ to find where the curve crosses the x-axis.

So $x = 3$

So the curve crosses the x-axis at $(3, 0)$.

When $x = 0$, $y = 3^3 = 27$ Put $x = 0$ to find where the curve crosses the y-axis.

So the curve crosses the y-axis at $(0, 27)$.

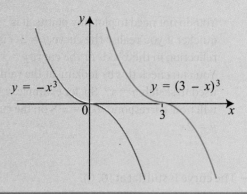

You can write the equation for the curve as $y = [-(x - 3)]^3$ so $y = -(x - 3)^3$ so the curve will have the same shape as $y = -x^3$.

You do not need to do any working if you realise the curve $y = (3 - x)^3 = -(x - 3)^3$ is a translation of $+3$ along the x-axis of the curve $y = -x^3$.

The point of inflexion is at $(3, 0)$.

Exercise 4B

1 Sketch the following curves and show their positions relative to the curve $y = x^3$:

   a $y = (x - 2)^3$ **b** $y = (2 - x)^3$ **c** $y = (x - 1)^3$

   d $y = (x + 2)^3$ **e** $y = -(x + 2)^3$

2 Sketch the following and indicate the coordinates of the points where the curves cross the axes:

   a $y = (x + 3)^3$ **b** $y = (x - 3)^3$ **c** $y = (1 - x)^3$

   d $y = -(x - 2)^3$ **e** $y = -(x - \frac{1}{2})^3$

4.3 *You need to be able to sketch the reciprocal function* $y = \dfrac{k}{x}$ *where k is a constant.*

Example 6

Sketch the curve $y = \dfrac{1}{x}$ and its asymptotes.

$y = \dfrac{1}{x}$

When $x = 0$, y is not defined.

When $y = 0$, x is not defined.

$x \to +\infty, y \to 0$

$x \to -\infty, y \to 0$

$y \to +\infty, x \to 0$

$y \to -\infty, x \to 0$

$y = \dfrac{1}{x}$

The curve does not cross the axes.

The curve tends towards the x-axis when x is large and positive or large and negative. The x-axis is a horizontal asymptote.

The curve tends towards the y-axis when y is large and positive or large and negative. The y-axis is a vertical asymptote.

x	-1	$-\frac{1}{2}$	$-\frac{1}{4}$	$\frac{1}{4}$	$\frac{1}{2}$	1
$y = \frac{1}{x}$	-1	-2	-4	4	2	1

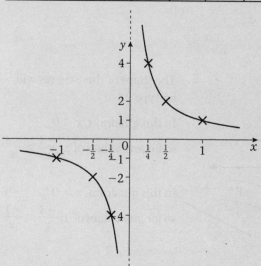

The curve does not cross the x-axis or y-axis. You need to plot some points.

You can draw a dashed line to indicate an asymptote. (In this case the asymptotes are the axes.)

- **The curves with equations** $y = \dfrac{k}{x}$ **fall into two categories:**

Type 1

$y = \dfrac{k}{x}, k > 0$

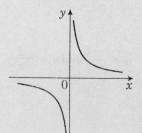

Type 2

$y = \dfrac{k}{x}, k < 0$

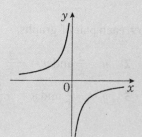

Example 7

Sketch on the same diagram:

a $y = \dfrac{4}{x}$ and $y = \dfrac{12}{x}$

b $y = -\dfrac{1}{x}$ and $y = -\dfrac{3}{x}$

a

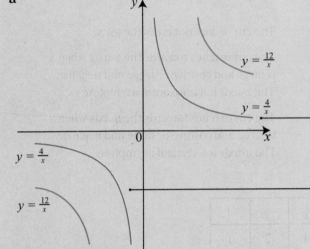

The shape of these curves will be Type 1.

In this quadrant, $x > 0$ so for any values of x: $\dfrac{12}{x} > \dfrac{4}{x}$

In this quadrant, $x < 0$ so for any values of x: $\dfrac{12}{x} > \dfrac{4}{x}$

b

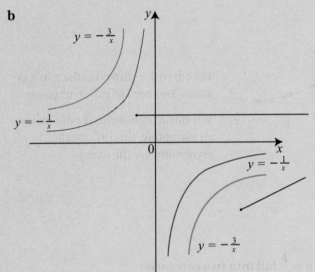

The shape of these curves will be Type 2.

In this quadrant, $x < 0$ so for any values of x: $\dfrac{-3}{x} > \dfrac{-1}{x}$

In this quadrant, $x > 0$ so for any values of x: $\dfrac{-3}{x} < \dfrac{-1}{x}$

Exercise 4C

Use a separate diagram to sketch each pair of graphs.

1 $y = \dfrac{2}{x}$ and $y = \dfrac{4}{x}$

2 $y = \dfrac{2}{x}$ and $y = -\dfrac{2}{x}$

3 $y = -\dfrac{4}{x}$ and $y = -\dfrac{2}{x}$

4 $y = \dfrac{3}{x}$ and $y = \dfrac{8}{x}$

5 $y = -\dfrac{3}{x}$ and $y = -\dfrac{8}{x}$

4.4 You can sketch curves of functions to show points of intersection and solutions to equations.

Example 8

a On the same diagram sketch the curves with equations $y = x(x - 3)$ and $y = x^2(1 - x)$.

b Find the coordinates of the point of intersection.

a $y = x(x - 3)$
    $0 = x(x - 3)$ Put $y = 0$ and solve for x.

So $x = 0$ or $x = 3$.
So the curve crosses the x-axis at $(0, 0)$ and $(3, 0)$.

$y = x^2(1 - x)$
$0 = x^2(1 - x)$ Put $y = 0$ and solve for x to find
                               where the curve crosses the x-axis.

So $x = 0$ or $x = 1$.
So the curve crosses the x-axis at $(0, 0)$ or $(1, 0)$.
The curve crosses the y-axis at $(0, 0)$.

$x \to \infty,\ y \to -\infty$ Check what happens to y for large positive
$x \to -\infty,\ y \to +\infty$ and negative values of x.

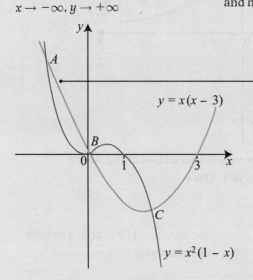

A cubic curve is always steeper than a quadratic curve, so it will cross over somewhere on this side of the y-axis.

b From the graph there are three points where the curves cross, labelled A, B and C. The x-coordinates are given by the solutions to the equation.

$$x(x - 3) = x^2(1 - x)$$
$$x^2 - 3x = x^2 - x^3 \quad \text{Multiply out brackets.}$$
$$x^3 - 3x = 0 \quad \text{Collect terms on one side.}$$
$$x(x^2 - 3) = 0 \quad \text{Factorise.}$$
$$x(x - \sqrt{3})(x + \sqrt{3}) = 0 \quad \text{Factorise using a difference of 2 squares.}$$

So $x = -\sqrt{3}, 0, \sqrt{3}$

You can use the equation $y = x^2(1 - x)$ to find the y-coordinates.
So the point where x is negative is $A(-\sqrt{3}, 3[1 + \sqrt{3}])$, B is $(0, 0)$ and C is the point $(\sqrt{3}, 3[1 - \sqrt{3}])$.

Example 9

a On the same diagram sketch the curves with equations $y = x^2(x - 1)$ and $y = \dfrac{2}{x}$.

b Explain how your sketch shows that there are two solutions to the equation
$x^2(x - 1) - \dfrac{2}{x} = 0$.

a
$$y = x^2(x - 1)$$
$$0 = x^2(x - 1) \qquad \text{Put } y = 0 \text{ and solve for } x.$$

So $x = 0$ or $x = 1$.
So the curve crosses the x-axis at $(0, 0)$ and $(1, 0)$.
The curve crosses the y-axis at $(0, 0)$.

$x \to \infty, y \to \infty$

$x \to \infty, y \to -\infty$

Check what happens to y for large positive and negative values of x.

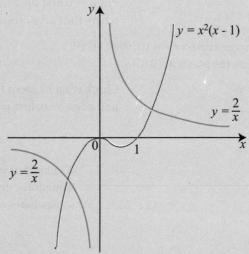

b From the sketch there are only two points of intersection of the curves.
This means there are only two values of x where

$$x^2(x - 1) = \dfrac{2}{x}$$

or $\qquad x^2(x - 1) - \dfrac{2}{x} = 0$

You would not be expected to solve this equation.

So this equation has two solutions.

Exercise 4D

1 In each case:

  i sketch the two curves on the same axes

  ii state the number of points of intersection

  iii write down a suitable equation which would give the x-coordinates of these points.
    (You are not required to solve this equation.)

  a $y = x^2, y = x(x^2 - 1)$ **b** $y = x(x + 2), y = -\dfrac{3}{x}$

  c $y = x^2, y = (x + 1)(x - 1)^2$ **d** $y = x^2(1 - x), y = -\dfrac{2}{x}$

e $y = x(x - 4)$, $y = \dfrac{1}{x}$

f $y = x(x - 4)$, $y = -\dfrac{1}{x}$

g $y = x(x - 4)$, $y = (x - 2)^3$

h $y = -x^3$, $y = -\dfrac{2}{x}$

i $y = -x^3$, $y = x^2$

j $y = -x^3$, $y = -x(x + 2)$

> **Hint:**
> In **If** check the point with $x = 2$ in both curves.

2 **a** On the same axes sketch the curves given by $y = x^2(x - 4)$ and $y = x(4 - x)$.

     b Find the coordinates of the points of intersection.

3 **a** On the same axes sketch the curves given by $y = x(2x + 5)$ and $y = x(1 + x)^2$

     b Find the coordinates of the points of intersection.

4 **a** On the same axes sketch the curves given by $y = (x - 1)^3$ and $y = (x - 1)(1 + x)$.

     b Find the coordinates of the points of intersection.

5 **a** On the same axes sketch the curves given by $y = x^2$ and $y = -\dfrac{27}{x}$.

     b Find the coordinates of the point of intersection.

6 **a** On the same axes sketch the curves given by $y = x^2 - 2x$ and $y = x(x - 2)(x - 3)$.

     b Find the coordinates of the point of intersection.

7 **a** On the same axes sketch the curves given by $y = x^2(x - 3)$ and $y = \dfrac{2}{x}$.

     b Explain how your sketch shows that there are only two solutions to the equation $x^3(x - 3) = 2$.

8 **a** On the same axes sketch the curves given by $y = (x + 1)^3$ and $y = 3x(x - 1)$.

     b Explain how your sketch shows that there is only one solution to the equation $x^3 + 6x + 1 = 0$.

9 **a** On the same axes sketch the curves given by $y = \dfrac{1}{x}$ and $y = -x(x - 1)^2$.

     b Explain how your sketch shows that there are no solutions to the equation $1 + x^2(x - 1)^2 = 0$.

10 **a** On the same axes sketch the curves given by $y = 1 - 4x^2$ and $y = x(x - 2)^2$.

     b State, with a reason, the number of solutions to the equation $x^3 + 4x - 1 = 0$.

11 **a** On the same axes sketch the curve $y = x^3 - 3x^2 - 4x$ and the line $y = 6x$.

     b Find the coordinates of the points of intersection.

12 **a** On the same axes sketch the curve $y = (x^2 - 1)(x - 2)$ and the line $y = 14x + 2$.

     b Find the coordinates of the points of intersection.

13 **a** On the same axes sketch the curves with equations $y = (x - 2)(x + 2)^2$ and $y = -x^2 - 8$.

     b Find the coordinates of the points of intersection.

If a curve has equation $y = f(x)$, then there are 4 basic transformations that you can use. They are described in terms of translations (a value is <u>added</u> to the x or y coordinates) or a stretch (the x or y coordinates are <u>multiplied</u> by the value)

① $f(x + a)$ is a horizontal translation of $-a$

(This means that the value a is subtracted from all the x coordinates whilst the y coordinates stay unchanged. In other words the curve moves a units to the left.)

② $f(x) + a$ is a vertical translation of $+a$

(This means that the value a is added to all the y coordinates whilst the x coordinates stay unchanged. In this case the curve moves a units up.)

③ $f(ax)$ is a horizontal stretch of scale factor $\dfrac{1}{a}$

(This means that all the x coordinates are multiplied by $\dfrac{1}{a}$ whilst the y coordinates are left unchanged. The curve is "squashed up" in a horizontal direction.)

④ $af(x)$ is a vertical stretch of scale factor a

(This means that all the y coordinates are multiplied by a but the x coordinates are left unchanged. The curve is "stretched" in a vertical direction.)

Example 10

Sketch the graph of $y = (x - 2)^2 + 3$.

Start with $f(x) = x^2$ **Step 1** using ①:
     $f(x - 2) = (x - 2)^2$ •————— Horizontal translation of $+2$.

Calling this $g(x)$, $g(x) = (x - 2)^2$ **Step 2** using ②:
     $g(x) + 3 = (x - 2)^2 + 3$ •———— Vertical translation of $+3$.

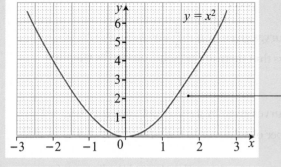

Sketch the graph of $f(x) = x^2$.

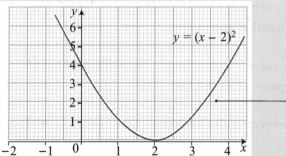

Step 1
Horizontal translation of +2.

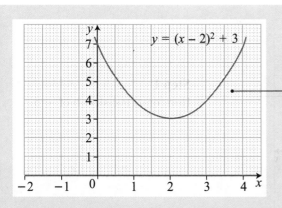

Step 2
Vertical translation of + 3.

Example 11

Sketch the graph of $y = \dfrac{2}{x + 5}$

Start with $f(x) = \dfrac{1}{x}$

$f(x + 5) = \dfrac{1}{x + 5}$

Step 1 using ①:
Horizontal translation of -5

Calling this $g(x)$, $g(x) = \dfrac{1}{x + 5}$

Step 2 using ④:
Vertical stretch, scale factor 2.

$2g(x) = \dfrac{2}{x + 5}$

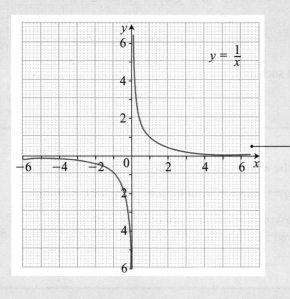

Sketch the graph of $f(x) = \dfrac{1}{x}$.

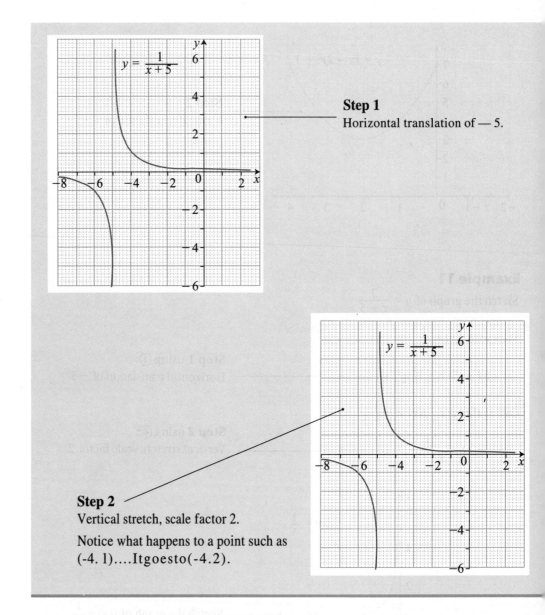

Step 1
Horizontal translation of — 5.

Step 2
Vertical stretch, scale factor 2.

Notice what happens to a point such as
(-4. 1)....Itgoesto(-4.2).

You should notice that the equation of the vertical asymptote has changed in the previous example. The asymptotes for $y = \dfrac{1}{x}$ are $y = 0$ and $x = 0$ but for $y = \dfrac{2}{x + 5}$ the horizontal asymptote is still $y = 0$ but the vertical asymptote has changed to $x = -5$ because the whole curve (including its asymptote) has moved 5 units to the left under the transformation $f(x + 5)$.

Example 12

Sketch the graph of $y = 3 + \dfrac{2}{4 - x}$ and state the equations of its asymptotes.

This graph involves several transformations but the basic starting point is a graph of the form $y = \dfrac{k}{x}$ which you met in Example 7.

The $-x$ term suggests starting with $y = -\dfrac{2}{x}$ as $y = f(x)$.

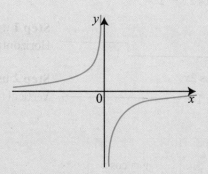

The denominator has $4 - x$ so this would be $y = -\dfrac{2}{x-4} = \dfrac{2}{4-x}$ so that is the transformation $y = f(x - 4)$. So move the curve 4 units to the <u>right</u>.

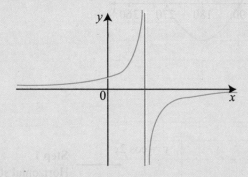

You should notice that the vertical asymptote has now changed to $x = 4$

Finally the curve you want to sketch is $y = 3 + \dfrac{2}{4-x}$ which is simply the previous curve $+ 3$.

This is a $f(x) + 3$ transformation so the previous curve will move <u>up</u> 3 units.

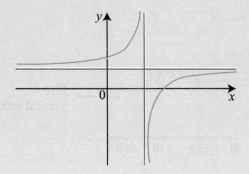

The effect of this final transformation is to alter the equation of the horizontal asymptote to $y = 3$.

So the equations of the asymptotes are $y = 3$ and $x = 4$.

The following example involves the graphs of trigonometric functions. You may have met the graphs of $y = \sin x$, $y = \cos x$ and $y = \tan x$ in your IGCSE, but they are also covered in Chapter 10.

Example 13

Sketch the graph of $y = \cos 2x - 1$.

Start with $f(x) = \cos x$

$\qquad f(2x) = \cos 2x$

Step 1 using ③:
Horizontal stretch, scale factor $\frac{1}{2}$.

Calling this $g(x)$, $g(x) = \cos 2x$

$\qquad g(x) - 1 = \cos 2x - 1$

Step 2 using ②:
Vertical translation of -1.

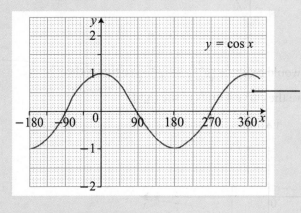

Sketch the graph of $f(x) = \cos x$.

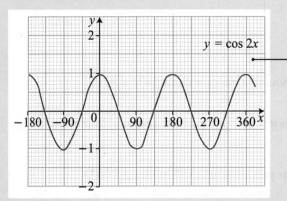

Step 1
Horizontal stretch, scale factor $\frac{1}{2}$.

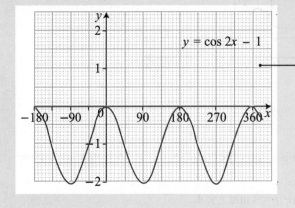

Step 2
Vertical translation of -1.

Exercise 4E

Sketch the following

1 $y = 2x^2 - 4$

2 $y = 3(x + 1)^2$

3 $y = \dfrac{3}{x} - 2$

4 $y = \dfrac{3}{x - 2}$

5 $y = 5\sin(x + 30°), 0 \leqslant x \leqslant 360°$

6 $y = 2x^3 - 3$

7 $y = 3 + \dfrac{1}{x + 1}$

8 $y = \dfrac{1}{x - 2} - 1$

> **Hint:** Write as
> $$\dfrac{2 + 2x + 1}{1 + x} = \dfrac{2(1 + x) + 1}{1 + x} \text{ and dIvIde}$$

9 $y = 2 + \dfrac{1}{x - 1}$

10 $y = \dfrac{3 + 2x}{1 + x}$

11 $y = 2 + \dfrac{3}{1 - x}$

12 $y = 5 - \dfrac{2}{3 + x}$

13 $y = \dfrac{3}{2 - x} - 4$

4.6 *You can sketch the graph of the exponential function $y = e^x$ and transformations of this*

Example 14

Sketch the graph of $f(x) = 2^x$ for the domain $x \in \mathbb{R}$.

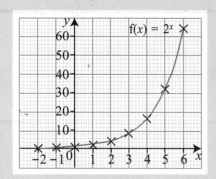

Draw up a table of values.

x	−2	−1	0	1	2	3	4	5	6
y	0.25	0.5	1	2	4	8	16	32	64

Plot points on a graph.

The exponential function $y = e^x$ (where $e = 2.718...$) is a function with a graph very similar to $y = 2^x$. The value of e gives special properties that are covered in work in Chapter 9.

Example 15

Draw the graphs of:

a $y = e^x$ **b** $y = e^{-x}$

a

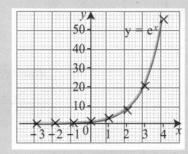

A table of values will show you how rapidly this curve grows.

x	-2	-1	0	1	2	3	4	5
y	0.14	0.37	1	2.7	7.4	20	55	148

With these curves it is worth keeping in mind:

- -as $x \rightarrow \infty$, $e^x \rightarrow \infty$ (it grows very rapidly)
- -when $x = 0$, $e^0 = 1$ [(0, 1) lies on the curve]
- -as $x \rightarrow -\infty$, $e^x \rightarrow 0$ (it approaches but never reaches the x-axis).

b

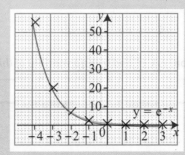

This curve is similar to the one in part **a** except that its value at $x = 2$ is e^{-2} and its value at $x = -2$ is e^2.

Hence it is a reflection of the curve of part **a** in the y-axis.

The graph in Example **15b** is often referred to as exponential decay. It is used as a model in many examples from real life including the fall in value of a car as well as the decay in radioactive isotopes.

Example 16

Draw graphs of the exponential functions:

a $y = e^{2x}$ **b** $y = 10e^{-x}$ **c** $y = 3 + 4e^{\frac{1}{2}x}$

a $y = e^{2x}$
$= (e^x)^2$

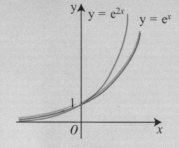

x	-3	0	3
y	0.002	1	403

If you calculate some values it can give you an idea of the shape of the graph.

The y values of $y = e^{2x}$ are the 'square' of the y values of $y = e^x$.

b $y = 10e^{-x}$

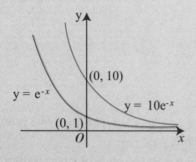

x	-3	0	3
y	201	10	0.5

Calculating some y values helps you sketch the curve.

The y values of $y = 10e^{-x}$ are 10 times bigger than the y values of $y = e^{-x}$.

c $y = 3 + 4e^{\frac{1}{2}x}$

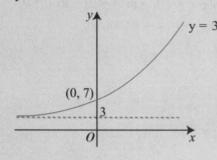

x	-3	0	3
y	3.9	7	21

Since $e^{\frac{1}{2}x} > 0$

$3 + 4e^{\frac{1}{2}x} > 3$.

The line $y = 3$ is an asymptote.

In Chapter 1 (Section 1.6) you saw the connection between $y = \log_a x$ and $y = a^x$
Because the function $y = \log_e x$ is particularly important in mathematics it has a special notation

- $\log_e x = \ln x$

Your calculator should have a special button for evaluating $\ln x$

Example 17

Solve the equations
a $e^x = 3$ **b** $\ln x = 4$

a When $e^x = 3$
     $x = \ln 3$

b When $\ln x = 4$
     $x = e^4$

The key to solving any equation is knowing the inverse operation.
(e.g. when $x^2 = 10$, $x = \sqrt{10}$.)

The inverse of e^x is $\ln x$ and vice versa.

Example 18

Sketch the graphs of

a $y = \ln(3 - x)$ **b** $y = 3 + \ln(2x)$

a $y = \ln(3 - x)$

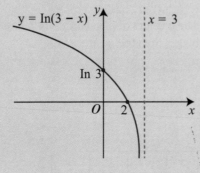

When $x \to 3$, $y \to -\infty$. The line $x = 3$ is an asymptote.

y does not exist for values of x bigger than 3.

When $x = 2$, $y = \ln(3 - 2) = \ln 1 = 0$.

As $x \to -\infty$, $y \to \infty$ (slowly).

b $y = 3 + \ln(2x)$

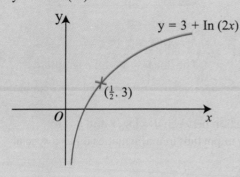

When $x \to 0$, $y \to -\infty$.

When $x = \frac{1}{2}$, $y = 3 + \ln 1 = 3$.

As $x \to \infty$, $y \to \infty$ (slowly).

Exercise 4F

1 Sketch the graphs of

   a $y = e^x + 1$ **b** $y = 4e^{-2x}$ **c** $y = 2e^x - 3$

   d $y = 4 - e^x$ **e** $y = 6 + 10e^{\frac{1}{2}x}$ **f** $y = 100e^{-x} + 10$

2 Sketch the following graphs stating any asymptotes and intersections with axes:

   a $y = \ln(x + 1)$ **b** $y = 2 \ln x$ **c** $y = \ln(2x)$

   d $y = 3\ln(x - 2)$, $x > 2$ **e** $y = \ln(4 - x)$ **f** $y = 3 + \ln(x + 2)$

4.7 *You can use graphs of functions to solve equations*

Example 18

a Complete the table below of values of $y = e^{\frac{1}{2}x} - 2$, giving your answers to 2 decimal places where appropriate.

x	0	1	2	3	4	5
y		−0.35	0.72		5.39	10.18

b Draw the graph of $y = e^{\frac{1}{2}x} - 2$ for $0 \leqslant x \leqslant 5$

c Use your graph to estimate, to 2 significant figures, the solution of the equation $e^{\frac{1}{2}x} = 8$ showing your method clearly.

d By drawing a suitable line on your graph estimate, to 2 significant figures, the solution of the equation $x = 2\ln(7 - 2x)$

a $x = 0, y = e^0 - 2 = 1 - 2 = -1$

From calculator

$x = 3, y = 2.4817... = 2.48$ (2 dp)

b

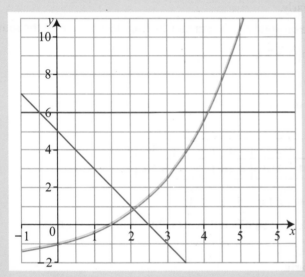

The blue and purple lines are for parts **c** and **d**.

c $e^{\frac{1}{2}x} = 8$ Make the LHS = $e^{\frac{1}{2}x} - 2$ i.e. the equation of the
$e^{\frac{1}{2}x} - 2 = 8 - 2$ graph. Therefore you need to subtract 2 from 8
$y = 6$ and draw the line $y = 6$.

So solution is intersection of the curve and the line $y = 6$.

From graph $x \approx 4.15$ In the exam a range of answers would be allowed say $4.10 - 4.20$.

d $x = 2\ln(7 - 2x)$

$\dfrac{x}{2} = \ln(7 - 2x)$ Using properties of logs from Chapter 1.

$e^{\frac{x}{2}} = 7 - 2x$

$e^{\frac{1}{2}x} - 2 = 7 - 2x - 2$ Make LHS equal to the given equation i.e. $e^{\frac{1}{2}x} - 2$.

$y = 5 - 2x$ Draw the line $y = 5 - 2x$ on your graph and find points of intersection.

From graph $x \approx 2.1$

Exercise 4G

1 a Complete the table below of values of $y = 3 + 2e^{-\frac{1}{2}x}$, giving your values of y to 2 decimal places.

x	0	1	2	3	4	5	6
y	5		3.74	3.45	3.27		3.10

b Draw the graph of $y = 3 + 2e^{-\frac{1}{2}x}$ for $0 \leqslant x \leqslant 6$

c Use your graph to estimate, to 2 significant figures, the solution of the equation

$$e^{-\frac{1}{2}x} = 0.5$$

showing your method clearly.

d By drawing a suitable line on your graph estimate, to 2 significant figures, the solution of the equation $x = -2\ln\left(\frac{x-2}{2}\right)$.

2 a Complete the table below of values of $y = 2 + \frac{1}{3}e^x$, giving your values of y to 2 decimal places.

x	-1	0	1	1.5	2	2.5	3
y	2.12		2.91	3.49	4.46		8.70

b Draw the graph of $y = 2 + \frac{1}{3}e^x$ for $-1 \leqslant x \leqslant 3$

c Use your graph to estimate, to 2 significant figures, the solution of the equation

$$e^x = 12$$

showing your method clearly.

d By drawing a suitable line on your graph estimate, to 1 significant figure, the solution of the equation $x = \ln(6 - 6x)$.

3 a Complete the table below of values of $y = 2 + \ln x$, giving your values of y to 2 decimal places.

x	0.1	0.5	1	1.5	2	3	4
y	-0.30	1.31		2.41	2.69	3.10	

b Draw the graph of $y = 2 + \ln x$ for $0.1 \leqslant x \leqslant 4$

c Use your graph to estimate, to 2 significant figures, the solution of the equation

$$\ln x = 0.5$$

showing your method clearly.

d By drawing a suitable line on your graph estimate, to 1 significant figure, the solution of the equation $x = e^{x-2}$.

4 a Complete the table below of values of $y = 5\sin 2x - 2\cos x$, giving your values of y to 2 decimal places.

x	0	15	30	45	60	75	90
y	-2	0.57		3.59	3.33		0

b Draw the graph of $y = 5\sin 2x - 2\cos x$ for $0 \leqslant x \leqslant 90$

c Use your graph to estimate, to 2 significant figures, the solution of the equation

$$2(1 + \cos x) = 5\sin 2x$$

showing your method clearly.

Mixed Exercise 4H

1 **a** On the same axes sketch the graphs of $y = x^2(x - 2)$ and $y = 2x - x^2$.

  b By solving a suitable equation find the points of intersection of the two graphs.

2 **a** On the same axes sketch the curves with equations $y = \dfrac{6}{x}$ and $y = 1 + x$.

  b The curves intersect at the points A and B. Find the coordinates of A and B.

  c The curve C with equation $y = x^2 + px + q$, where p and q are integers, passes through A and B. Find the values of p and q.

  d Add C to your sketch.

3 Sketch the following indicating any intersections with the coordinate axes.

  a $y = x^2 - 2x - 3$ **b** $y = x^2 - 2x + 4$

> **Hint:**
> **b** Complete the square.

4 Sketch the following indicating any intersections with the coordinate axes.

  a $y = 4x - 3 - x^2$ **b** $y = 4x - 5 - x^2$

5 Sketch the graph of

  a $y = \frac{1}{2}e^x + 4$ **b** $y = \ln(x + 1) + 2$

6 **a** Complete the table below of values of $y = 1 - \ln(x - 1)$, giving your values of y to 2 decimal places.

x	2	3	4	5	6	7
y	1	0.31	-0.10			-0.79

  b Draw the graph of $y = 1 - \ln(x - 1)$ for $2 \leqslant x \leqslant 7$

  c Use your graph to estimate, to 2 significant figures, the solution of the equation

$$\ln(x - 1) = 0.8$$

showing your method clearly.

  d By drawing a suitable line on your graph estimate, to 2 significant figures, the solution of the equation $x = 1 + e^{1 - \frac{x}{4}}$.

1 You should know the shapes of the following basic curves.

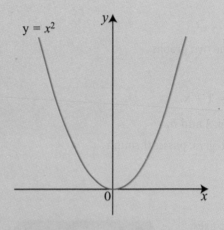

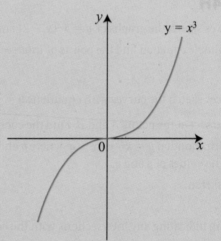

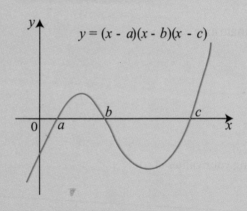

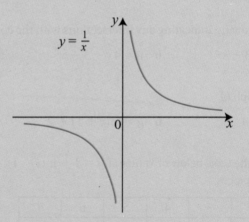

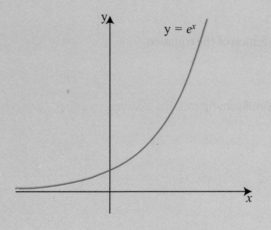

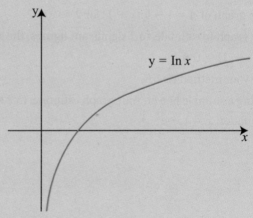

2 Transformations:

$f(x + a)$ is a translation of $-a$ in the x-direction.

$f(x) + a$ is a translation of $+a$ in the y-direction.

$f(ax)$ is a stretch of $\dfrac{1}{a}$ in the x-direction $\left(\text{multiply } x\text{-coordinates by } \dfrac{1}{a}\right)$.

$af(x)$ is a stretch of a in the y-direction (multiply y-coordinates by a).

Chapter 5: Series

5.1 *A sequence that increases by a constant amount each time is called an arithmetic sequence.*

The following are examples of arithmetic sequences:

$3, 7, 11, 15, 19, \ldots$ (because you add 4 each time)
$2, 7, 12, 17, 22, \ldots$ (because you add 5 each time)
$17, 14, 11, 8, \ldots$ (because you add -3 each time)
$a, a + d, a + 2d, a + 3d, \ldots$ (because you add d each time)

- **A recurrence relationship of the form**

$$U_{k+1} = U_k + n, \ k \geqslant 1 \ \ n \in \mathbb{Z}$$

is called an arithmetic sequence.

Example 1

Find the **a** 10th, **b** nth and **c** 50th terms of the arithmetic sequence $3, 7, 11, 15, 19, \ldots$

Sequence is $3, 7, 11, 15, \ldots$	The sequence is going up in fours.
First term $= 3$	It is starting at 3.
Second term $= 3 + 4$	The first term is $3 + 0 \times 4$.
Third term $= 3 + 4 + 4$	The second term is $3 + 1 \times 4$.
Fourth term $= 3 + 4 + 4 + 4$	The third term is $3 + 2$ lots of 4.
	The fourth term is $3 + 3$ lots of 4.

a 10th term is
$3 + 9 \times 4 = 3 + 36 = 39$ 10th term = first term + 9 fours.

b nth term is
$3 + (n - 1) \times 4 = 4n - 1$ nth term = first term + $(n - 1)$ fours.

c 50th term is
$3 + (50 - 1) \times 4 = 3 + 196 = 199$ 50th term = first term + 49 fours.

Example 2

A 6 metre high tree is planted in a garden. If it grows 1.5 metres a year:

a How high will it be after it has been in the garden for 8 years?

b After how many years will it be 24 metres high?

a $6 + \underline{8 \times 1.5}$ It starts at 6 m.

    $= 6 + 12$ It has 8 years' growth at 1.5 m a year.

    $= 18$ metres

b $24 - 6 = 18$ metres   Find out how much it has grown in total.

    So number of years $= \dfrac{18}{1.5}$ It grows at 1.5 metres a year.

            $= 12$ years

Example 3

Find the number of terms in the arithmetic sequence 7, 11, 15, ..., 143:

The sequence goes up in fours. •————————— Work out how to get from one term

It goes from 7 to 143, a difference of 136. •——┐ to the next.

136 in fours is $\frac{136}{4} = 34$ jumps. └—— Work out the difference between

7, 11, 15, ..., ..., 143   largest and smallest numbers.
‿‿‿‿‿

There is one more term than the number of jumps, so 34 jumps means 35 terms.

Exercise 5A

1 Which of the following sequences are arithmetic?

   a   3, 5, 7, 9, 11, ...   **b**   10, 7, 4, 1, ...   **c** $y, 2y, 3y, 4y, ...$

   d   1, 4, 9, 16, 25, ...   **e**   16, 8, 4, 2, 1, ...   **f**   1, −1, 1, −1, 1, ...

   g $y, y^2, y^3, y^4, ...$ **h** $U_{n+1} = U_n + 2, U_1 = 3$ **i** $U_{n+1} = 3U_n - 2, U_1 = 4$

   j $U_{n+1} = (U_n)^2, U_1 = 2$ **k** $U_n = n(n+1)$ **l** $U_n = 2n + 3$

2 Find the 10th and nth terms in the following arithmetic progressions:

   a   5, 7, 9, 11, ...   **b**   5, 8, 11, 14, ...   **c**   24, 21, 18, 15, ...

   d   −1, 3, 7, 11, ...   **e** $x, 2x, 3x, 4x, ...$ **f** $a, a + d, a + 2d, a + 3d, ...$

3 An investor puts £4000 in an account. Every month thereafter she deposits another £200. How much money in total will she have invested at the start of **a** the 10th month and **b** the mth month? (Note that at the start of the 6th month she will have made only 5 deposits of £200.)

4 Calculate the number of terms in the following arithmetic sequences:

   a   3, 7, 11, ..., 83, 87   **b**   5, 8, 11, ..., 119, 122

   c   90, 88, 86, ..., 16, 14   **d**   4, 9, 14, ..., 224, 229

   e $x, 3x, 5x, ..., 35x$ **f** $a, a + d, a + 2d, ..., a + (n-1)d$

5.2 *Arithmetic series are formed by adding together the terms of an arithmetic sequence*
    $U_1 + U_2 + U_3 + ... + U_n.$

In an arithmetic series the next term is found by adding (or subtracting) a constant number.

This number is called the common difference d.

The first term is represented by a.

• **Therefore all arithmetic series can be put in the form**

$$a + (a + d) + (a + 2d) + (a + 3d) + (a + 4d) + (a + 5d)$$

   1st term   2nd term   3rd term   4th term   5th term   6th term

Look at the relationship between the number of the term and the coefficient of d. You should be able to see that the coefficient of d is one less than the number of the term.

We can use this fact to produce a formula for the nth term of an arithmetic series.

• **The nth term of an arithmetic series is $a + (n-1)d$, where a is the first term and d is the common difference.**

Example 4

Find **i** the 20th and **ii** the 50th terms of the following series:

a $4 + 7 + 10 + 13 + \dots$ **b** $100 + 93 + 86 + 79 + \dots$

a $4 + 7 + 10 + 13 + \dots$

In this series $a = 4$ and $d = 3$

First calculate the values of a and d. (In this case d is $7 - 4$.)

i 20th term
$$= 4 + (20 - 1) \times 3$$
$$= 4 + 19 \times 3$$
$$= 61$$

ii 50th term
$$= 4 + (50 - 1) \times 3$$
$$= 4 + 49 \times 3$$
$$= 151$$

Use the formula $a + (n - 1)d$, with $n = 20$ for the 20th term and $n = 50$ for the 50th term.

b $100 + 93 + 86 + 79 + \dots$

In this series $a = 100$ and $d = -7$

d is negative this time.
$d = (93 - 100) = -7$.
To calculate d you can use $U_2 - U_1$ or $U_3 - U_2$ or $U_4 - U_3$, etc.

i 20th term
$$= 100 + (20 - 1) \times -7$$
$$= 100 + 19 \times -7$$
$$= -33$$

ii 50th term
$$= 100 + (50 - 1) \times -7$$
$$= 100 + 49 \times -7$$
$$= -243$$

Example 5

For the arithmetic series $5 + 9 + 13 + 17 + 21 + \dots + 805$:

a find the number of terms   **b** which term of the series would be 129?

Series is $5 + 9 + 13 + 17 + 21 + \dots + 805$.

In this series $a = 5$ and $d = 4$.

A good starting point in all questions is to find the values of a and d.
Here $a = 5$ and $a + d = 9$, so $d = 4$.

a Using nth term $= a + (n - 1)d$
$$805 = 5 + (n - 1) \times 4$$
$$805 = 5 + 4n - 4$$
$$805 = 4n + 1$$
$$804 = 4n$$
$$n = 201$$

The nth term is $a + (n - 1)d$.
So replace U_n with 805 and solve for n.
Subtract 1.
Divide by 4.

There are 201 terms in this series.

b Using nth term $= a + (n - 1)d$
$$129 = 5 + (n - 1) \times 4$$
$$129 = 4n + 1$$
$$128 = 4n$$
$$n = 32$$

This time the nth term is 129.
So replace U_n with 129.
Subtract 1.
Divide by 4.

The 32nd term is 129.

Example 6

Given that the 3rd term of an arithmetic series is 20 and the 7th term is 12:

a find the first term   **b** find the 20th term.

(Note: These are very popular questions and involve setting up and solving simultaneous equations.)

a 3rd term = 20, so $a + 2d = 20$.   ①   Use nth term = $a + (n - 1)d$,
7th term = 12, so $a + 6d = 12$.   ②   with $n = 3$ and $n = 7$.

Taking ① from ②:

$$4d = -8$$
$$d = -2$$

The common difference is -2.
$$a + 2 \times -2 = 20$$ Substitute $d = -2$ back into equation ①.
$$a - 4 = 20$$ Add 4 to both sides.
$$a = 24$$

The first term is 24.

b 20th term = $a + 19d$ ————— Use nth term is $a + (n - 1)d$ with $n = 20$.

$$= 24 + 19 \times -2$$ ——— Substitute a = 24 and d = -2.
$$= 24 - 38$$
$$= -14$$

The 20th term is -14.

Exercise 5B

1 Find **i** the 20th and **ii** the nth terms of the following arithmetic series:

    a $2 + 6 + 10 + 14 + 18 \ldots$ **b** $4 + 6 + 8 + 10 + 12 + \ldots$
    c $80 + 77 + 74 + 71 + \ldots$ **d** $1 + 3 + 5 + 7 + 9 + \ldots$
    e $30 + 27 + 24 + 21 + \ldots$ **f** $2 + 5 + 8 + 11 + \ldots$
    g $p + 3p + 5p + 7p + \ldots$ **h** $5x + x + (-3x) + (-7x) + \ldots$

2 Find the number of terms in the following arithmetic series:

    a $5 + 9 + 13 + 17 + \ldots + 121$ **b** $1 + 1.25 + 1.5 + 1.75 \ldots + 8$
    c $-4 + -1 + 2 + 5 \ldots + 89$ **d** $70 + 61 + 52 + 43 \ldots + -200$
    e $100 + 95 + 90 + \ldots + (-1000)$ **f** $x + 3x + 5x \ldots + 153x$

3 The first term of an arithmetic series is 14. If the fourth term is 32, find the common difference.

4 Given that the 3rd term of an arithmetic series is 30 and the 10th term is 9 find a and d. Hence find which term is the first one to become negative.

5 In an arithmetic series the 20th term is 14 and the 40th term is -6. Find the 10th term.

6 The first three terms of an arithmetic series are $5x$, 20 and $3x$. Find the value of x and hence the values of the three terms.

7 For which values of x would the expression -8, x^2 and $17x$ form the first three terms of an arithmetic series?

> **Hint:**
> Question 6 – Find two expressions equal to the common difference and set them equal to each other.

5.3 You can find the sum of an arithmetic series.

The method of finding this sum is attributed to a famous mathematician called Carl Friedrich Gauss (1777–1855). He reputedly solved the following sum whilst in Junior School:

$$1 + 2 + 3 + 4 + 5 + \ldots + 99 + 100$$

Here is how he was able to work it out:

Let $\qquad\qquad\qquad\quad S = 1 + 2 + 3 + 4 \ldots + 98 + 99 + 100$

Reversing the sum $\qquad\; S = 100 + 99 + 98 + 97 \ldots + 3 + 2 + 1$

Adding the two sums $2S = 101 + 101 + 101 + \ldots + 101 + 101 + 101$

$$2S = 100 \times 101$$

$$S = (100 \times 101) \div 2$$

$$S = 5050$$

In general:

$$S_n = a + (a + d) + (a + 2d) + \ldots + (a + (n - 2)d) + (a + (n - 1)d)$$

Reversing the sum:

$$S_n = (a + (n - 1)d) + (a + (n - 2)d) + (a + (n - 3)d) + \ldots + (a + d) + a$$

Adding the two sums:

$$2S_n = [2a + (n - 1)d] + [2a + (n - 1)d] + \ldots + [2a + (n - 1)d]$$

$$2S_n = n[2a + (n - 1)d]$$

$$S_n = \frac{n}{2}[2a + (n - 1)d]$$

Hint: There are n lots of $2a + (n - 1)d$.

Prove for yourself that it could be $S_n = \frac{n}{2}(a + L)$ where $L = a + (n - 1)d$.

- **The formula for the sum of an arithmetic series is**

$$S_n = \frac{n}{2}[2a + (n - 1)d]$$

or $\quad S_n = \frac{n}{2}(a + L)$

You will not be asked to prove these formulae.

where a is the first term, d is the common difference, n is the number of terms and L is the last term in the series.

Example 7

Find the sum of the first 100 odd numbers.

$S = 1 + 3 + 5 + 7 + \ldots$

$\quad = \frac{n}{2}[2a + (n - 1)d]$

$\quad = \frac{100}{2}[2 \times 1 + (100 - 1)2]$

$\quad = 50[2 + 198]$

$\quad = 50 \times 200$

$\quad = 10\,000$

This can be found simply using the formula

$$S = \frac{n}{2}[2a + (n - 1)d]$$

with $a = 1$, $d = 2$ and $n = 100$.

$$L = a + (n-1)d$$
$$= 1 + 99 \times 2$$
$$= 199$$
$$S = \frac{n}{2}(a+L)$$
$$= \frac{100}{2}(1+199)$$
$$= 10\,000$$

Alternatively, find L and use
$$S = \frac{n}{2}(a+L)$$
This is a very useful formula and is well worth remembering.

You will not be asked to prove these formulae.

Example 8

Find the greatest number of terms required for the sum of $4 + 9 + 14 + 19 + \ldots$ to exceed 2000.

$$4 + 9 + 14 + 19 + \ldots > 2000$$

Always establish what you are given in a question. As you are adding on positive terms, it is easier to solve the equality $S_n = 2000$.

Using $\quad S = \frac{n}{2}[2a + (n-1)d]$

$$2000 = \frac{n}{2}[2 \times 4 + (n-1)5]$$

Knowing $a = 4$, $d = 5$ and $S_n = 2000$, you need to find n.

$$4000 = n(8 + 5n - 5)$$
$$4000 = n(5n + 3)$$
$$4000 = 5n^2 + 3n$$
$$0 = 5n^2 + 3n - 4000$$

Substitute into $S = \frac{n}{2}[2a + (n-1)d]$.

$$n = \frac{-3 \pm \sqrt{(9 + 80\,000)}}{10}$$

Solve using formula $n = \frac{-b \pm \sqrt{(b^2 - 4ac)}}{2a}$

$$= 27.9, -28.5$$

28 terms are needed.

Accept positive answer and round up.

Example 9

Robert starts his new job on a salary of £15 000. He is promised rises of £1000 a year, at the end of every year, until he reaches his maximum salary of £25 000. Find his total earnings (since appointed) after **a** 8 years with the firm and **b** 14 years with the firm.

a Total earnings

Note that it will take Robert 11 years to reach his maximum (his first year and 10 wage rises).

$$= £15\,000 + £16\,000 + \ldots \text{ (for 8 years)}$$

$$a = 15\,000, d = 1000 \text{ and } n = 8$$

Write down what you know.

$$S = \frac{n}{2}[2a + (n-1)d]$$

Use $S = \frac{n}{2}[2a + (n-1)d]$

$$S = \frac{8}{2}[30\,000 + 7 \times 1000]$$

$$= £148\,000$$

b Total earnings

$$= £15\,000 + £16\,000 + \dots + £25\,000$$
$$+ £25\,000 + £25\,000 + £25\,000$$

$a = 15\,000$, $d = 1000$ and

$n = 11$ for the first 11 years.

$$S = \frac{n}{2}[2a + (n-1)d]$$

$$S = \frac{11}{2}[30\,000 + 10 \times 1000]$$

$$= £220\,000$$

3 years at £25 000 = £75 000.

Total amount earned = £295 000.

This time there are 10 years of increases, taking him to the end of his 11th year, and 3 years of the same salary.

Use $S = \frac{n}{2}[2a + (n-1)d]$ for the first 11 years.

Example 10

Show that the sum of the first n natural numbers is $\frac{1}{2}n(n+1)$.

$S = 1 + 2 + 3 + 4 + \dots + n$

This is an arithmetic series with

$a = 1, d = 1, n = n$.

$$S = \frac{n}{2}[2a + (n-1)d]$$

$$S = \frac{n}{2}[2 \times 1 + (n-1) \times 1]$$

$$S = \frac{n}{2}[(2 + n - 1)$$

$$S = \frac{n}{2}[(n + 1)$$

$$= \frac{1}{2}n(n+1)$$

Use $S = \frac{n}{2}[2a + (n-1)d]$

with $a = 1, d = 1$ and $n = n$.

Exercise 5C

1 Find the sums of the following series:

  a $3 + 7 + 11 + 14 + \dots$ (20 terms)

  b $2 + 6 + 10 + 14 + \dots$ (15 terms)

  c $30 + 27 + 24 + 21 + \dots$ (40 terms)

  d $5 + 1 + -3 + -7 + \dots$ (14 terms)

  e $5 + 7 + 9 + \dots + 75$

  f $4 + 7 + 10 + \dots + 91$

  g $34 + 29 + 24 + 19 + \dots + -111$

  h $(x + 1) + (2x + 1) + (3x + 1) + \dots + (21x + 1)$

2 Find how many terms of the following series are needed to make the given sum:

  a $5 + 8 + 11 + 14 + \dots = 670$ **b** $3 + 8 + 13 + 18 + \dots = 1575$

  c $64 + 62 + 60 + \dots = 0$ **d** $34 + 30 + 26 + 22 + \dots = 112$

3 Find the sum of the first 50 even numbers.

4 Carol starts a new job on a salary of £20 000. She is given an annual wage rise of £500 at the end of every year until she reaches her maximum salary of £25 000. Find the total amount she earns (assuming no other rises), **a** in the first 10 years and **b** over 15 years.

5 Find the sum of the multiples of 3 less than 100. Hence or otherwise find the sum of the numbers less than 100 which are not multiples of 3.

6 James decides to save some money during the six-week holiday. He saves 1p on the first day, 2p on the second, 3p on the third and so on. How much will he have at the end of the holiday (42 days)? If he carried on, how long would it be before he has saved £100?

7 The first term of an arithmetic series is 4. The sum to 20 terms is -15. Find, in any order, the common difference and the 20th term.

8 The sum of the first three numbers of an arithmetic series is 12. If the 20th term is -32, find the first term and the common difference.

9 Show that the sum of the first $2n$ natural numbers is $n(2n + 1)$.

10 Prove that the sum of the first n odd numbers is n^2.

5.4 *You can use $\sum$ to signify 'the sum of'.*

For example:

$$\sum_{n=1}^{10} 2n \text{ means the sum of } 2n \text{ from } n = 1 \text{ to } n = 10$$

$$= 2 + 4 + 6 + 8 + 10 + 12 + 14 + 16 + 18 + 20$$

$$\sum_{n=1}^{10} U_n = U_1 + U_2 + U_3 + \ldots + U_{10}$$

$$\sum_{r=0}^{10} (2 + 3r) \text{ means the sum of } (2 + 3r) \text{ from } r = 0 \text{ to } r = 10$$

$$= 2 + 5 + 8 + \ldots + 32$$

$$\sum_{r=5}^{=15} (10 - 2r) \text{ means the sum of } (10 - 2r) \text{ from } r = 5 \text{ to } r = 15$$

$$= 0 + -2 + -4 + \ldots + -20$$

Example 11

Calculate $\displaystyle\sum_{r=1}^{r=20} (4r + 1)$

$= 5 + 9 + 13 + \ldots + 81$ Substitute $r = 1$, 2, etc. to find terms in series.

$S = \dfrac{n}{2}[2a + (n - 1)d]$ Substitute $a = 5$, $d = 4$ and $n = 20$ into $S = \dfrac{n}{2}[2a + (n - 1)d]$.

$= \dfrac{20}{2}[2 \times 5 + (20 - 1)4]$

$= 10[10 + (19) \times 4]$

$= 10 \times 86$

$= 860$

Exercise 5D

1 Rewrite the following sums using $\sum$ notation:

a $4 + 7 + 10 + \ldots + 31$

b $2 + 5 + 8 + 11 + \ldots + 89$

c $40 + 36 + 32 + \ldots + 0$

d The multiples of 6 less than 100

2 Calculate the following:

a $\displaystyle\sum_{r=1}^{5} 3r$

b $\displaystyle\sum_{r=1}^{10} (4r - 1)$

c $\displaystyle\sum_{r=1}^{20} (5r - 2)$

d $\displaystyle\sum_{r=0}^{5} r(r + 1)$

3 For what value of n does $\displaystyle\sum_{r=1}^{n} (5r + 3)$ first exceed 1000?

4 For what value of n would $\displaystyle\sum_{r=1}^{n} (100 - 4r) = 0$?

5.5 *The following sequences are called geometric sequences. To get from one term to the next we multiply by the same number each time. This number is called the common ratio, r.*

1, 2, 4, 8, 16, ...

100, 25, 6.25, 1.5625, ...

2, −6, 18, −54, 162, ...

Example 12

Find the common ratios in the following geometric sequences:

a $2, 10, 50, 250, \ldots$

b $90, -30, 10, -3\frac{1}{3}$

a $2, 10, 50, 250, \ldots$ — Use u_1, u_2 etc. to refer to the individual terms in a sequence.

Common ratio $= \dfrac{10}{2} = 5$ — Here $u_1 = 2$, $u_2 = 10$, $u_3 = 50$.

To find the common ratio calculate $\dfrac{u_2}{u_1}$ or $\dfrac{u_3}{u_2}$.

b $90, -30, 10, -3\frac{1}{3}$ — Common ratio $= \dfrac{u_2}{u_1}$.

Common ratio $= \dfrac{-30}{90} = -\dfrac{1}{3}$ — A common ratio can be negative or a fraction (or both).

Exercise 5E

1 Which of the following are geometric sequences? For the ones that are, give the value of 'r' in the sequence:

a $1, 2, 4, 8, 16, 32, \ldots$

b $2, 5, 8, 11, 14, \ldots$

c $40, 36, 32, 28, \ldots$

d $2, 6, 18, 54, 162, \ldots$

e $10, 5, 2.5, 1.25, \ldots$

f $5, -5, 5, -5, 5, \ldots$

g $3, 3, 3, 3, 3, 3, 3, \ldots$

h $4, -1, 0.25, -0.0625, \ldots$

2 Continue the following geometric sequences for three more terms:

  a $5, 15, 45, \ldots$ **b** $4, -8, 16, \ldots$

  c $60, 30, 15, \ldots$ **d** $1, \frac{1}{4}, \frac{1}{16}, \ldots$

  e $1, p, p^2, \ldots$ **f** $x, -2x^2, 4x^3, \ldots$

3 If 3, x and 9 are the first three terms of a geometric sequence. Find:

  a the exact value of x,

  b the exact value of the 4th term.

> **Hint for question 3:**
> In a geometric sequence the common ratio can be calculated by $\dfrac{u_2}{u_1}$ or $\dfrac{u_3}{u_2}$.

5.6 *You can define a geometric sequence using the first term a and the common ratio r:*

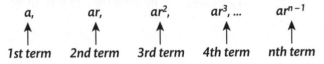

$$a, \qquad ar, \qquad ar^2, \qquad ar^3, \ldots \qquad ar^{n-1}$$

1st term   2nd term   3rd term   4th term   nth term

> Sometimes a geometric sequence is called a geometric progression.

Example 13

Find the **i** 10th and **ii** nth terms in the following geometric sequences:

  a $3, 6, 12, 24, \ldots$

  b $40, -20, 10, -5, \ldots$

a $3, 6, 12, 24, \ldots$ For this sequence $a = 3$ and $r = \frac{6}{3} = 2$.

  i 10th term $= 3 \times (2)^9$ For the 10th term use ar^{n-1} with $a = 3$,

            $= 3 \times 512$ $r = 2$ and $n = 10$.

            $= 1536$

  ii nth term $= 3 \times 2^{n-1}$ For the nth term use ar^{n-1} with $a = 3$ and $r = 2$.

b $40, -20, 10, -5, \ldots$ For this sequence $a = 40$ and $r = -\frac{20}{40} = -\frac{1}{2}$.

  i 10th term $= 40 \times \left(-\frac{1}{2}\right)^9$ Use ar^{n-1} with $a = 40$, $r = -\frac{1}{2}$ and $n = 10$.

            $= 40 \times -\frac{1}{512}$

            $= -\frac{5}{64}$

  ii nth term $= 40 \times \left(-\frac{1}{2}\right)^{n-1}$ Use ar^{n-1} with $a = 40$, $r = -\frac{1}{2}$ and $n = n$.

            $= 5 \times 8 \times \left(-\frac{1}{2}\right)^{n-1}$

            $= 5 \times 2^3 \times \left(-\frac{1}{2}\right)^{n-1}$ Use laws of indices $\dfrac{x^m}{x^n} = \dfrac{1}{x^{n-m}}$.

            $= (-1)^{n-1} \times \dfrac{5}{2^{n-4}}$ So $2^3 \times \dfrac{1}{2^{n-1}} = \dfrac{1}{2^{n-1-3}}$.

> **Hint**
> Look at the relationship between the position of the term in the sequence and the index of the term. You should be able to see that the index of r is one less than its position in the sequence. So the nth term of a geometric sequence is ar^{n-1}.

Example 14

The second term of a geometric sequence is 4 and the 4th term is 8.
Find the exact values of **a** the common ratio, **b** first term and **c** the 10th term:

a 2nd term = 4, $ar = 4$ ① $\longrightarrow$ Using nth term = ar^{n-1}

4th term = 6, $ar^3 = 8$ ② $\longrightarrow$ with $n = 2$

② ÷ ① $r^2 = 2$ and $n = 4$.

$r = \sqrt{2}$

So   common ratio = $\sqrt{2}$

b Substitute back in ① $a\sqrt{2} = 4$ Divide equation by $\sqrt{2}$.

$a = \dfrac{4}{\sqrt{2}}$

$= \dfrac{4\sqrt{2}}{2}$ To rationalise $\dfrac{4}{\sqrt{2}}$, multiply top and bottom by $\sqrt{2}$.

$a = 2\sqrt{2}$

So first term = $2\sqrt{2}$

c 10th term = ar^9

$= 2\sqrt{2}(\sqrt{2})^9$ Substitute the values of $a(= 2\sqrt{2})$ and $r(= \sqrt{2})$

$= 2(\sqrt{2})^{10}$ back into ar^{n-1} with $n = 10$.

$= 2 \times 2^5$ $(\sqrt{2})^{10} = (2^{\frac{1}{2}})^{10} = 2^{\frac{1}{2} \times 10} = 2^5$

$= 2^6$

$= 64$

So 10th term = 64

Example 15

The numbers 3, x and $(x + 6)$ form the first three terms of a positive geometric sequence.
Find:

a the possible values of x,   **b** the 10th term of the sequence.

a $\dfrac{u_2}{u_1} = \dfrac{u_3}{u_2}$ The sequence is geometric so $\dfrac{u_2}{u_1} = \dfrac{u_3}{u_2}$

$\dfrac{x}{3} = \dfrac{x + 6}{x}$ Cross multiply.

$x^2 = 3(x + 6)$

$x^2 = 3x + 18$

$x^2 = 3x - 18 = 0$ Factorise.

$(x - 6)(x + 3) = 0$

$x = 6$ or -3

So x is either 6 or -3, but there are no   If there are no negative terms then -3
negative terms so $x = 6$.   cannot be an answer.

Accept $x = 6$, as terms are positive.

b 10th term $= ar^9$

$\qquad = 3 \times 2^9$ Use the formula nth term $= ar^{n-1}$ with $n = 9$, $a = 3$

$\qquad = 3 \times 512$ and $r = \dfrac{x}{3} = \dfrac{6}{3} = 2$.

$\qquad = 1536$

The 10th term is 1536.

Exercise 5F

1 Find the sixth, tenth and nth terms of the following geometric sequences:

    a 2, 6, 18, 54, ...

    b 100, 50, 25, 12.5, ...

    c 1, −2, 4, −8, ...

    d 1, 1.1, 1.21, 1.331, ...

2 The nth term of a geometric sequence is $2 \times (5)^n$. Find the first and 5th terms.

3 The sixth term of a geometric sequence is 32 and the 3rd term is 4. Find the first term and the common ratio.

4 Given that the first term of a geometric sequence is 4, and the third is 1, find possible values for the 6th term.

5 The expressions $x - 6$, $2x$ and x^2 form the first three terms of a geometric progression. By calculating two different expressions for the common ratio, form and solve an equation in x to find possible values of the first term.

5.7 *You need to be able to find the sum of a geometric series.*

Example 16

Find the general term for the sum of the first n terms of a geometric series a, ar, ar^2, ..., ar^n.

Let $S_n = a + ar + ar^2 + ar^3 + ... + ar^{n-2} + ar^{n-1}$ ①   Multiply by r.

$\qquad rS_n = ar + ar^2 + ar^3 + ... + ar^{n-1} + ar^n$ ②

① − ② gives $S_n - rS_n = a - ar^n$ Subtract rS_n from S_n.

$\qquad\quad S_n(1 - r) = a(1 - r^n)$ Take out the common factor.

$\qquad\qquad\quad S_n = \dfrac{a(1 - r^n)}{1 - r}$ Divide by $(1 - r)$.

• **The general rule for the sum of a geometric series is** $S_n = \dfrac{a(r^n - 1)}{r - 1}$ **or** $\dfrac{a(1 - r^n)}{1 - r}$

You will not be asked to prove these formulae.

Example 17

Find the sum of the following series:

a $2 + 6 + 18 + 54 + \dots$ (for 10 terms)

b $1024 - 512 + 256 - 128 + \dots + 1$

a Series is

$2 + 6 + 18 + 54 + \dots$ (for 10 terms)

So $a = 2$, $r = \frac{6}{2} = 3$ and $n = 10$

As in all questions, write down what is given.

So $S_{10} = \dfrac{2(3^{10} - 1)}{3 - 1} = 59\,048$

As $r = 3$ (> 1), it is easier to use the formula $S_n = \dfrac{a(r^n - 1)}{r - 1}$ as it avoids minus signs.

b Series is

$1024 - 512 + 256 - 128 + \dots + 1$

So $a = 1024$, $r = -\frac{512}{1024} = -\frac{1}{2}$

and nth term $= 1$

$$1024\left(-\tfrac{1}{2}\right)^{n-1} = 1$$

$$(-2)^{n-1} = 1024$$

$$2^{n-1} = 1024$$

$$n - 1 = \frac{\log 1024}{\log 2}$$

$$n - 1 = 10$$

$$n = 11$$

First solve $ar^{n-1} = 1$ to find n.

$(-2)^{n-1} = (-1)^{n-1}(2^{n-1}) = 1024$, so $(-1)^{n-1}$ must be positive and $2^{n-1} = 1024$.

$1024 = 2^{10}$

So $S_{11} = \dfrac{1024\left[1 - \left(-\tfrac{1}{2}\right)^{11}\right]}{1 - \left(-\tfrac{1}{2}\right)}$

As $r = -\frac{1}{2}$ (< 1) we use the formula $S_n = \dfrac{a(1 - r^n)}{1 - r}$.

$$= \dfrac{1024\left(1 + \tfrac{1}{2048}\right)}{1 + \tfrac{1}{2}}$$

$$= \dfrac{1024.5}{\tfrac{3}{2}} = 683$$

Example 18

An investor invests £2000 on January 1st every year in a savings account that guarantees him 4% per annum for life. If interest is calculated on the 31st of December each year, how much will be in the account at the end of the 10th year?

End of year 1, amount $= 2000 \times 1.04$

A rate of 4% means $\times 1.04$.

Start of year 2, amount $= 2000 \times 1.04 + 2000$

Every new year he invests £2000.

End of year 2, amount $= (2000 \times 1.04 + 2000) \times 1.04$

$\qquad\qquad\qquad = 2000 \times 1.04^2 + 2000 \times 1.04$

At the end of every year the total amount in the account is multiplied by 1.04.

Start of year 3,

amount $= 2000 \times 1.04^2 + 2000 \times 1.04 + 2000$

End of year 3.

amount $= (2000 \times 1.04^2 + 2000 \times 1.04 + 2000) \times 1.04$

$\qquad = 2000 \times 1.04^3 + 2000 \times 1.04^2 + 2000 \times 1.04$

So by end of year 10.   Look at the values for the end of year 3 and extend this for 10 years.

amount $= 2000 \times 1.04^{10} + 2000 \times 1.04^9 + \ldots + 2000 \times 1.04$

$\qquad = 2000(1.04^{10} + 1.04^9 + \ldots + 1.04)$ This is a geometric series. Substitute $a = 1.04$,

$\qquad = 2000 \times \dfrac{1.04(1.04^{10} - 1)}{1.04 - 1}$ $r = 1.04$ and $n = 10$ in S

$\qquad = 2000 \times 12.486 \ldots = £24\,972.70$ $= \dfrac{a(r^n - 1)}{r - 1}$

Example 19

Find the least value of n such that the sum of $1 + 2 + 4 + 8 + \ldots$ to n terms would exceed $2\,000\,000$.

Sum to n terms is $S_n = 1\dfrac{(2^n - 1)}{2 - 1}$ Substitute $a = 1$, $r = 2$ into $S_n = \dfrac{a(r^n - 1)}{r - 1}$.

$\qquad\qquad\qquad = 2^n - 1$

If this is to exceed $2\,000\,000$ then

$\qquad S_n > 2\,000\,000$

$\qquad 2^n - 1 > 2\,000\,000$

$\qquad 2^n > 2\,000\,001$ Add 1.

$\qquad n\log(2) > \log(2\,000\,001)$

$\qquad n > \dfrac{\log(2\,000\,001)}{\log(2)}$ Use laws of logs: $\log a^n = n\log a$.

$\qquad n > 20.9$

It needs 21 terms to exceed $2\,000\,000$ Round up n to the nearest integer.

Example 20

Find $\displaystyle\sum_{r=1}^{10} (3 \times 2^r)$.

$S_{10} = \displaystyle\sum_{r=1}^{10} (3 \times 2^r)$ '$\sum$' means 'sum of' – in this case the sum of (3×2^r) from $r = 1$ to $r = 10$.

$\qquad = 3 \times 2^1 + 3 \times 2^2 + 3 \times 2^3 + \ldots + 3 \times 2^{10}$

$\qquad = 3(2^1 + 2^2 + 2^3 + \ldots + 2^{10})$ This is a geometric series with $a = 2$, $r = 2$ and $n = 10$.

$\qquad = 3 \times 2\dfrac{(2^{10} - 1)}{2 - 1}$ Use $s = \dfrac{a(r^n - 1)}{r - 1}$

So $S_{10} = 6138$

Exercise 5G

1 Find the sum of the following geometric series (to 3 d.p. if necessary):

    a $1 + 2 + 4 + 8 + \ldots$ (8 terms)   **b** $32 + 16 + 8 + \ldots$ (10 terms)

    c $4 - 12 + 36 - 108 \ldots$ (6 terms)   **d** $729 - 243 + 81 - \ldots - \frac{1}{3}$

    e $\sum_{r=1}^{6} 4^r$ **f** $\sum_{r=1}^{8} 2 \times (3)^r$

    g $\sum_{r=1}^{10} 6 \times (\frac{1}{2})^r$ **h** $\sum_{r=1}^{6} 60 \times (-\frac{1}{3})^r$

2 The sum of the first three terms of a geometric series is 30.5. If the first term is 8, find possible values of r.

3 The man who invented the game of chess was asked to name his reward. He asked for 1 grain of corn to be placed on the first square of his chessboard, 2 on the second, 4 on the third and so on until all 64 squares were covered. He then said he would like as many grains of corn as the chessboard carried. How many grains of corn did he claim as his prize?

4 Jane invests £4000 at the start of every year. She negotiates a rate of interest of 4% per annum, which is paid at the end of the year. How much is her investment worth at the end of **a** the 10th year and **b** the 20th year?

5 A ball is dropped from a height of 10 m. It bounces to a height of 7 m and continues to bounce. Subsequent heightsto which it bounces follow a geometric sequence. Find out:

    a   how high it will bounce after the fourth bounce,

    b   the total distance travelled until it hits the ground for the sixth time.

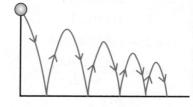

6 Find the least value of n such that the sum $3 + 6 + 12 + 24 + \ldots$ to n terms would first exceed 1.5 million.

7 Find the least value of n such that the sum $5 + 4.5 + 4.05 + \ldots$ to n terms would first exceed 45.

8 Richard is sponsored to cycle 1000 miles over a number of days. He cycles 10 miles on day 1, and increases this distance by 10% a day. How long will it take him to complete the challenge? What was the greatest number of miles he completed in a single day?

9 A savings scheme is offering a rate of interest of 3.5% per annum for the lifetime of the plan. Alan wants to save up £20 000. He works out that he can afford to save £500 every year, which he will deposit on 1 January. If interest is paid on 31 December, how many years will it be before he has saved up his £20 000?

5.8 You need to be able to find the sum to infinity of a convergent geometric series.

Consider the series $\quad S = 3 + 1.5 + 0.75 + 0.375 + ...$

No matter how many terms of the series you take, the sum never exceeds a certain number. We call this number the limit of the sum, or more often, its sum to infinity.

We can find out what this limit is.

As $a = 3$ and $r = \frac{1}{2}$, $S = \dfrac{a(1 - r^n)}{1 - r} = \dfrac{3(1 - (\frac{1}{2})^n)}{1 - \frac{1}{2}} = 6(1 - (\frac{1}{2})^n)$

If we replace n with certain values to find the sum we find that

when $n = 3$, $S_3 = 5.25$

when $n = 5$, $S_5 = 5.8125$

when $n = 10$, $S_{10} = 5.9994$

when $n = 20$, $S_{20} = 5.999\,994$

You can see that as n gets larger, S becomes closer and closer to 6.

We say that this infinite series is **convergent**, and has a sum to infinity of 6. Convergent means the series tends towards a specific value as more terms are added.

Not all series converge. The reason that this one does is that the terms of the sequence are getting smaller.

This happens because $-1 < r < 1$.

The sum to infinity of a series exists only if $-1 < r < 1$.

$S = \dfrac{a(1 - r^n)}{1 - r}$

If $-1 < r < 1$, $r^n \to 0$ as $n \to \infty$

Hint: You can write 'the sum to infinity' is S_∞.

$S_\infty = \dfrac{a}{1 - r}$

- **The sum to infinity of a geometric series is $\dfrac{a}{1 - r}$ if $|r| < 1$.**

Hint: $|r|$ means $-1 < r < 1$.

Example 21

Find the sums to infinity of the following series:

a $40 + 10 + 2.5 + 0.625 + ...$

b $1 + \dfrac{1}{p} + \dfrac{1}{p^2} + ...$

a $40 + 10 + 2.5 + 0.625 + ...$

In this series $a = 40$ and $r = \dfrac{10}{40} = \dfrac{1}{4}$

$-1 < r < 1$, so S_∞ exists

$S = \dfrac{a}{1 - r} = \dfrac{40}{1 - \frac{1}{4}} = \dfrac{40}{\frac{3}{4}} = \dfrac{160}{3}$

Always write down the values of a and r, using $\dfrac{u_2}{u_1}$ for r.

Substitute $a = 40$ and $r = \dfrac{10}{4} = \dfrac{1}{4}$ into $S = \dfrac{a}{1 - r}$.

b $1 + \dfrac{1}{p} + \dfrac{1}{p^2} + \ldots$

In this series $a = 1$ and $r = \dfrac{u_2}{u_1} = \dfrac{\frac{1}{p}}{1} = \dfrac{1}{p}$.

S will exist if $\left| \dfrac{1}{p} \right| < 1$ so $p > 1$.

If $p > 1$, $S_\infty = \dfrac{1}{1 - \frac{1}{p}}$

$= \dfrac{p}{p - 1}$ Multiply top and bottom by p.

Example 22

The sum to 4 terms of a geometric series is 15 and the sum to infinity is 16.

a Find the possible values of r.

b Given that the terms are all positive, find the first term in the series.

a $\dfrac{a(1 - r^4)}{1 - r} = 15$ ① $S_4 = 15$ so use the formula $S_n = \dfrac{a(1 - r^n)}{1 - r}$ with $n = 4$.

$\dfrac{a}{1 - r} = 16$ ② $S_\infty = 16$ so use the formula $S_\infty = \dfrac{a}{1 - r}$ with $S_\infty = 16$.

$16(1 - r^4) = 15$ Solve equations simultaneously.

$1 - r^4 = \dfrac{15}{16}$ Replace $\dfrac{a}{1 - r}$ by 16 in equation ①

$r^4 = \dfrac{1}{16}$ Divide by 16.

$r = \pm\dfrac{1}{2}$ Rearrange.
Take the 4th root of $\dfrac{1}{16}$.

b As all terms positive, $r = +\dfrac{1}{2}$
Substitute $r = +\dfrac{1}{2}$ back into
equation ② to find a

$\dfrac{a}{1 - \frac{1}{2}} = 16$

$16(1 - \tfrac{1}{2}) = a$

$a = 8$

The first term in the series is 8.

Exercise 5H

1 Find the sum to infinity, if it exists, of the following series:

a $1 + 0.1 + 0.01 + 0.001 + \ldots$ **b** $1 + 2 + 4 + 8 + 16 + \ldots$

c $10 - 5 + 2.5 - 1.25 + \ldots$ **d** $2 + 6 + 10 + 14$

e $1 + 1 + 1 + 1 + 1 + \ldots$ **f** $3 + 1 + \dfrac{1}{3} + \dfrac{1}{9} + \ldots$

g $0.4 + 0.8 + 1.2 + 1.6 + \ldots$ **h** $9 + 8.1 + 7.29 + 6.561 + \ldots$

i $1 + r + r^2 + r^3 + \ldots$ **j** $1 - 2x + 4x^2 - 8x^3 + \ldots$

2 Find the common ratio of a geometric series with a first term of 10 and a sum to infinity of 30.

3 Find the common ratio of a geometric series with a first term of -5 and a sum to infinity of -3.

4 Find the first term of a geometric series with a common ratio of $\frac{2}{3}$ and a sum to infinity of 60.

5 Find the first term of a geometric series with a common ratio of $-\frac{1}{3}$ and a sum to infinity of 10.

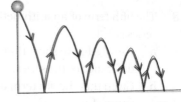

Hint for question 6:
Write 0.232 323 232 3 as
$\frac{23}{100} + \frac{23}{10\,000} + \frac{23}{1\,000\,000}$

6 Find the fraction equal to the recurring decimal 0.232 323 232 3.

7 Find $\sum\limits_{r=1}^{\infty} 4(0.5)^r$.

8 A ball is dropped from a height of 10 m. It bounces to a height of 6 m, then 3.6, and so on following a geometric sequence.
Find the total distance travelled by the ball.

9 The sum to three terms of geometric series is 9 and its sum to infinity is 8. What could you deduce about the common ratio. Why? Find the first term and common ratio.

10 The sum to infinity of a geometric series is three times the sum to 2 terms. Find all possible values of the common ratio.

Mixed Exercise 5I

1 Find a rule that describes the following sequences:

   a   5, 11, 17, 23, ...   **b**   3, 6, 9, 12, ...

   c   1, 3, 9, 27, ...   **d**   10, 5, 0, -5, ...

   e   1, 4, 9, 16, ...   **f**   1, 1.2, 1.44, 1.728, ...

   Which of the above are arithmetic sequences?
   For the ones that are, state the values of a and d.

2 For the arithmetic series $5 + 9 + 13 + 17 + ...$
   Find **a** the 20th term, and **b** the sum of the first 20 terms.

3 Find the least value of n for which $\sum\limits_{r=1}^{n} (4r - 3) > 2000$.

4 A salesman is paid commission of £10 per week for each life insurance policy that he has sold. Each week he sells one new policy so that he is paid £10 commission in the first week, £20 commission in the second week. £30 commission in the third week and so on.

   a   Find his total commission in the first year of 52 weeks.

   b   In the second year the commission increases to £11 per week on new policies sold, although it remains at £10 per week for policies sold in the first year. He continues to sell one policy per week. Show that he is paid £542 in the second week of his second year.

   c   Find the total commission paid to him in the second year.

© Edexcel Limited

5 The sum of the first two terms of an arithmetic series is 47.
The thirtieth term of this series is -62. Find:
a the first term of the series and the common difference
b the sum of the first 60 terms of the series. © Edexcel Limited

6 **a** Find the sum of the integers which are divisible by 3 and lie between 1 and 400.
b Hence, or otherwise, find the sum of the integers, from 1 to 400 inclusive, which are **not** divisible by 3. © Edexcel Limited

7 A polygon has 10 sides. The lengths of the sides, starting with the smallest, form an arithmetic series. The perimeter of the polygon is 675 cm and the length of the longest side is twice that of the shortest side. Find, for this series:
a the common difference
b the first term. © Edexcel Limited

8 The fifth term of an arithmetic series is 14 and the sum of the first three terms of the series is -3.
a Use algebra to show that the first term of the series is -6 and calculate the common difference of the series.
b Given that the nth term of the series is greater than 282, find the least possible value of n. © Edexcel Limited

9 The fourth term of an arithmetic series is $3k$, where k is a constant, and the sum of the first six terms of the series is $7k + 9$.
a Show that the first term of the series is $9 - 8k$.
b Find an expression for the common difference of the series in terms of k.
Given that the seventh term of the series is 12, calculate:
c the value of k
d the sum of the first 20 terms of the series. © Edexcel Limited

10 State which of the following series are geometric. For the ones that are, give the value of the common ratio r.
a $4 + 7 + 10 + 13 + 16 + \dots$ **b** $4 + 6 + 9 + 13.5 + \dots$
c $20 + 10 + 5 + 2.5 + \dots$ **d** $4 - 8 + 16 - 32 + \dots$
e $4 - 2 - 8 - 14 - \dots$ **f** $1 + 1 + 1 + 1 + \dots$

11 Find the 8th and nth terms of the following geometric sequences:
a $10, 7, 4.9, \dots$ **b** $5, 10, 20, \dots$
c $4, -4, 4, \dots$ **d** $3, -1.5, 0.75, \dots$

12 Find the sum to 10 terms of the following geometric series:
a $4 + 8 + 16 + \dots$ **b** $30 - 15 + 7.5, \dots$
c $5 + 5 + 5, \dots$ **d** $2 + 0.8 + 0.32, \dots$

13 Determine which of the following geometric series converge. For the ones that do, give the limiting value of this sum (i.e. S_∞).
a $6 + 2 + -23- + \dots$ **b** $4 - 2 + 1 - \dots$
c $5 + 10 + 20 + \dots$ **d** $4 + 1 + 0.25 + \dots$

14 A geometric series has third term 27 and sixth term 8:
a Show that the common ratio of the series is $\frac{2}{3}$.
b Find the first term of the series.

c Find the sum to infinity of the series.

d Find, to 3 significant figures, the difference between the sum of the first 10 terms of the series and the sum to infinity of the series.

15 The second term of a geometric series is 80 and the fifth term of the series is 5.12:

a Show that the common ratio of the series is 0.4.

Calculate:

b the first term of the series,

c the sum to infinity of the series, giving your answer as an exact fraction,

d the difference between the sum to infinity of the series and the sum of the first 14 terms of the series, giving your answer in the form $a \times 10^n$, where $1 \leqslant a < 10$ and n is an integer.

16 The nth term of a sequence is u_n, where $u_n = 95\left(\frac{4}{5}\right)^n$, $n = 1, 2, 3, \ldots$

a Find the value of u_1 and u_2.

Giving your answers to 3 significant figures, calculate:

b the value of u_{21},

c $\displaystyle\sum_{15}^{n=1} u_n$,

d Find the sum to infinity of the series whose first term is u_1 and whose nth term is u_n.

17 A sequence of numbers $u_1, u_2, \ldots, u_n, \ldots$ is given by the formula $u_n = 3\left(\frac{2}{3}\right)^n - 1$ where n is a positive integer.

a Find the values of u_1, u_2 and u_3.

b Show that $\displaystyle\sum_{15}^{n=1} u_n = -9.014$ to 4 significant figures.

c Prove that $u_{n+1} = 2\left(\frac{2}{3}\right)^n - 1$.

18 The third and fourth terms of a geometric series are 6.4 and 5.12 respectively. Find:

a the common ratio of the series,

b the first term of the series,

c the sum to infinity of the series.

d Calculate the difference between the sum to infinity of the series and the sum of the first 25 terms of the series.

19 The first three terms of a geometric series are $p(3q + 1)$, $p(2q + 2)$ and $p(2q - 1)$ respectively, where p and q are non-zero constants.

a Use algebra to show that one possible value of q is 5 and to find the other possible value of q.

b For each possible value of q, calculate the value of the common ratio of the series.

Given that $q = 5$ and that the sum to infinity of the geometric series is 896, calculate:

c the value of p,

d the sum, to 2 decimal places, of the first twelve terms of the series.

20 A savings scheme pays 5% per annum compound interest. A deposit of £100 is invested in this scheme at the start of each year.

a Show that at the start of the third year, after the annual deposit has been made, the amount in the scheme is £315.25.

b Find the amount in the scheme at the start of the fortieth year, after the annual deposit has been made.

1. You can use Σ to signify 'sum of'. You can use Σ to write series in a more concise way

   e.g. $\displaystyle\sum_{r=1}^{10} (5 + 2r) = 7 + 9 + \ldots + 25$

2. All arithmetic series can be put in the form

   $$a + (a + d) + (a + 2d) + (a + 3d) + (a + 4d) + (a + 5d)$$

       1st term   2nd term   3rd term   4th term   5th term   6th term

3. The nth term of an arithmetic series is $a + (n - 1)d$, where a is the first term and d is the common difference.

4. The formula for the sum of an arithmetic series is

   $$S_n = \frac{n}{2}[2a + (n - 1)d]$$

   or $S_n = \dfrac{n}{2}(a + L)$

   where a is the first term, d is the common difference, n is the number of terms and L is the last term in the series.

5. In a geometric series you get from one term to the next by multiplying by a constant called the common ratio.

6. The formula for the nth term $= ar^{n-1}$ where $a =$ first term and $r =$ common ratio.

7. The formula for the sum to n terms is

   $$S_n = \frac{a(1 - r^n)}{1 - r} \text{ or } S_n = \frac{a(r^n - 1)}{r - 1}$$

8. The sum to infinity exists if $|r| < 1$ and is $S_\infty = \dfrac{a}{1 - r}$

Chapter 6: The binomial series

6.1 You need to be able to expand $(1 + ax)^n$ using the binomial expansion.

$(1 + x)^n = \binom{n}{0}1^n + \binom{n}{1}1^{n-1}x^1 + \binom{n}{2}1^{n-2}x^2 + \binom{n}{3}1^{n-3}x^3 + \binom{n}{4}1^{n-4}x^4 + \dots + \binom{n}{r}1^{n-r}x^r$

$$= 1 + nx + \frac{n(n-1)}{2!}x^2 + \frac{n(n-1)(n-2)}{3!}x^3 + \frac{n(n-1)(n-2)(n-3)}{4!}x^4 + \dots$$

When n is a positive integer the coefficient $\binom{n}{r}$ is sometimes written as ^nC_r and this can be evaluated on most calculators.

Example 1

Find the first 3 terms in the binomial expansion of $(1 - \frac{1}{2}x)^6$ in ascending powers of x.

$(1 - \frac{1}{2}x)^6 = 1 + \binom{6}{1}(-\frac{1}{2}x) + \binom{6}{2}(-\frac{1}{2}x)^2 + \dots$ — Use the expansion for $(1 + y)^n$ with $y = -\frac{1}{2}x$

$\quad = 1 + 6(-\frac{1}{2}x) + 15(-\frac{1}{2}x)^2 \dots$ — Note the brackets

$\quad = 1 - 3x + \frac{15}{4}x^2$ — $\binom{6}{2} = \frac{6!}{4!2!} = 15$ You should check that you can evaluate this as $^6C_2$ on your calculator.

Simplify the terms. The brackets mean that the 3rd term is positive since "-" is squared.

Example 2

Find the first four terms in the binomial expansion of $(1 + 2x)^5$:

$(1 + 2x)^5 = 1 + nx + \frac{n(n-1)}{2!}x^2 + \frac{n(n-1)(n-2)}{3!}x^3 + \dots$ — Compare $(1 + x)^n$ with $(1 + 2x)^n$.

$\quad = 1 + 5(2x) + \frac{5(4)}{2!}(2x)^2 + \frac{5(4)(3)}{3!}(2x)^3 + \dots$ — Replace n by 5 and 'x' by $2x$.

$\quad = 1 + 10x + 40x^2 + 80x^3 + \dots$

Example 3

Find the coefficient of **a** x^3 and **b** x^8 in the binomial expansion of $(1 - 2x)^{12}$.

a $(1 - 2x)^{12} = \dots + \binom{12}{3}(-2x)^3 + \dots$ — You do not need the whole expansion just the required terms.

Coefficient of $x^3 = 220 \times (-2)^3 = -1760$

NB $\binom{12}{3} = {}^{12}C_3 = \frac{12!}{9!3!} = 220$

b $(1 - 2x)^{12} = \dots + \binom{12}{8}(-2x)^8 + \dots$

Coefficient of $x^8 = 495 \times (-2)^8 = 126720$

NB $\binom{12}{8} = {}^{12}C_8 = \frac{12!}{8!4!} = 495$

Exercise 6A

Use the binomial expansion to find the first four terms of

1 $(1 + x)^8$

2 $(1 - 2x)^6$

3 $\left(1 + \dfrac{x}{2}\right)^{10}$

4 $(1 - 3x)^5$

5 When $(1 - 2x)^p$ is expanded, the coefficient of x^2 is 40. Given that $p > 0$, use this information to find:
  a The value of the constant p.
  b The coefficient of x.
  c The coefficient of x^3.

6 Write down the first four terms in the expansion of $\left(1 - \dfrac{x}{10}\right)^6$.

  By substituting an appropriate value for x, find an approximate value to $(0.99)^6$. Use your calculator to find the degree of accuracy of your approximation.

7 Find the term in x^3 of the following expansions:
  a $(1 - x)^6$ **b** $(1 + x)^{10}$ **c** $(1 + x)^{20}$

8 **a** Expand $(3 + 2x)^4$ in ascending powers of x, giving each coefficient as an integer.
  b Hence, or otherwise, write down the expansion of $(3 - 2x)^4$ in ascending powers of x.
  c Hence by choosing a suitable value for x show that $(3 + 2\sqrt{2})^4 + (3 - 2\sqrt{2})^4$ is an integer and state its value.

6.2 You can use the binomial expansion $(1 + x)^n = 1 + nx + \dfrac{n(n-1)}{2!}x^2 + \dfrac{n(n-1)(n-2)}{3!}x^3 + \ldots$

when n is not a positive integer.

When n is not a positive integer then none of the $(n - r)$ terms in the coefficients will be equal to zero and so the series will be **infinite.** In this case the expansion of $(1 + x)^n$ will only be valid for values of x in the range $-1 < x < 1$. This is sometimes written using the modulus function as $|x| < 1$

Example 4

Use the binomial expansion to find the first four terms of   **a** $\dfrac{1}{(1 + x)}$ **b** $\sqrt{(1 - 3x)}$

a $\dfrac{1}{(1 + x)} = (1 + x)^{-1}$

Write in index form.
Replace n by -1 in the expansion.

$= 1 + (-1)(x) + \dfrac{(-1)(-2)(x)^2}{2!} + \dfrac{(-1)(-2)(-3)(x)^3}{3!} + \ldots$

$= 1 - 1x + 1x^2 - 1x^3 + \ldots$

$= 1 - x + x^2 - x^3 + \ldots$

As n is not a positive integer, no coefficient will ever be equal to zero.
The expansion is **infinite**, and convergent when $|x| < 1$.

b $\sqrt{(1-3x)} = (1-3x)^{\frac{1}{2}}$ Write in index form.

$$= 1 + \left(\tfrac{1}{2}\right)(-3x)$$ Replace n by $\tfrac{1}{2}$ and x by $-3x$.

$$+ \frac{\left(\tfrac{1}{2}\right)\left(\tfrac{1}{2}-1\right)(-3x)^2}{2!}$$ Be careful to write this as $(-3x)^2$, not $-3x^2$.

$$+ \frac{\left(\tfrac{1}{2}\right)\left(\tfrac{1}{2}-1\right)\left(\tfrac{1}{2}-2\right)(-3x)^3}{3!} + \ldots$$

$$= 1 - \frac{3x}{2} + \frac{\left(\tfrac{1}{2}\right)\left(-\tfrac{1}{2}\right)9x^2}{2}$$ Simplify terms.

$$+ \frac{\left(\tfrac{1}{2}\right)\left(-\tfrac{1}{2}\right)\left(-\tfrac{3}{2}\right)(-27x^3)}{6} + \ldots$$ Because n is not a positive integer, no coefficient will ever be equal to zero.

$$= 1 - \frac{3x}{2} - \frac{9x^2}{8} - \frac{27x^3}{16} + \ldots$$ The expansion is **infinite**, and convergent when $|x| < \tfrac{1}{3}$ because $|3x| < 1$

Example 5

Find the binomial expansions of **a** $(1-x)^{\frac{1}{3}}$, **b** $\dfrac{1}{(1+4x)^2}$, up to and including the term in x^3.

State the range of values of x for which the expansions are valid.

a $(1-x)^{\frac{1}{3}}$

$$= 1 + \left(\tfrac{1}{3}\right)(2x)$$ Replace n by $\tfrac{1}{3}$, x by $(-x)$.

$$+ \frac{\left(\tfrac{1}{3}\right)\left(\tfrac{1}{3}-1\right)(-x)^2}{2!}$$ Simplify brackets.

$$+ \frac{\left(\tfrac{1}{3}\right)\left(\tfrac{1}{3}-1\right)\left(\tfrac{1}{3}-2\right)(-x)^3}{3!} + \ldots$$

$$= 1 + \left(\tfrac{1}{3}\right)(-x) + \frac{\left(\tfrac{1}{3}\right)\left(-\tfrac{2}{3}\right)(-x)^2}{2}$$ Simplify coefficients.

$$+ \frac{\left(\tfrac{1}{3}\right)\left(-\tfrac{2}{3}\right)\left(-\tfrac{5}{3}\right)(-x)^3}{6} + \ldots$$ Terms in expansion are $(-x)$, $(-x)^2$, $(-x)^3$.

$$= 1 - \tfrac{1}{3}x - \tfrac{1}{9}x^2 - \tfrac{5}{81}x^3 + \ldots$$

Expansion is valid as long as $|-x| < 1 \Rightarrow |x| < 1$

b $\dfrac{1}{(1+4x)^2}$ Write in index form.

$$= (1+4x)^{-2}$$

$$= 1 + (-2)(4x)$$ Replace n by -2, x by '$4x$'.

$$+ \frac{(-2)(-2-1)(4x)^2}{2!}$$

$$+ \frac{(-2)(-2-1)(-2-2)(4x)^3}{3!} + \ldots$$ Simplify brackets.

$$= 1 + (-2)(4x)$$

$$+ \frac{(-2)(-3)16x^2}{2}$$ Simplify coefficients.

$$+ \frac{(-2)(-3)(-4)64x^3}{6} + \ldots$$

$$= 1 - 8x + 48x^2 - 256x^3 + \ldots$$ Terms in expansion are $(4x), (4x)^2, (4x)^3$.

Expansion is valid as long as $|4x| < 1$

$$\Rightarrow |x| < \tfrac{1}{4}.$$

Example 6

Find the expansion of $\sqrt{(1 - 2x)}$ up to and including the term in x^3. By substituting in $x = 0.01$, find a suitable decimal approximation to $\sqrt{2}$.

$$\sqrt{(1 - 2x)} = (1 - 2x)^{\frac{1}{2}}$$ Write in index form.

$$= 1 + (\tfrac{1}{2})(-2x)$$ Replace n by $\tfrac{1}{2}$, x by $(-2x)$.

$$+ \frac{(\tfrac{1}{2})(\tfrac{1}{2} - 1)(-2x)^2}{2!}$$

$$+ \frac{(\tfrac{1}{2})(\tfrac{1}{2} - 1)(\tfrac{1}{2} - 2)(-2x)^3}{3!} + \ldots$$ Simplify brackets.

$$= 1 + (\tfrac{1}{2})(-2x)$$

$$+ \frac{(\tfrac{1}{2})(-\tfrac{1}{2})(4x^2)}{2}$$ Simplify coefficients.

$$+ \frac{(\tfrac{1}{2})(-\tfrac{1}{2})(-\tfrac{3}{2})(-8x^3)}{6} + \ldots$$ Terms in expansion are $(-2x), (-2x)^2, (-2x)^3$.

$$= 1 - x - \frac{x^2}{2} - \frac{x^3}{2} + \ldots$$

Expansion is valid as long as $|2x| < 1$

$$\Rightarrow |x| < \tfrac{1}{2}.$$

$$\sqrt{(1 - 2 \times 0.01)} \approx 1 - 0.01 - \frac{(0.01)^2}{2} - \frac{(0.01)^3}{2}$$

Substitute $x = 0.01$ into both sides of expansion. This is valid as $|x| < \tfrac{1}{2}$.

$$\sqrt{0.98} \approx 1 - 0.01 - 0.00005 - 0.0000005$$ Simplify both sides. Note that the terms are getting smaller.

$$\sqrt{\frac{98}{100}} \approx 0.9899495$$ Write 0.98 as $\frac{98}{100}$.

$$\sqrt{\frac{49 \times 2}{100}} \approx 0.9899495$$ Use rules of surds.

$$\frac{7\sqrt{2}}{10} \approx 0.9899495$$ $\times 10, \div 7$

$$\sqrt{2} \approx \frac{0.9899495 \times 10}{7}$$ Simplify.

$$\sqrt{2} \approx 1.414213571$$

Exercise 6B

1 Find the binomial expansion of the following up to and including the terms in x^3. State the range values of x for which these expansions are valid.

   a $(1 + 2x)^3$ **b** $\dfrac{1}{1 - x}$ **c** $\sqrt{(1 + x)}$ **d** $\dfrac{1}{(1 + 2x)^3}$

   e $\sqrt[3]{(1 - 3x)}$ **f** $(1 - 10x)^{\frac{3}{2}}$ **g** $\left(1 + \dfrac{x}{4}\right)^{-4}$ **h** $\dfrac{1}{(1 + 2x^2)}$

2 By first writing $\dfrac{(1 + x)}{(1 - 2x)}$ as $(1 + x)(1 - 2x)^{-1}$ show that the cubic approximation

to $\dfrac{(1 + x)}{(1 - 2x)}$ is $1 + 3x + 6x^2 + 12x^3$. State the range of values of x for which this expansion is valid.

3 Find the binomial expansion of $\sqrt{(1 + 3x)}$ in ascending powers of x up to and including the term in x^3. By substituting $x = 0.01$ in the expansion, find an approximation to $\sqrt{103}$. By comparing it with the exact value, comment on the accuracy of your approximation.

4 In the expansion of $(1 + ax)^{-\frac{1}{2}}$ the coefficient of x^2 is 24. Find possible values of the constant a and the corresponding term in x^3.

5 Show that if x is small, the expression $\sqrt{\dfrac{1 + x}{1 - x}}$ is approximated by $1 + x + \frac{1}{2}x^2$.

> **Hint:**
>
> Multiply by $\sqrt{\dfrac{1 + x}{1 - x}}$ first

6 Find the first four terms in the expansion of $(1 - 3x)^{\frac{3}{2}}$. By substituting in a suitable value of x, find an approximation to $97^{\frac{3}{2}}$.

Mixed Exercise 6C

1 When $(1 - \frac{3}{2}x)^p$ is expanded in ascending powers of x, the coefficient of x is -24.

   a Find the value of p.

   b Find the coefficient of x^2 in the expansion.

   c Find the coefficient of x^3 in the expansion.   © Edexcel Limited

2 **a** Expand $(1 - 2x)^{10}$ in ascending powers of x up to and including the term in x^3, simplifying each coefficient in the expansion.

   b Use your expansion to find an approximation to $(0.98)^{10}$, stating clearly the substitution which you have used for x.   © Edexcel Limited

3 The coefficient of x^2 in the binomial expansion of $\left(1 + \dfrac{x}{2}\right)^n$, where n is a positive integer, is 7.

   a Find the value of n.

   b Using the value of n found in part **a**, find the coefficient of x^4.   © Edexcel Limited

4 **a** Expand $(1 + 2x)^{12}$ in ascending powers of x up to and including the term in x^3, simplifying each coefficient.

   b By substituting a suitable value for x, which must be stated, into your answer to part **a**, calculate an approximate value of $(1.02)^{12}$.

   c Use your calculator, writing down all the digits in your display, to find a more exact value of $(1.02)^{12}$.

   d Calculate, to 3 significant figures, the percentage error of the approximation found in part **b**.   © Edexcel Limited

5 Find binomial expansions of the following in ascending powers of x as far as the term in x^3. State the set of values of x for which the expansion is valid.

    a $(1 - 4x)^3$ **b** $\dfrac{1}{(1 - 2x)}$ **c** $\dfrac{1 + x}{1 + 3x}$

6 Find the first four terms of the expansion in ascending powers of x of:

    $(1 - \tfrac{1}{2}x)^{\frac{1}{2}}, \ |x| < 2$

    and simplify each coefficient.   © Edexcel Limited

                                                                      (adapted)

7 Obtain the first four non-zero terms in the expansion, in ascending powers of x,

    of the function $f(x)$ where $f(x) = \dfrac{1}{\sqrt{(1 + 3x^2)}}, \ 3x^2 < 1$.   © Edexcel Limited

8 Give the binomial expansion of $(1 + x)^{\frac{1}{2}}$ up to and including the term in x^3. By substituting $x = \tfrac{1}{4}$, find the fraction that is an approximation to $\sqrt{5}$.

9 When $(1 + ax)^n$ is expanded as a series in ascending powers of x, the coefficients of x and x^2 are -6 and 27 respectively.

    a   Find the values of a and n.

    b   Find the coefficient of x^3.

    c   State the values of x for which the expansion is valid.   © Edexcel Limited

                                                                       (adapted)

1 The binomial expansion $(1 + x)^n = 1 + nx + \dfrac{n(n-1)x^2}{2!} + \dfrac{n(n-1)(n-2)x^3}{3!} + \dots$ can be used to give an exact expression if n is a positive integer, or an approximate expression for any other rational number.

- $(1 + 2x)^3 = 1 + 3(2x) + 3 \times 2 \dfrac{(2x)^2}{2!} + 3 \times 2 \times 1 \times \dfrac{(2x)^3}{3!} + 3 \times 2 \times 1 \times 0 \times \dfrac{(2x)^4}{4!} \dots$

$$= 1 + 6x + 12x^2 + 8x^3 \text{ (Expansion is \textit{finite} and \textit{exact}.)}$$

- $\sqrt{(1-x)} = (1-x)^{\frac{1}{2}} = 1 + \left(\dfrac{1}{2}\right)(-x) + \dfrac{1}{2}\left(-\dfrac{1}{2}\right)\dfrac{(-x^2)}{2!} + \left(\dfrac{1}{2}\right)\left(-\dfrac{1}{2}\right)\left(-\dfrac{3}{2}\right)\dfrac{(-x)^3}{3!} + \dots$

$$= 1 - \dfrac{1}{2}x - \dfrac{1}{8}x^2 - \dfrac{1}{16}x^3 + \dots$$

(Expansion is *infinite* and *approximate*.)

2 The expansion $(1 + x)^n = 1 + nx + n(n-1)\dfrac{x^2}{2!} + n(n-1)(n-2)\dfrac{x^3}{3!} + \dots$, where n is negative or a fraction, is only valid if $|x| < 1$.

Chapter 7: Scalar and vector quantities

7.1 *You need to know the difference between a scalar and a vector, and how to write down vectors and draw vector diagrams.*

A scalar quantity can be described by using a single number (the *magnitude* or *size*).

- **A vector quantity has both magnitude and direction.**

For example:

Scalar: The distance from *P* to *Q* is 100 metres.   Distance is a scalar.

Vector: From *P* to *Q* you go 100 metres north.   This is called the displacement from *P* to *Q*. Displacement is a vector.

Scalar: A ship is sailing at $12\,\text{km}\,\text{h}^{-1}$.   Speed is a scalar.

Vector: A ship is sailing at $12\,\text{km}\,\text{h}^{-1}$, on a bearing of 060°.   This is called the velocity of the ship. Velocity is a vector.

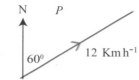

Example 1

Show on a diagram the displacement vector from P to Q, where Q is 500 m due north of P.

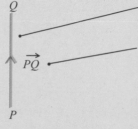

This is called a 'directed line segment'.
The direction of the arrow shows the direction of the vector.

The vector is written as $\overrightarrow{PQ}$.

The length of the line segment *PQ* represents distance 500 m. In accurate diagrams a scale could be used (e.g. 1 cm represents 100 m).

Sometimes, instead of using the endpoints *P* and *Q*, a small (lower case) letter is used.

In print, the small letter will be in **bold type**. In writing, you should underline the small letter to show it is a vector:

$$\underline{a} \text{ or } \underline{a}$$

- Vectors that are equal have both the same magnitude and the same direction.

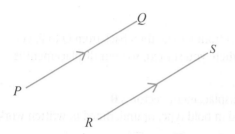

Here $\overrightarrow{PQ} = \overrightarrow{RS}$.

- Two vectors are added using the 'triangle law'.

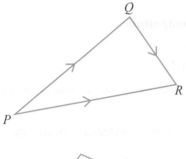

> **Hint:**
> Think of displacement vectors.
> If you travel from P to Q, then from Q to R, the resultant journey is P to R:
> $$\overrightarrow{PQ} + \overrightarrow{QR} = \overrightarrow{PR}$$

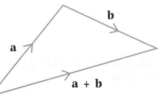

When you add the vectors **a** and **b**, the resultant vector **a** + **b** goes from 'the start of **a** to the finish of **b**'.

This is sometimes called the triangle law for vector addition.

Example 2

The diagram shows the vectors **a**, **b** and **c**. Draw another diagram to illustrate the vector addition **a** + **b** + **c**.

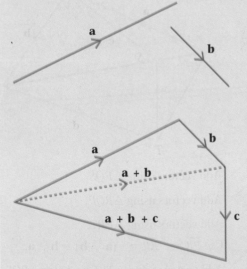

First use the triangle law for **a** + **b**, then use it again for (**a** + **b**) + **c**.

The resultant goes from the start of **a** to the finish of **c**.

- Adding the vectors $\overrightarrow{PQ}$ and $\overrightarrow{QP}$ gives the zero vector 0. $\overrightarrow{PQ} + \overrightarrow{QP} = 0$

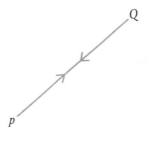

Hint:

If you travel from P to Q, then back from Q to P, you are back where you started, so your displacement is zero.

The zero displacement vector is **0**.
It is printed in bold type, or underlined in written work.

You can also write $\overrightarrow{QP}$ as $-\overrightarrow{PQ}$.
So $\overrightarrow{PQ} + \overrightarrow{QP} = \mathbf{0}$ or $\overrightarrow{PQ} - \overrightarrow{PQ} = \mathbf{0}$.

- **The modulus of a vector is another name for its magnitude.**
  - **The modulus of the vector a is written as $|\mathbf{a}|$.**
  - **The modulus of the vector $\overrightarrow{PQ}$ is written as $|\overrightarrow{PQ}|$.**

Example 3

The vector **a** is directed due east and $|\mathbf{a}| = 12$. The vector **b** is directed due south and $|\mathbf{b}| = 5$. Find $|\mathbf{a} + \mathbf{b}|$.

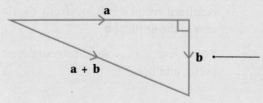

Use the triangle law for adding the vectors **a** and **b**.

$|\mathbf{a} + \mathbf{b}|^2 = 12^2 + 5^2 = 169$ ————— Use Pythagoras' Theorem.

$|\mathbf{a} + \mathbf{b}| = 13$

Example 4

In the diagram, $\overrightarrow{QP} = \mathbf{a}$, $\overrightarrow{QR} = \mathbf{b}$, $\overrightarrow{QS} = \mathbf{c}$ and $\overrightarrow{RT} = \mathbf{d}$.

Find in terms of **a**, **b**, **c** and **d**:

a $\overrightarrow{PS}$ **b** $\overrightarrow{RP}$ **c** $\overrightarrow{PT}$ **d** $\overrightarrow{TS}$

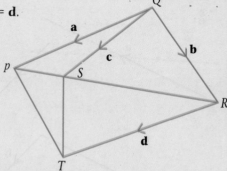

a $\overrightarrow{PS} = \overrightarrow{PQ} + \overrightarrow{QS} = -\mathbf{a} + \mathbf{c}$
            $= \mathbf{c} - \mathbf{a}$

b $\overrightarrow{RP} = \overrightarrow{RQ} + \overrightarrow{QP} = -\mathbf{b} + \mathbf{a}$
            $= \mathbf{a} - \mathbf{b}$

c $\overrightarrow{PT} = \overrightarrow{PR} + \overrightarrow{RT} = (\mathbf{b} - \mathbf{a}) + \mathbf{d}$
            $= \mathbf{b} + \mathbf{d} - \mathbf{a}$

d $\overrightarrow{TS} = \overrightarrow{TR} + \overrightarrow{RS} = -\mathbf{d} + (\overrightarrow{RQ} + \overrightarrow{QS})$
            $= -\mathbf{d} + (-\mathbf{b} + \mathbf{c})$
            $= \mathbf{c} - \mathbf{b} - \mathbf{d}$

Add vectors using $\triangle PQS$.

Add vectors using $\triangle RQP$.

Add vectors using $\triangle PRT$.
Use $\overrightarrow{PR} = -\overrightarrow{RP} = -(\mathbf{a} - \mathbf{b}) = \mathbf{b} - \mathbf{a}$.

Add vectors using $\triangle TRS$ and also $\triangle RQS$.

Exercise 7A

1 The diagram shows the vectors **a**, **b**, **c** and **d**.
   Draw a diagram to illustrate the vector
   addition **a** + **b** + **c** + **d**.

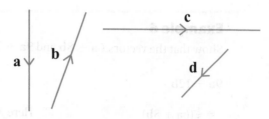

2 The vector **a** is directed due north and $|\mathbf{a}| = 24$. The vector **b** is directed due west and
   $|\mathbf{b}| = 7$. Find $|\mathbf{a} + \mathbf{b}|$.

3 The vector **a** is directed north-east and $|\mathbf{a}| = 20$. The vector **b** is directed south-east
   and $|\mathbf{b}| = 13$. Find $|\mathbf{a} + \mathbf{b}|$.

4 In the diagram, $PQ = \mathbf{a}$, $QS = \mathbf{b}$, $SR = \mathbf{c}$
   and $\overrightarrow{PT} = \mathbf{d}$. Find in terms of **a**, **b**, **c** and **d**:

   a $\overrightarrow{QT}$
   b $\overrightarrow{PR}$
   c $\overrightarrow{TS}$
   d $\overrightarrow{TR}$

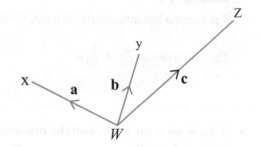

5 In the diagram, $\overrightarrow{WX} = \mathbf{a}$, $\overrightarrow{WY} = \mathbf{b}$ and
   $\overrightarrow{WZ} = \mathbf{c}$. It is given that $\overrightarrow{XY} = \overrightarrow{YZ}$.
   Prove that $\mathbf{a} + \mathbf{c} = 2\mathbf{b}$.
   ($2\mathbf{b}$ is equivalent to $\mathbf{b} + \mathbf{b}$).

7.2 You need to be able to perform simple vector arithmetic, and to know the definition of
a unit vector.

Example 5

The diagram shows the vector **a**. Draw diagrams to illustrate
the vectors $3\mathbf{a}$ and $-2\mathbf{a}$.

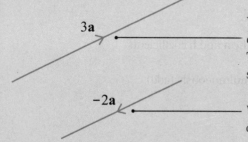

Vector $3\mathbf{a}$ is $\mathbf{a} + \mathbf{a} + \mathbf{a}$, so is in the same
direction as **a** with 3 times its magnitude.
The vector **a** has been multiplied by the
scalar 3 (a scalar multiple).

Vector $-2\mathbf{a}$ is $-\mathbf{a} - \mathbf{a}$, so is in the opposite
direction to **a** with 2 times its magnitude.

- Any vector parallel to the vector **a** may be written as λ**a**, where λ is a non-zero scalar

Example 6

Show that the vectors $6\mathbf{a} + 8\mathbf{b}$ and $9\mathbf{a} + 12\mathbf{b}$ are parallel.

$9\mathbf{a} + 12\mathbf{b}$

$= \frac{3}{2}(6\mathbf{a} + 8\mathbf{b})$ Here $\lambda = \frac{3}{2}$.

∴ the vectors are parallel.

- Subtracting a vector is equivalent to 'adding a negative vector', so $\mathbf{a} - \mathbf{b}$ is defined to be $\mathbf{a} + (-\mathbf{b})$.

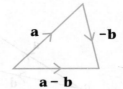

Hint:
To subtract **b**, you reverse the direction of **b** then add.

- A unit vector is a vector which has magnitude (or modulus) 1 unit.

Example 7

The vector **a** has magnitude 20 units. Write down a unit vector that is parallel to **a**.

The unit vector is $\frac{\mathbf{a}}{20}$ or $\frac{1}{20}\mathbf{a}$.   Divide **a** by the magnitude.

In general, the unit vector is $\frac{\mathbf{a}}{|\mathbf{a}|}$.

- If $\lambda\mathbf{a} + \mu\mathbf{b} = \alpha\mathbf{a} + \beta\mathbf{b}$, and the non-zero vectors a and b are not parallel, then $\lambda = \alpha$ and $\mu = \beta$.

The above result can be shown as follows:

$\lambda\mathbf{a} + \mu\mathbf{b} = \alpha\mathbf{a} + \beta\mathbf{b}$ can be written as $(\lambda - \alpha)\mathbf{a} = (\beta - \mu)\mathbf{b}$, but two vectors cannot be equal unless they are parallel or zero.

Since **a** and **b** are not parallel or zero, $(\lambda - \alpha) = 0$ and $(\beta - \mu) = 0$, so $\lambda = \alpha$ and $\beta = \mu$.

Example 8

Given that $5\mathbf{a} - 4\mathbf{b} = (2s + t)\mathbf{a} + (s - t)\mathbf{b}$, where **a** and **b** are non-zero, non-parallel vectors, find the values of the scalars s and t.

$2s + t = 5$
$s - t = -4$ Equate the **a** and **b** coefficients.

$3s = 1$ Solve simultaneously (add).

$s = \frac{1}{3}$

$t = 5 - 2s = 4\frac{1}{3}$

So $s = \frac{1}{3}$ and $t = 4\frac{1}{3}$.

Example 9

In the diagram, $\vec{PQ} = 3\mathbf{a}$, $\vec{QR} = \mathbf{b}$, $\vec{SR} = 4\mathbf{a}$ and $\vec{PX} = k\vec{PR}$.
Find, in terms of $\mathbf{a}$, $\mathbf{b}$ and k:

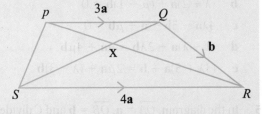

a $\vec{PS}$ **b** $\vec{PX}$

c $\vec{SQ}$ **d** $\vec{SX}$

Use the fact that X lies on SQ to find the
value of k.

a $\vec{PS} = \vec{PR} + \vec{RS} = \vec{PQ} + \vec{QR} + \vec{RS}$ Add using the triangle law.
  $= 3\mathbf{a} + \mathbf{b} - 4\mathbf{a} = \mathbf{b} - \mathbf{a}$

b $\vec{PR} = \vec{PQ} + \vec{QR} = 3\mathbf{a} + \mathbf{b}$ Find $\vec{PR}$ and use $\vec{PX} = k\vec{PR}$.
  $\vec{PX} = k\vec{PR} = k(3\mathbf{a} + \mathbf{b})$

c $\vec{SQ} = 4\mathbf{a} - \mathbf{b}$ Use the triangle law on $\triangle SRQ$.

d $\vec{SX} = \vec{SP} + \vec{PX}$
  $= -(\mathbf{b} - \mathbf{a}) + k(3\mathbf{a} + \mathbf{b})$ Use $\vec{SP} = -\vec{PS}$, and the answers
  $= -\mathbf{b} + \mathbf{a} + k(3\mathbf{a} + \mathbf{b})$ to parts **a** and **b**.
  $= (3k + 1)\mathbf{a} + (k - 1)\mathbf{b}$

X lies on SQ, so $\vec{SQ}$ and $\vec{SX}$ are parallel.

$(3k + 1)\mathbf{a} + (k - 1)\mathbf{b} = \lambda(4\mathbf{a} - \mathbf{b})$ ——— Use the fact that, for parallel vectors,
$(3k + 1)\mathbf{a} + (k - 1)\mathbf{b} = 4\lambda\mathbf{a} - \lambda\mathbf{b}$ one is a scalar multiple of the other.

So $(3k + 1) = 4\lambda$ and $(k - 1) = -\lambda$ ——— $\mathbf{a}$ and $\mathbf{b}$ are non-parallel and non-zero,
  $(3k + 1) = 4(1 - k)$ so equate coefficients.

  $k = \frac{3}{7}$ ——— Eliminate λ and solve for k.

Exercise 7B

1 In the triangle PQR, $PQ = 2\mathbf{a}$ and $QR = 2\mathbf{b}$. The mid-point of PR is M.
Find, in terms of $\mathbf{a}$ and $\mathbf{b}$:

  a $\vec{PR}$ **b** $\vec{PM}$ **c** $\vec{QM}$.

2 $ABCD$ is a trapezium with AB parallel to DC and $DC = 3AB$.
M is the mid-point of DC, $\vec{AB} = \mathbf{a}$ and $\vec{BC} = \mathbf{b}$.
Find, in terms of $\mathbf{a}$ and $\mathbf{b}$:

  a $\vec{AM}$ **b** $\vec{BD}$ **c** $\vec{MB}$ **d** $\vec{DA}$.

3 In each part, find whether the given vector is parallel to $\mathbf{a} - 3\mathbf{b}$:

  a $2\mathbf{a} - 6\mathbf{b}$ **b** $4\mathbf{a} - 12\mathbf{b}$ **c** $\mathbf{a} + 3\mathbf{b}$

  d $3\mathbf{b} - \mathbf{a}$ **e** $9\mathbf{b} - 3\mathbf{a}$ **f** $\frac{1}{2}\mathbf{a} - \frac{2}{3}\mathbf{b}$

4   The non-zero vectors **a** and **b** are not parallel. In each part, find the value of λ and the value of μ:

   a $\mathbf{a} + 3\mathbf{b} = 2\lambda\mathbf{a} - \mu\mathbf{b}$

   b $(\lambda + 2)\mathbf{a} + (\mu - 1)\mathbf{b} = 0$

   c $4\lambda\mathbf{a} - 5\mathbf{b} - \mathbf{a} + \mu\mathbf{b} = 0$

   d $(1 + \lambda)\mathbf{a} + 2\lambda\mathbf{b} = \mu\mathbf{a} + 4\mu\mathbf{b}$

   e $(3\lambda + 5)\mathbf{a} + \mathbf{b} = 2\mu\mathbf{a} + (\lambda - 3)\mathbf{b}$

5   In the diagram, $\overrightarrow{OA} = \mathbf{a}$, $\overrightarrow{OB} = \mathbf{b}$ and C divides AB in the ratio 5:1.

   a   Write down, in terms of **a** and **b**, expressions for $\overrightarrow{AB}$, $\overrightarrow{AC}$ and $\overrightarrow{OC}$.

   Given that $\overrightarrow{OE} = \lambda\mathbf{b}$, where λ is a scalar:

   b   Write down, in terms of **a**, **b** and λ, an expression for $\overrightarrow{CE}$.

   Given that $\overrightarrow{OD} = \mu(\mathbf{b} - \mathbf{a})$, where μ is a scalar:

   c   Write down, in terms of **a**, **b**, λ and μ, an expression for $\overrightarrow{ED}$.

   Given also that E is the mid-point of CD:

   d   Deduce the values of λ and μ.

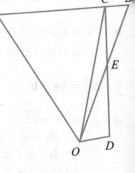

6   In the diagram $\overrightarrow{OA} = \mathbf{a}$, $\overrightarrow{OB} = \mathbf{b}$, $3\overrightarrow{OC} = 2\overrightarrow{OA}$ and $4\overrightarrow{OD} = 7\overrightarrow{OB}$. The line DC meets the line AB at E.

   a   Write down, in terms of **a** and **b**, expressions for

      i $\overrightarrow{AB}$ ii $\overrightarrow{DC}$

   Given that $\overrightarrow{DE} = \lambda\overrightarrow{DC}$ and $\overrightarrow{EB} = \mu\overrightarrow{AB}$ where λ and μ are constants:

   b   Use $\triangle EBD$ to form an equation relating to **a**, **b**, λ and μ.

   Hence:

   c   Show that $\lambda = \frac{9}{13}$.

   d   Find the exact value of μ.

   e   Express $\overrightarrow{OE}$ in terms of **a** and **b**.

   The line $\overrightarrow{OE}$ produced meets the line AD at F.

   Given that $\overrightarrow{OF} = k\overrightarrow{OE}$ where k is a constant and that $\overrightarrow{AF} = \frac{1}{10}(7\mathbf{b} - 4\mathbf{a})$:

   f   Find the value of k.

   © Edexcel Limited

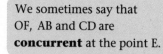

We sometimes say that OF, AB and CD are **concurrent** at the point E.

7   In $\triangle OAB$, P is the mid-point of AB and Q is the point on OP such that $Q = \frac{3}{4}P$.

   Given that $\overrightarrow{OA} = \mathbf{a}$ and $\overrightarrow{OB} = \mathbf{b}$, find, in terms of **a** and **b**:

   a $\overrightarrow{AB}$ b $\overrightarrow{OP}$ c $\overrightarrow{OQ}$ d $\overrightarrow{AQ}$

   The point R on OB is such that $OR = kOB$, where $0 < k < 1$.

   e   Find, in terms of **a**, **b** and k, the vector $\overrightarrow{AR}$.

   Given that AQR is a straight line:

   f   Find the ratio in which Q divides AR and the value of k.

   © Edexcel Limited

8 In the figure $OE:EA = 1:2$, $AF:FB = 3:1$ and $OG:OB = 3:1$. The vector $\overrightarrow{OA} = \mathbf{a}$ and the vector $\overrightarrow{OB} = \mathbf{b}$.

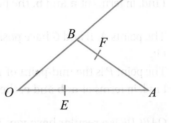

Find, in terms of **a**, **b** or a and b, expressions for:

a $\overrightarrow{OE}$ b $\overrightarrow{OF}$ c $\overrightarrow{EF}$

d $\overrightarrow{BG}$ e $\overrightarrow{FB}$ f $\overrightarrow{FG}$

g Use your results in **c** and **f** to show that the points E, F and G are collinear and find the ratio $EF:FG$.

h Find $\overrightarrow{EB}$ and $\overrightarrow{AG}$ and hence prove that EB is parallel to AG.

> **Collinear** means that the points lie on a straight line

7.3 *You need to be able to use vectors to describe the position of a point in two or three dimensions.*

- **The position vector of a point A is the vector $\overrightarrow{OA}$, where O is the origin. $\overrightarrow{OA}$ is usually written as vector a.**

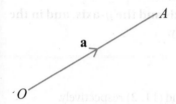

$$\overrightarrow{OA} = \mathbf{a}$$

- $\overrightarrow{AB} = \mathbf{b} - \mathbf{a}$, **where a and b are the position vectors of A and B respectively.**

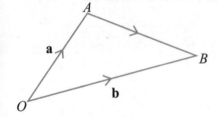

> **Hint:**
> Use the triangle law to give
> $\overrightarrow{AB} = \overrightarrow{AO} + \overrightarrow{OB} = -\mathbf{a} + \mathbf{b}$
> So $\overrightarrow{AB} = \mathbf{b} - \mathbf{a}$

Example 10

In the diagram the points A and B have position vectors **a** and **b** respectively (referred to the origin O). The point P divides AB in the ratio $1:2$.

Find the position vector of P.

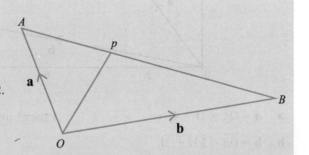

$\overrightarrow{AB} = \mathbf{b} - \mathbf{a}$

$\overrightarrow{OP} = \overrightarrow{OA} + \overrightarrow{AP}$ $\overrightarrow{OP}$ is the position vector of P.

$\overrightarrow{AP} = \frac{1}{3}(\mathbf{b} - \mathbf{a})$ Use the $1:2$ ratio (AP is one third of AB).

$\overrightarrow{OP} = \mathbf{a} + \frac{1}{3}(\mathbf{b} - \mathbf{a})$

$\overrightarrow{OP} = \frac{2}{3}\mathbf{a} + \frac{1}{3}\mathbf{b}$ You could write $\mathbf{p} = \frac{2}{3}\mathbf{a} + \frac{1}{3}\mathbf{b}$.

Exercise 7C

1   The points A and B have position vectors **a** and **b** respectively (referred to the origin O).
   The point P divides AB in the ratio $1:5$.
   Find, in terms of **a** and **b**, the position vector of P.

2   The points A, B and C have position vectors **a**, **b** and **c** respectively (referred to the origin O).
   The point P is the mid-point of AB.
   Find, in terms of **a**, **b** and **c**, the vector $\overrightarrow{PC}$.

3 $OABCDE$ is a regular hexagon. The points A and B have position vectors **a** and **b** respectively, referred to the origin O.
   Find, in terms of **a** and **b**, the position vectors of C, D and E.

7.4   *You need to know how to write down and use the Cartesian components of a vector in two dimensions.*

- **The vectors i and j are unit vectors parallel to the x-axis and the y-axis, and in the direction of x increasing and y increasing, respectively.**

Example 11

The points A and B in the diagram have coordinates $(3, 4)$ and $(11, 2)$ respectively.
Find, in terms of **i** and **j**:

a the position vector of A **b** the position vector of B **c** the vector $\overrightarrow{AB}$

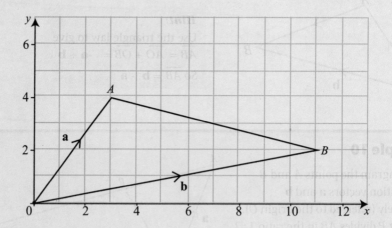

a $\mathbf{a} = \overrightarrow{OA} = 3\mathbf{i} + 4\mathbf{j}$ **i** goes 1 unit 'across', **j** goes 1 unit 'up':

b $\mathbf{b} = \overrightarrow{OB} = 11\mathbf{i} + 2\mathbf{j}$

c $\overrightarrow{AB} = \mathbf{b} - \mathbf{a}$
   $= (11\mathbf{i} + 2\mathbf{j}) - (3\mathbf{i} + 4\mathbf{j})$
   $= 8\mathbf{i} - 2\mathbf{j}$

You can see from the diagram that the vector $\overrightarrow{AB}$ goes 8 units 'across' and 2 units 'down'.

- You can write a vector with Cartesian components as a column matrix:

$$x\mathbf{i} + y\mathbf{j} = \begin{pmatrix} x \\ y \end{pmatrix}$$

Hint:
This standard notation is easy to read and also avoids the need to write out lengthy expressions with **i** and **j** terms.

Example 12

Given that $\mathbf{a} = 2\mathbf{i} + 5\mathbf{j}$, $\mathbf{b} = 12\mathbf{i} - 10\mathbf{j}$ and $\mathbf{c} = -3\mathbf{i} + 9\mathbf{j}$, find $\mathbf{a} + \mathbf{b} + \mathbf{c}$, using column matrix notation in your working.

$$\mathbf{a} + \mathbf{b} + \mathbf{c} = \begin{pmatrix} 2 \\ 5 \end{pmatrix} + \begin{pmatrix} 12 \\ -10 \end{pmatrix} + \begin{pmatrix} -3 \\ 9 \end{pmatrix}$$

$$= \begin{pmatrix} 11 \\ 4 \end{pmatrix}$$

Add the numbers in the top line to get 11 (the x component), and the bottom line to get 4 (the y component). This is $11\mathbf{i} + 4\mathbf{j}$.

- The modulus (or magnitude) of $x\mathbf{i} + y\mathbf{j}$ is $\sqrt{x^2 + y^2}$

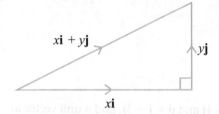

Hint:
From Pythagoras' Theorem, the magnitude of $x\mathbf{i} + y\mathbf{j}$, represented by the hypotenuse, is $\sqrt{x^2 + y^2}$.

Example 13

The vector $\mathbf{a}$ is equal to $5\mathbf{i} - 12\mathbf{j}$.
Find $|\mathbf{a}|$, and find a unit vector in the same direction as $\mathbf{a}$.

$$|\mathbf{a}| = \sqrt{5^2 + (-12)^2} = \sqrt{169} = 13$$

Unit vector is $\dfrac{\mathbf{a}}{|\mathbf{a}|}$ — Look back to Section 7.2.

$$= \frac{5\mathbf{i} - 12\mathbf{j}}{13}$$

$$= \tfrac{1}{13}(5\mathbf{i} - 12\mathbf{j})$$

or $\tfrac{5}{13}\mathbf{i} - \tfrac{12}{13}\mathbf{j}$

or $\tfrac{1}{13}\begin{pmatrix} 5 \\ -12 \end{pmatrix}$

Example 14

Given that $\mathbf{a} = 5\mathbf{i} + \mathbf{j}$ and $\mathbf{b} = -2\mathbf{i} - 4\mathbf{j}$, find the exact value of $|2\mathbf{a} + \mathbf{b}|$.

$$2\mathbf{a} + \mathbf{b} = 2\begin{pmatrix} 5 \\ 1 \end{pmatrix} + \begin{pmatrix} -2 \\ -4 \end{pmatrix}$$

$$= \begin{pmatrix} 10 \\ 2 \end{pmatrix} + \begin{pmatrix} -2 \\ -4 \end{pmatrix}$$

$$= \begin{pmatrix} 8 \\ -2 \end{pmatrix}$$

$$|2\mathbf{a} + \mathbf{b}| = \sqrt{8^2 + (-2)^2}$$

$$= \sqrt{68}$$

$$= \sqrt{4}\sqrt{17}$$

$$= 2\sqrt{17}$$

You must give the answer as a surd because the question asks for an exact answer.

Exercise 7D

1   Given that $\mathbf{a} = 9\mathbf{i} + 7\mathbf{j}$, $\mathbf{b} = 11\mathbf{i} - 3\mathbf{j}$ and $\mathbf{c} = -8\mathbf{i} - \mathbf{j}$, find:

    a $\mathbf{a} + \mathbf{b} + \mathbf{c}$

    b $2\mathbf{a} - \mathbf{b} + \mathbf{c}$

    c $2\mathbf{b} + 2\mathbf{c} - 3\mathbf{a}$

    (Use column matrix notation in your working.)

2   The points A, B and C have coordinates $(3, -1)$, $(4, 5)$ and $(-2, 6)$ respectively. and O is the origin.

    Find, in terms of $\mathbf{i}$ and $\mathbf{j}$:

    a the position vectors of A, B and C

    b $\overrightarrow{AB}$

    c $\overrightarrow{AC}$

Find, in surd form:

    d $|\overrightarrow{OC}|$

    e $|\overrightarrow{AB}|$

    f $|\overrightarrow{AC}|$

3   Given that $\mathbf{a} = 4\mathbf{i} + 3\mathbf{j}$, $\mathbf{b} = 5\mathbf{i} - 12\mathbf{j}$, $\mathbf{c} = -7\mathbf{i} + 24\mathbf{j}$ and $\mathbf{d} = \mathbf{i} - 3\mathbf{j}$, find a unit vector in the direction of $\mathbf{a}$, $\mathbf{b}$, $\mathbf{c}$ and $\mathbf{d}$.

4   Given that $\mathbf{a} = 5\mathbf{i} + \mathbf{j}$ and $\mathbf{b} = \lambda\mathbf{i} + 3\mathbf{j}$, and that $|3\mathbf{a} + \mathbf{b}| = 10$, find the possible values of λ.

Mixed Exercise 7E

1   Given that $2\mathbf{p} - 3\mathbf{q} = \begin{pmatrix} 5 \\ 15 \end{pmatrix}$, where $\mathbf{p} = \begin{pmatrix} 4 \\ m \end{pmatrix}$, $\mathbf{q} = \begin{pmatrix} n \\ -3 \end{pmatrix}$ and m and n are constants, find the values of m and n.

2   If $\mathbf{r} = \begin{pmatrix} 4 \\ -1 \end{pmatrix}$, $\mathbf{s} = \begin{pmatrix} 3 \\ 7 \end{pmatrix}$ and $m\mathbf{r} + n\mathbf{s} = \begin{pmatrix} 7 \\ 37 \end{pmatrix}$, find constants m and n.

3   In the diagram, OXYZ is a parallelogram. M is the mid-point of XY.

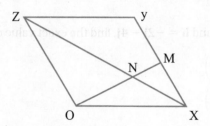

    a Given that $\overrightarrow{OX} = \begin{pmatrix} 8 \\ 0 \end{pmatrix}$ and $\overrightarrow{OZ} = \begin{pmatrix} -2 \\ 6 \end{pmatrix}$, write down the vectors $\overrightarrow{XM}$ and $\overrightarrow{XZ}$.

    b Given that $\overrightarrow{ON} = v\overrightarrow{OM}$, write down in terms of v the vector $\overrightarrow{ON}$.

    c Given that $\overrightarrow{ON} = \overrightarrow{OX} + w\overrightarrow{XZ}$, find in tems of w the vector $\overrightarrow{ON}$.

    d Solve two simultaneous equations to find v and w.

4 ABCD is a parallelogram in which $\overrightarrow{AB} = \mathbf{x}$
and $\overrightarrow{BC} = \mathbf{y}$.
AE : ED = 1 : 2.

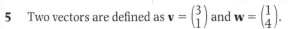

  a Express in terms of $\mathbf{x}$ and $\mathbf{y}$. $\overrightarrow{AC}$ and $\overrightarrow{BE}$.

  b AC and BE intersect at F. such that $\overrightarrow{BF} = v\overrightarrow{BE}$.

    i Express $\overrightarrow{BF}$ in terms of $\mathbf{x}$, $\mathbf{y}$ and v.

    ii Show that $\overrightarrow{AF} = (1 - v)\mathbf{x} + \frac{1}{3}v\mathbf{y}$.

    iii Use this expression for $\overrightarrow{AF}$ to find the value of v.

5 Two vectors are defined as $\mathbf{v} = \begin{pmatrix} 3 \\ 1 \end{pmatrix}$ and $\mathbf{w} = \begin{pmatrix} 1 \\ 4 \end{pmatrix}$.

Express $\mathbf{v} + \mathbf{w}$, $2\mathbf{v} - \mathbf{w}$ and $\mathbf{v} - 2\mathbf{w}$ as column vectors, find the magnitude and draw the resultant vector triangle for each vector.

6 Two vectors are defined as $\mathbf{p} = \begin{pmatrix} 2 \\ -1 \end{pmatrix}$ and $\mathbf{q} = \begin{pmatrix} 3 \\ 5 \end{pmatrix}$.

Express $\mathbf{p} + \mathbf{q}$, $3\mathbf{p} + \mathbf{q}$ and $\mathbf{p} - 3\mathbf{q}$ as column vectors, find the magnitude and draw the resultant vector triangle for each vector.

7 Chloe, Leo and Max enter an orienteering competition. Each decides to take a different route, described using these column vectors, where the units are in km:

$$\mathbf{s} = \begin{pmatrix} 1 \\ 1 \end{pmatrix} \qquad \mathbf{t} = \begin{pmatrix} 2 \\ 3 \end{pmatrix}$$

They all start from the same point P, and take 3 hours to complete their routes.

Chloe	$\mathbf{s} + 2\mathbf{t}$
Leo	$2\mathbf{s} + \mathbf{t}$
Max	$5\mathbf{s} - \mathbf{t}$

  a Express each journey as a column vector.

  b Find the length of each journey, and hence calculate the average speed of each orienteer in km/hour.

1   A vector is a quantity that has both magnitude and direction.

2   Vectors that are equal have both the same magnitude and the same direction.

3   Two vectors are added using the 'triangle law'.

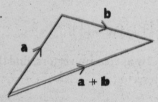

4   Adding the vectors $\overrightarrow{PQ}$ and $\overrightarrow{QP}$ gives the zero vector **0**.
    $(\overrightarrow{PQ} + \overrightarrow{QP} = \mathbf{0})$

5   The modulus of a vector is another name for its magnitude.
    - The modulus of the vector **a** is written as $|\mathbf{a}|$.
    - The modulus of the vector $\overrightarrow{PQ}$ is written as $|\overrightarrow{PQ}|$.

6   The vector $-\mathbf{a}$ has the same magnitude as the vector **a** but is in the opposite direction.

7   Any vector parallel to the vector **a** may be written as $\lambda\mathbf{a}$, where λ is a non-zero scalar.

8   $\mathbf{a} - \mathbf{b}$ is defined to be $\mathbf{a} + (-\mathbf{b})$.

9   A unit vector is a vector which has magnitude (or modulus) 1 unit.

10 If $\lambda\mathbf{a} + \mu\mathbf{b} = \alpha\mathbf{a} + \beta\mathbf{b}$, and the non-zero vectors **a** and **b** are not parallel, then $\lambda = \alpha$ and $\mu = \beta$.

11 The position vector of a point A is the vector $\overrightarrow{OA}$, where O is the origin. $\overrightarrow{OA}$ is usually written as vector **a**.

12 $\overrightarrow{AB} = \mathbf{b} - \mathbf{a}$, where **a** and **b** are the position vectors of A and B respectively.

13 The modulus (or magnitude) of $x\mathbf{i} + y\mathbf{j}$ is $\sqrt{x^2 + y^2}$.

Chapter 8: Rectangular Cartesian coordinates

8.1 *You can write the equation of a straight line in the form y = mx + c or ax + by + c = 0.*

- In the general form $y = mx + c$, m is the gradient and $(0, c)$ is the intercept on the y-axis.

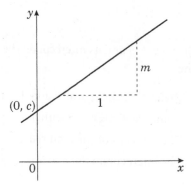

- In the general form $ax + by + c = 0$, a, b and c are integers.

Example 1

Write down the gradient and intercept on the y-axis of these lines:

a $y = -3x + 2$
b $4x - 2y + 5 = 0$

a $y = -3x + 2$
   The gradient $= -3$ and the intercept on the y-axis $= (0, 2)$.

    Compare $y = -3x + 2$ with $y = mx + c$.
From this, $m = -3$ and $c = 2$.

b $4x - 2y + 5 = 0$

    $4x + 5 = 2y$

So $2y = 4x + 5$

        $y = 2x + \frac{5}{2}$

The gradient $= 2$ and the intercept on the y-axis $= (0, \frac{5}{2})$.

    Rearrange the equation into the form $y = mx + c$.

Add $2y$ to each side.

Put the term in y at the front of the equation.

Divide each term by 2, so that:
    $2y \div 2 = y$
    $4 \div 2 = 2$
    $5 \div 2 = \frac{5}{2}$. (Do not write this as 2.5)
Compare $y = 2x + \frac{5}{2}$ to $y = mx + c$.
From this, $m = 2$ and $c = \frac{5}{2}$.

Example 2

Write these lines in the form $ax + by + c = 0$:

a $y = 4x + 3$
b $y = -\frac{1}{2}x + 5$

a

$$y = 4x + 3$$
$$0 = 4x + 3 - y$$
So $4x - y + 3 = 0$

Rearrange the equation into the form $ax + by + c = 0$.

Subtract y from each side.

b

$$y = -\tfrac{1}{2}x + 5$$
$$\tfrac{1}{2}x + y = 5$$
$$\tfrac{1}{2}x + y - 5 = 0$$
So $x + 2y - 10 = 0$

Collect all the terms on one side of the equation.

Add $\tfrac{1}{2}x$ to each side.

Subtract 5 from each side.

Multiply each term by 2 to clear the fraction.

Example 3

A line is parallel to the line $y = \tfrac{1}{2}x - 5$ and its intercept on the y-axis is $(0, 1)$. Write down the equation of the line.

$$y = \tfrac{1}{2}x + 1$$

Remember that parallel lines have the same gradient.

Compare $y = \tfrac{1}{2}x - 5$ with $y = mx + c$, so $m = \tfrac{1}{2}$.

The gradient of the required line $= \tfrac{1}{2}$.

The intercept on the y-axis is $(0, 1)$, so $c = 1$.

Example 4

A line is parallel to the line $6x + 3y - 2 = 0$ and it passes through the point $(0, 3)$. Work out the equation of the line.

$$6x + 3y - 2 = 0$$
$$3y - 2 = -6x$$
$$3y = -6x + 2$$
$$y = -2x + \tfrac{2}{3}$$

Rearrange the equation into the form $y = mx + c$ to find m.

Subtract $6x$ from each side.

Add 2 to each side.

Divide each term by 3, so that
$$3y \div 3 = y$$
$$-6x \div 3 = -2x$$
$$2 \div 3 = \tfrac{2}{3}. \text{ (Do not write this as a decimal.)}$$

The gradient of this line is -2.

Compare $y = -2x + \tfrac{2}{3}$ with $y = mx + c$, so $m = -2$.

The equation of the line is $y = -2x + 3$.

Parallel lines have the same gradient, so the gradient of the required line $= -2$. $(0, 3)$ is the intercept on the y-axis, so $c = 3$.

Example 5

The line $y = 4x - 8$ meets the x-axis at the point P. Work out the coordinates of P.

$y = 4x - 8$
Substituting,

$$4x - 8 = 0$$
$$4x = 8$$
$$x = 2$$
So $P(2, 0)$.

The line meets the x-axis when $y = 0$, so substitute $y = 0$ into $y = 4x - 8$.

Rearrange the equation for x.

Add 8 to each side.

Divide each side by 4.

Always write down the coordinates of the point.

Exercise 8A

1   Work out the gradients of these lines:

   a $y = -2x + 5$ **b** $y = -x + 7$

   c $y = 4 + 3x$ **d** $y = \frac{1}{3}x - 2$

   e $y = -\frac{2}{3}x$ **f** $y = \frac{5}{4}x + \frac{2}{3}$

   g $2x - 4y + 5 = 0$ **h** $10x - 5y + 1 = 0$

   i $-x + 2y - 4 = 0$ **j** $-3x + 6y + 7 = 0$

   k $4x + 2y - 9 = 0$ **l** $9x + 6y + 2 = 0$

2   These lines intercept the y-axis at $(0, c)$. Work out the value of c in each case.

   a $y = -x + 4$ **b** $y = 2x - 5$

   c $y = \frac{1}{2}x - \frac{2}{3}$ **d** $y = -3x$

   e $y = \frac{6}{7}x + \frac{7}{5}$ **f** $y = 2 - 7x$

   g $3x - 4y + 8 = 0$ **h** $4x - 5y - 10 = 0$

   i $-2x + y - 9 = 0$ **j** $7x + 4y + 12 = 0$

   k $7x - 2y + 3 = 0$ **l** $-5x + 4y + 2 = 0$

3   Write these lines in the form $ax + by + c = 0$.

   a $y = 4x + 3$ **b** $y = 3x - 2$

   c $y = -6x + 7$ **d** $y = \frac{4}{5}x - 6$

   e $y = \frac{5}{3}x + 2$ **f** $y = \frac{7}{3}x$

   g $y = 2x - \frac{4}{7}$ **h** $y = -3x + \frac{2}{9}$

   i $y = -6x - \frac{2}{3}$ **j** $y = -\frac{1}{3}x + \frac{1}{2}$

   k $y = \frac{2}{3}x + \frac{5}{6}$ **l** $y = \frac{3}{5}x + \frac{1}{2}$

4   A line is parallel to the line $y = 5x + 8$ and its intercept on the y-axis is $(0, 3)$. Write down the equation of the line.

5   A line is parallel to the line $y = -\frac{2}{5}x + 1$ and its intercept on the y-axis is $(0, -4)$. Work out the equation of the line. Write your answer in the form $ax + by + c = 0$, where a, b and c are integers.

6   A line is parallel to the line $3x + 6y + 11 = 0$ and its intercept on the y-axis is $(0, 7)$. Write down the equation of the line.

7   A line is parallel to the line $2x - 3y - 1 = 0$ and it passes through the point $(0, 0)$. Write down the equation of the line.

8   The line $y = 6x - 18$ meets the x-axis at the point P. Work out the coordinates of P.

9   The line $3x + 2y - 5 = 0$ meets the x-axis at the point R. Work out the coordinates of R.

10 The line $5x - 4y + 20 = 0$ meets the y-axis at the point A and the x-axis at the point B. Work out the coordinates of the points A and B.

8.2 You can work out the gradient m of the line joining the point with coordinates (x_1, y_1) to the point with coordinates (x_2, y_2) by using the formula $m = \dfrac{y_2 - y_1}{x_2 - x_1}$.

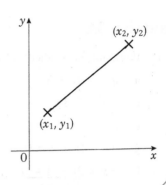

Example 6

Work out the gradient of the line joining the points $(2, 3)$ and $(5, 7)$.

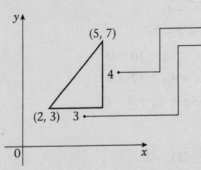

The gradient of the line is $\frac{4}{3}$.

Draw a sketch.

$7 - 3 = 4$

$5 - 2 = 3$

Remember the gradient of a line

$= \dfrac{\text{difference in } y\text{-coordinates}}{\text{difference in } x\text{-coordinates}}$,

so $m = \dfrac{7 - 3}{5 - 2}$.

This is $m = \dfrac{y_2 - y_1}{x_2 - x_1}$ with $(x_1, y_1) = (2, 3)$ and $(x_2, y_2) = (5, 7)$.

Example 7

Work out the gradient of the line joining these pairs of points:

a $(-2, 7)$ and $(4, 5)$ **b** $(2d, -5d)$ and $(6d, 3d)$

a $m = \dfrac{5 - 7}{4 - (-2)}$

$= \dfrac{-2}{6}$

$= -\dfrac{1}{3}$

The gradient of the line is $-\dfrac{1}{3}$.

Use $m = \dfrac{y_2 - y_1}{x_2 - x_1}$. Here $(x_1, y_1) = (-2, 7)$ and $(x_2, y_2) = (4, 5)$.

$-(-2) = +2$, so $4 + 2 = 6$

Remember to simplify the fraction when possible, so divide by 2.

$\dfrac{-1}{3}$ is the same as $-\dfrac{1}{3}$.

b $m = \dfrac{3d - (-5d)}{6d - 2d}$

$= \dfrac{8d}{4d}$

$= 2$

The gradient of the line is 2.

Here $(x_1, y_1) = (2d, -5d)$ and $(x_2, y_2) = (6d, 3d)$.

$-(-5d) = +5d$, so $3d + 5d = 8d$.

$8d \div 4d = 2$.

Example 8

The line joining $(2, -5)$ to $(4, a)$ has gradient -1. Work out the value of a.

$$\frac{a - (-5)}{4 - 2} = -1$$

Use $m = \dfrac{y_2 - y_1}{x_2 - x_1}$. Here $m = -1$, $(x_1, y_1) = (2, -5)$ and $(x_2, y_2) = (4, a)$.

So $\dfrac{a + 5}{2} = -1$ ◄——— $a - (-5) = a + 5$

$a + 5 = -2$ — Multiply each side of the equation by 2 to clear the fraction.

$a = -7$ — Subtract 5 from each side of the equation.

Exercise 8B

1 Work out the gradient of the line joining these pairs of points:

a $(4, 2), (6, 3)$

b $(-1, 3), (5, 4)$

c $(-4, 5), (1, 2)$

d $(2, -3), (6, 5)$

e $(-3, 4), (7, -6)$

f $(-12, 3), (-2, 8)$

g $(-2, -4), (10, 2)$

h $(\frac{1}{2}, 2), (\frac{3}{4}, 4)$

i $(\frac{1}{4}, \frac{1}{2}), (\frac{1}{2}, \frac{2}{3})$

j $(-2.4, 9.6), (0, 0)$

k $(1.3, -2.2), (8.8, -4.7)$

l $(0, 5a), (10a, 0)$

m $(3b, -2b), (7b, 2b)$

n $(p, p^2), (q, q^2)$

2 The line joining $(3, -5)$ to $(6, a)$ has gradient 4. Work out the value of a.

3 The line joining $(5, b)$ to $(8, 3)$ has gradient -3. Work out the value of b.

4 The line joining $(c, 4)$ to $(7, 6)$ has gradient $\frac{3}{4}$. Work out the value of c.

5 The line joining $(-1, 2d)$ to $(1, 4)$ has gradient $-\frac{1}{4}$. Work out the value of d.

6 The line joining $(-3, -2)$ to $(2e, 5)$ has gradient 2. Work out the value of e.

7 The line joining $(7, 2)$ to $(f, 3f)$ has gradient 4. Work out the value of f.

8 The line joining $(3, -4)$ to $(-g, 2g)$ has gradient -3. Work out the value of g.

9 Show that the points $A(2, 3), B(4, 4), C(10, 7)$ can be joined by a straight line.
(Hint: Find the gradient of the lines joining the points: **i** A and B and **ii** A and C.)

10 Show that the points $(-2a, 5a), (0, 4a), (6a, a)$ are collinear (i.e. on the same straight line).

8.3 You can find the equation of a line with gradient m that passes through the point with coordinates (x_1, y_1) by using the formula $y - y_1 = \mathbf{m}(x - x_1)$.

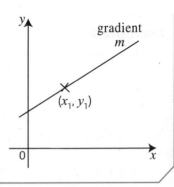

Example 9

Find the equation of the line with gradient 5 that passes through the point (3, 2).

(x, y) is *any* point on the line.

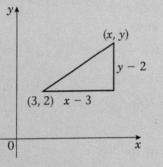

The gradient = 5, so $\dfrac{y - 2}{x - 3} = 5$.

$y - 2 = 5(x - 3)$

$y - 2 = 5x - 15$

$y = 5x - 13$

Multiply each side of the equation by $x - 3$ to clear the fraction, so that:

$$\frac{y - 2}{x - 3} \times \frac{x - 3}{1} = y - 2$$

$$5 \times (x - 3) = 5(x - 3)$$

This is in the form $y - y_1 = m(x - x_1)$. Here $m = 5$ and $(x_1, y_1) = (3, 2)$.

Expand the brackets.

Add 2 to each side.

Example 10

Find the equation of the line with gradient $-\frac{1}{2}$ that passes through the point $(4, -6)$.

$y - (-6) = -\frac{1}{2}(x - 4)$

So $y + 6 = -\frac{1}{2}(x - 4)$

$y + 6 = -\frac{1}{2}x + 2$

$y = -\frac{1}{2}x - 4$

Use $y - y_1 = m(x - x_1)$. Here $m = -\frac{1}{2}$ and $(x_1, y_1) = (4, -6)$.

Expand the brackets. Remember $-\frac{1}{2} \times -4 = +2$.

Subtract 6 from each side.

Example 11

The line $y = 3x - 9$ meets the x-axis at the point A. Find the equation of the line with gradient $\frac{2}{3}$ that passes through the point A. Write your answer in the form $ax + by + c = 0$, where a, b and c are integers.

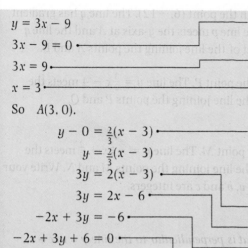

$y = 3x - 9$ ——— The line meets the x-axis when $y = 0$,
$3x - 9 = 0$ ——— so substitute $y = 0$ into $y = 3x - 9$.
$3x = 9$ ——— Rearrange the equation to find x.
$x = 3$ ——— Always write down the coordinates of
So $A(3, 0)$. the point.
$y - 0 = \frac{2}{3}(x - 3)$ ——— Use $y - y_1 = m(x - x_1)$. Here $m = \frac{2}{3}$
$y = \frac{2}{3}(x - 3)$ and $(x_1, y_1) = (3, 0)$.
$3y = 2(x - 3)$ ——— Rearrange the equation into the form
$ax + by + c = 0$.
$3y = 2x - 6$ ——— Multiply by 3 to clear the fraction.
$-2x + 3y = -6$ ——— Expand the brackets.
$-2x + 3y + 6 = 0$ ——— Subtract $2x$ from each side.
——— Add 6 to each side.

Exercise 8C

1 Find the equation of the line with gradient m that passes through the point (x_1, y_1) when:

  a $m = 2$ and $(x_1, y_1) = (2, 5)$ **b** $m = 3$ and $(x_1, y_1) = (-2, 1)$

  c $m = -1$ and $(x_1, y_1) = (3, -6)$ **d** $m = -4$ and $(x_1, y_1) = (-2, -3)$

  e $m = \frac{1}{2}$ and $(x_1, y_1) = (-4, 10)$ **f** $m = -\frac{2}{3}$ and $(x_1, y_1) = (-6, -1)$

  g $m = 2$ and $(x_1, y_1) = (a, 2a)$ **h** $m = -\frac{1}{2}$ and $(x_1, y_1) = (-2b, 3b)$

2 The line $y = 4x - 8$ meets the x-axis at the point A. Find the equation of the line with gradient 3 that passes through the point A.

3 The line $y = -2x + 8$ meets the y-axis at the point B. Find the equation of the line with gradient 2 that passes through the point B.

4 The line $y = \frac{1}{2}x + 6$ meets the x-axis at the point C. Find the equation of the line with gradient $\frac{2}{3}$ that passes through the point C. Write your answer in the form $ax + by + c = 0$, where a, b and c are integers.

5 The line $y = \frac{1}{4}x + 2$ meets the y-axis at the point B. The point C has coordinates $(-5, 3)$. Find the gradient of the line joining the points B and C.

6 The lines $y = x$ and $y = 2x - 5$ intersect at the point A. Find the equation of the line with gradient $\frac{2}{5}$ that passes through the point A.

Hint:
Solve $y = x$ and $y = 2x - 5$ simultaneously.

7 The lines $y = 4x - 10$ and $y = x - 1$ intersect at the point T. Find the equation of the line with gradient $-\frac{2}{3}$ that passes through the point T. Write your answer in the form $ax + by + c = 0$, where a, b and c are integers.

8 The line p has gradient $\frac{2}{3}$ and passes through the point $(6, -12)$. The line q has gradient -1 and passes through the point $(5, 5)$. The line p meets the y-axis at A and the line q meets the x-axis at B. Work out the gradient of the line joining the points A and B.

Hint:
First work out the gradient of the line joining the points P and Q.

9 The line $y = -2x + 6$ meets the x-axis at the point P. The line $y = \frac{3}{2}x - 4$ meets the y-axis at the point Q. Find the equation of the line joining the points P and Q.

10 The line $y = 3x - 5$ meets the x-axis at the point M. The line $y = -\frac{2}{3}x + \frac{2}{3}$ meets the y-axis at the point N. Find the equation of the line joining the points M and N. Write your answer in the form $ax + by + c = 0$, where a, b and c are integers.

8.4 *You can work out the gradient of a line that is perpendicular to the line* $y = mx + c$.

- **If a line has a gradient of m, a line perpendicular to it has a gradient of $-\dfrac{1}{m}$.**

- **If two lines are perpendicular, the product of their gradients is -1.**

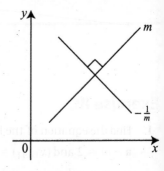

Example 12

Work out the gradient of the line that is perpendicular to the lines with these gradients:

a 3   **b** $\frac{1}{2}$ **c** $-\frac{2}{5}$

a $m = 3$

So the gradient of the perpendicular line is $-\frac{1}{3}$.   Use $-\dfrac{1}{m}$ with $m = 3$.

b $m = \frac{1}{2}$

So the gradient of the perpendicular line is   Use $-\dfrac{1}{m}$ with $m = \frac{1}{2}$.

$$-\frac{1}{\left(\frac{1}{2}\right)}$$

Remember $\dfrac{1}{\left(\frac{a}{b}\right)} = \dfrac{b}{a}$, so $\dfrac{1}{\left(\frac{1}{2}\right)} = \dfrac{2}{1}$.

$$= -\frac{2}{1}$$

$$= -2$$

c $m = -\frac{2}{5}$ Use $-\dfrac{1}{m}$ with $m = -\frac{2}{5}$.

So the gradient of the perpendicular line is

$$-\frac{1}{\left(-\frac{2}{5}\right)}$$

Here $\dfrac{1}{\left(\frac{2}{5}\right)} = \dfrac{5}{2}$, so $\dfrac{1}{\left(-\frac{2}{5}\right)} = -\dfrac{5}{2}$.

$$= -\left(-\frac{5}{2}\right)$$

$$= \frac{5}{2}$$

Example 13

Show that the line $y = 3x + 4$ is perpendicular to the line $x + 3y - 3 = 0$.

$y = 3x + 4$

The gradient of this line is 3.

$$x + 3y - 3 = 0$$
$$3y - 3 = -x$$
$$3y = -x + 3$$
$$y = -\tfrac{1}{3}x + 1$$

The gradient of this line is $-\tfrac{1}{3}$.

$$3 \times -\tfrac{1}{3} = -1$$

The lines are perpendicular because the product of their gradients is -1.

Compare $y = 3x + 4$ with $y = mx + c$, so $m = 3$.

Rearrange the equation into the form $y = mx + c$ to find m.

Subtract x from each side.

Add 3 to each side.

Divide each term by 3.

$$-x \div 3 = \frac{-x}{3} = -\tfrac{1}{3}x$$

Compare $y = -\tfrac{1}{3}x + 1$ with $y = mx + c$, so $m = -\tfrac{1}{3}$.

Multiply the gradients of the lines.

Example 14

Work out whether these pairs of lines are parallel, perpendicular or neither:

a $y = -2x + 9$
$y = -2x - 3$

b $3x - y - 2 = 0$
$x + 3y - 6 = 0$

c $y = \tfrac{1}{2}x$
$2x - y + 4 = 0$

a $y = -2x + 9$

The gradient of this line is -2.

$y = -2x - 3$

The gradient of this line is -2.

So the lines are parallel, since the gradients are equal.

Compare $y = -2x + 9$ with $y = mx + c$, so $m = -2$.

Compare $y = -2x - 3$ with $y = mx + c$, so $m = -2$.

Remember that parallel lines have the same gradient.

b $3x - y - 2 = 0$

$3x - 2 = y$

So $y = 3x - 2$

The gradient of this line is 3.

$x + 3y - 6 = 0$

$3y - 6 = -x$

$3y = -x + 6$

$y = -\tfrac{1}{3} + 2$

The gradient of this line is $-\tfrac{1}{3}$.

So the lines are perpendicular as
$3 \times \tfrac{1}{3} = -1$.

Rearrange the equation into the form $y = mx + c$.

Add y to each side.

Compare $y = 3x - 2$ with $y = mx + c$, so $m = 3$.

Subtract x from each side.

Add 6 to each side.

Divide each term by 3.

Compare $y = -\tfrac{1}{3}x + 2$ with $y = mx + c$, so $m = -\tfrac{1}{3}$.

c $\quad y = \frac{1}{2}x$ —————————————— Compare $y = \frac{1}{2}x$ with $y = mx + c$, so $m = \frac{1}{2}$.

The gradient of this line is $\frac{1}{2}$.

$\qquad 2x - y + 4 = 0$ ————————— Rearrange the equation into the form

$\qquad\qquad 2x + 4 = y$ ————————— $y = mx + c$ to find m.

So $\qquad\qquad y = 2x + 4$ ——————————— Add y to each side.

The gradient of this line is 2. ————— Compare $y = 2x + 4$ with $y = mx + c$, so

$\qquad\qquad\qquad\qquad\qquad\qquad\qquad m = 2$.

The lines are not parallel as they have different gradients.

The lines are not perpendicular as $\frac{1}{2} \times 2 = 1$.

Example 15

Find an equation of the line that passes through the point $(3, -1)$ and is perpendicular to the line $y = 2x - 4$.

$y = 2x - 4$ —————————————— Compare $y = 2x - 4$ with $y = mx + c$.

$m = 2$ ————————————————— Use the rule $-\dfrac{1}{m}$ with $m = 2$.

So the gradient of the ———————— Use $y - y_1 = m(x - x_1)$.

perpendicular line is $-\frac{1}{2}$.

$\qquad\qquad\qquad\qquad\qquad\qquad\qquad$ Here $m = -\frac{1}{2}$ and $(x_1, y_1) = (3, -1)$.

$y - (-1) = -\frac{1}{2}(x - 3)$ —————

$\qquad y + 1 = -\frac{1}{2}x + \frac{3}{2}$ ————— Expand the brackets.

$\qquad\qquad\qquad\qquad\qquad\qquad\qquad -\frac{1}{2} \times -3 = \frac{3}{2}$

$\qquad\qquad y = -\frac{1}{2}x + \frac{1}{2}$ ————— Subtract 1 from each side, so that $\frac{3}{2} - 1 = \frac{1}{2}$.

Exercise 8D

1 Work out whether these pairs of lines are parallel, perpendicular or neither:

a $\quad y = 4x + 2$ $\qquad\qquad$ **b** $\quad y = \frac{2}{3}x - 1$ $\qquad\qquad$ **c** $\quad y = \frac{1}{5}x + 9$

$\quad\;\; y = -\frac{1}{4}x - 7$ $\qquad\qquad\quad y = \frac{2}{3}x - 11$ $\qquad\qquad\quad\;\; y = 5x + 9$

d $\quad y = -3x + 2$ $\qquad\quad$ **e** $\quad y = \frac{3}{5}x + 4$ $\qquad\qquad$ **f** $\quad y = \frac{5}{7}x$

$\quad\;\; y = \frac{1}{3}x - 7$ $\qquad\qquad\qquad y = -\frac{5}{3}x - 1$ $\qquad\qquad\quad y = \frac{5}{7}x - 3$

g $\quad y = 5x - 3$ $\qquad\qquad$ **h** $\quad 5x - y - 1 = 0$ $\qquad$ **i** $\quad y = -\frac{3}{2}x + 8$

$\quad\;\; 5x - y + 4 = 0$ $\qquad\qquad\quad y = -\frac{1}{5}x$ $\qquad\qquad\quad\;\; 2x - 3y - 9 = 0$

j $\quad 4x - 5y + 1 = 0$ $\qquad$ **k** $\quad 3x + 2y - 12 = 0$ $\qquad$ **l** $\quad 5x - y + 2 = 0$

$\quad\;\; 8x - 10y - 2 = 0$ $\qquad\qquad 2x + 3y - 6 = 0$ $\qquad\qquad 2x + 10y - 4 = 0$

2 Find an equation of the line that passes through the point $(6, -2)$ and is perpendicular to the line $y = 3x + 5$.

3 Find an equation of the line that passes through the point $(-2, 7)$ and is parallel to the line $y = 4x + 1$. Write your answer in the form $ax + by + c = 0$.

4 Find an equation of the line:

    a parallel to the line $y = -2x - 5$, passing through $\left(-\frac{1}{2}, \frac{3}{2}\right)$

    b parallel to the line $x - 2y - 1 = 0$, passing through $(0, 0)$

    c perpendicular to the line $y = x - 4$, passing through $(-1, -2)$

    d perpendicular to the line $2x + y - 9 = 0$, passing through $(4, -6)$.

5 Find an equation of the line:

    a parallel to the line $y = 3x + 6$, passing through $(-2, 5)$

    b perpendicular to the line $y = 3x + 6$, passing through $(-2, 5)$

    c parallel to the line $4x - 6y + 7 = 0$, passing through $(3, 4)$

    d perpendicular to the line $4x - 6y + 7 = 0$, passing through $(3, 4)$.

6 Find an equation of the line that passes through the point $(5, -5)$ and is perpendicular to the line $y = \frac{2}{3}x + 5$. Write your answer in the form $ax + by + c = 0$, where a, b and c are integers.

7 Find an equation of the line that passes through the point $(-2, -3)$ and is perpendicular to the line $y = -\frac{4}{7}x + 5$. Write your answer in the form $ax + by + c = 0$, where a, b and c are integers.

8 The line r passes through the points $(1, 4)$ and $(6, 8)$ and the line s passes through the points $(5, -3)$ and $(20, 9)$. Show that the lines r and s are parallel.

9 The line l passes through the points $(-3, 0)$ and $(3, -2)$ and the line n passes through the points $(1, 8)$ and $(-1, 2)$. Show that the lines l and n are perpendicular.

10 The vertices of a quadrilateral $ABCD$ has coordinates $A(-1, 5)$, $B(7, 1)$, $C(5, -3)$, $D(-3, 1)$. Show that the quadrilateral is a rectangle.

8.5 You can find the distance d between (x_1, y_1) and (x_2, y_2) by using the formula
$d = \sqrt{[(x_2 - x_1)^2 + (y_2 - y_1)^2]}$.

Example 16

Find the distance between these pairs of points:

    a $(2, 3), (5, 7)$ **b** $(4a, a), (-3a, 2a)$

a

Draw a sketch.

Let the distance between the points be d.

The difference in the y-coordinates is $7 - 3 = 4$.

The difference in the x-coordinates is $5 - 2 = 3$.

$d^2 = (5 - 2)^2 + (7 - 3)^2$

$d^2 = 3^2 + 4^2$

$d = \sqrt{(3^2 + 4^2)}$

   $= \sqrt{25}$

   $= 5$

Use Pythagoras' theorem:
$d^2 = (x_2 - x_1)^2 + (y_2 - y_1)^2$

Take the square root of each side.

This is $d = \sqrt{[(x_2 - x_1)^2 + (y_2 - y_1)^2]}$ with $(x_1, y_1) = (2, 3)$ and $(x_2, y_2) = (5, 7)$.

b $d = \sqrt{[(-3a - 4a)^2 + (2a - a)^2]}$ ———— Use $d = \sqrt{[(x_2 - x_1)^2 + (y_2 - y_1)^2]}$. Here

$\quad = \sqrt{[(-7a)^2 + a^2]}$ $\qquad\qquad\qquad (x_1, y_1) = (4a, a)$ and $(x_2, y_2) = (-3a, 2a)$.

$\quad = \sqrt{(49a^2 + a^2)}$ $\qquad\qquad\qquad\qquad (-7a)^2 = -7a \times -7a$

$\quad = \sqrt{50a^2}$ $\qquad\qquad\qquad\qquad\qquad\qquad = 49a^2$

$\quad = \sqrt{25 \times 2 \times a^2}$ $\qquad\qquad\qquad$ Simplify.

$\quad = \sqrt{25} \times \sqrt{2} \times \sqrt{a^2}$

$\quad = 5\sqrt{2}a$

Exercise 8E

Find the distance between these pairs of points:

1 $(0, 1), (6, 9)$ $\qquad\qquad$ **2** $(4, -6), (9, 6)$ $\qquad\qquad$ **3** $(3, 1), (-1, 4)$

4 $(3, 5), (4, 7)$ $\qquad\qquad$ **5** $(2, 9), (4, 3)$ $\qquad\qquad$ **6** $(0, -4), (5, 5)$

7 $(-2, -7), (5, 1)$ $\qquad\qquad$ **8** $(-4a, 0), (3a, -2a)$ $\qquad$ **9** $(-b, 4b), (-4b, -2b)$

10 $(2c, c), (6c, 4c)$ $\qquad\quad$ **11** $(-4d, d), (2d, -4d)$ $\qquad$ **12** $(-e, -e), (-3e, -5e)$

8.6   *You can find the coordinates of a point that divides a line in a given ratio.*

• **The coordinates of the point dividing the line joining (x_1, y_1) and (x_2, y_2) in the ratio $m:n$ are given by** $\left(\dfrac{nx_1 + mx_2}{m + n}, \dfrac{ny_1 + my_2}{m + n}\right)$

In Exercise 7B you saw how to find the position vector of such a point

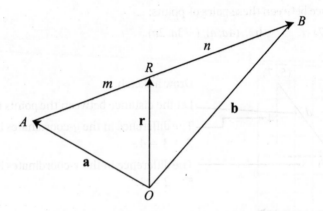

Using the vector triangle: $\qquad \mathbf{r} = \mathbf{a} + \dfrac{m}{m + n}\overrightarrow{AB} = \mathbf{a} + \dfrac{m}{m + n}(\mathbf{b} - \mathbf{a})$

and so $\qquad\qquad\qquad\qquad \mathbf{r} = \dfrac{(m + n)\mathbf{a} + m\mathbf{b} - m\mathbf{a}}{m + n} = \dfrac{n\mathbf{a} + m\mathbf{b}}{m + n}$

and this coordinate formula uses the same idea with $\mathbf{a} = \begin{pmatrix} x_1 \\ y_1 \end{pmatrix}$ and $\mathbf{b} = \begin{pmatrix} x_2 \\ y_2 \end{pmatrix}$.

Example 17

$A(-1, 5)$ and $B(3, 9)$

Find the coordinates of the point C that divides AB in the ratio $1 : 3$

C is $\dfrac{3(-1) + 1 \times 3}{1 + 3}, \dfrac{3 \times 5 + 1 \times 9}{1 + 3}$ Use the formula. Remember the second part of the ratio (the 3) multiplies the first point(A's) coordinates.

i.e. C is $\left(0, \dfrac{15 + 9}{4}\right)$

so C is $(0, 6)$

Exercise 8F

Find the coordinates of the point which divides AB in the given ratio:

a $A(0, 6)$; $B(4, 10)$ ratio $3 : 1$ **b** $A(1, 5)$; $B(-2, 8)$ ratio $1 : 2$

c $A(3, -7)$; $B(-2, 8)$ ratio $3 : 2$ **d** $A(-2, 5)$; $B(5, 2)$ ratio $4 : 3$

Find the mid-point of the line joining the following pairs of points:

a $(4, 2)$ and $(6, 8)$ **b** $(0, 6)$ and $(12, 2)$

c $(2, 2)$ and $(-4, 6)$ **d** $(-6, 4)$ and $(6, -4)$

Mixed Exercise 8G

1   The points A and B have coordinates $(-4, 6)$ and $(2, 8)$ respectively. A line p is drawn through B perpendicular to AB to meet the y-axis at the point C.
   a   Find an equation of the line p.
   b   Determine the coordinates of C.   © Edexcel Limited

2   The line l has equation $2x - y - 1 = 0$.
   The line m passes through the point $A(0, 4)$ and is perpendicular to the line l.
   a   Find an equation of m and show that the lines l and m intersect at the point $P(2, 3)$.
   The line n passes through the point $B(3, 0)$ and is parallel to the line m.
   b   Find an equation of n and hence find the coordinates of the point Q where the lines l and n intersect.   © Edexcel Limited

3   The line L_1 has gradient $\frac{1}{7}$ and passes through the point $A(2, 2)$. The line L_2 has gradient -1 and passes through the point $B(4, 8)$. The lines L_1 and L_2 intersect at the point C.
   a   Find an equation for L_1 and an equation for L_2.
   b   Determine the coordinates of C.   © Edexcel Limited

4   The straight line passing through the point $P(2, 1)$ and the point $Q(k, 11)$ has gradient $-\frac{5}{12}$.
   a   Find the equation of the line in terms of x and y only.
   b   Determine the value of k.   © Edexcel Limited

5   **a**   Find an equation of the line l which passes through the points $A(1, 0)$ and $B(5, 6)$.
   The line m with equation $2x + 3y = 15$ meets l at the point C.
   b   Determine the coordinates of the point C.   © Edexcel Limited

6 The line L passes through the points $A(1, 3)$ and $B(-19, -19)$.
Find an equation of L in the form $ax + by + c = 0$, where a, b and c are integers.

7 The straight line l_1 passes through the points A and B with coordinates $(2, 2)$ and $(6, 0)$ respectively.
  a Find an equation of l_1.
The straight line l_2 passes through the point C with coordinates $(-9, 0)$ and has gradient $\frac{1}{4}$.
  b Find an equation of l_2.

8 The straight line l_1 passes through the points A and B with coordinates $(0, -2)$ and $(6, 7)$ respectively.
  a Find the equation of l_1 in the form $y = mx + c$.
The straight line l_2 with equation $x + y = 8$ cuts the y-axis at the point C. The lines l_1 and l_2 intersect at the point D.
  b Calculate the coordinates of the point D.
  c Calculate the area of $\triangle ACD$.

9 The points A and B have coordinates $(2, 16)$ and $(12, -4)$ respectively. A straight line l_1 passes through A and B.
  a Find an equation for l_1 in the form $ax + by = c$.
The line l_2 passes through the point C with coordinates $(-1, 1)$ and has gradient $\frac{1}{3}$.
  b Find an equation for l_2.

10 The points $A(-1, -2)$, $B(7, 2)$ and $C(k, 4)$, where k is a constant, are the vertices of $\triangle ABC$. Angle ABC is a right angle.
  a Find the gradient of AB.
  b Calculate the value of k.
  c Find an equation of the straight line passing through B and C. Give your answer in the form $ax + by + c = 0$, where a, b and c are integers.

11 The point C divides the line joining $A(-1, 1)$ and $B(4, 11)$ in the ratio $3 : 2$.
  a Find the coordinates of the point C.
The line l is perpendicular to AB and passes through the point C.
  b Find an equation of l, giving your answer in the form $ax + by + c = 0$, where a, b and c are integers.
The line l cuts the y-axis at the point D.
  c Write down the coordinates of D.
  d Find the area of triangle ABD.

12 The points A and B have coordinates $(k, 1)$ and $(8, 2k - 1)$ respectively, where k is a constant. Given that the gradient of AB is $\frac{1}{3}$:
  a show that $k = 2$
  b find an equation for the line through A and B.

1 • In the general form of the equation of a straight line $y = mx + c$,
  m is the gradient and $(0, c)$ is the intercept on the y-axis.
  • Another general form of the equation of a straight line that you may see is
    $$ax + by + c = 0,$$
  where a, b and c are integers.

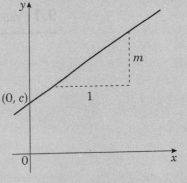

2 You can work out the gradient m of the line joining the point with
  coordinates (x_1, y_1) to the point with coordinates (x_2, y_2) by using
  the formula

  $$m = \frac{y_2 - y_1}{x_2 - x_1}$$

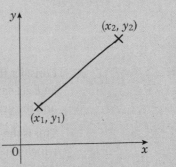

3 You can find the equation of a line with gradient m that passes through
  the point with coordinates (x_1, y_1) by using the formula
    $$y - y_1 = m(x - x_1)$$

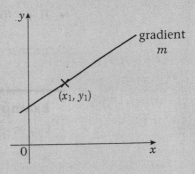

4 If a line has a gradient m, a line perpendicular to it has a gradient of $-\dfrac{1}{m}$.

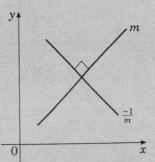

5 If two lines are perpendicular, the product of their gradients is -1.

6 The coordinates of the point dividing the line joining (x_1, y_1) and (x_2, y_2) in the ratio $m:n$
  are given by $\left(\dfrac{nx_1 + mx_2}{m + n}, \dfrac{ny_1 + my_2}{m + n} \right)$.

9.1 *You can find the gradient function f'(x) of a curve when f(x) = xⁿ.*

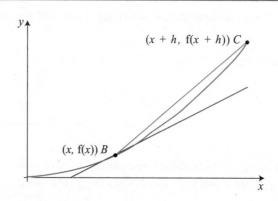

Consider the gradient of the chord BC where B and C are two points on the (red) curve. If you let h get smaller (mathematically we say $h \to 0$) then the point C will move closer to the point B and the gradient of the blue chord will get closer to the gradient of the green tangent.

This is the basic idea behind the process of **differentiation** and there are some simple rules which you will need to learn:

● **If $y = \mathrm{f}(x) = x^n$ then the gradient function $\mathrm{f}'(x) = nx^{n-1}$**

Sometimes we write $\dfrac{\mathrm{d}y}{\mathrm{d}x} = \mathrm{f}'(x)$.

Example 1

Find $\mathrm{f}'(x)$ when $\mathrm{f}(x)$ equals:

a $\quad x^6$ **b** $x^{\frac{1}{2}}$ **c** x^{-2} **d** $\dfrac{x}{x^5}$ **e** $x^2 \times x^3$

a $\quad 6x^5$

The power 6 is reduced to power 5 and the 6 multiplies the answer.

b $\quad \mathrm{f}(x) = x^{\frac{1}{2}}$

$\mathrm{f}'(x) = \frac{1}{2}x^{-\frac{1}{2}}$

$\quad = \dfrac{1}{2\sqrt{x}}$

The power $\frac{1}{2}$ is reduced to $\frac{1}{2} - 1 = -\frac{1}{2}$, and the $\frac{1}{2}$ multiplies the answer. This can be rewritten in an alternative form.

c $\quad \mathrm{f}(x) = x^{-2}$

$\mathrm{f}'(x) = -2x^{-3}$

$\quad = -\dfrac{2}{x^3}$

The power -2 is reduced to -3 and the -2 multiplies the answer. This can be rewritten in an alternative form using knowledge of negative powers.

d Let $f(x) = x \div x^5$

$\qquad = x^{-4}$ — Simplify using rules of powers to give one simple power, i.e. subtract $1 - 5 = -4$.

So $f'(x) = -4x^{-5}$ — Reduce the power -4 to give -5, then multiply your answer by -4.

$\qquad = -\dfrac{4}{x^5}$

e Let $f(x) = x^2 \times x^3$ — Add the powers this time to give $2 + 3 = 5$.

$\qquad = x^5$ — Reduce the power 5 to 4 and multiply your answer by 5.

So $f'(x) = 5x^4$

Exercise 9A

Find $f'(x)$, given $f(x)$ equals:

1	x^7	**2**	x^8	**3**	x^4	**4**	$x^{\frac{1}{3}}$
5	$x^{\frac{1}{4}}$	**6**	$\sqrt[3]{x}$	**7**	x^{-3}	**8**	x^{-4}
9	$\dfrac{1}{x^2}$	**10**	$\dfrac{1}{x^5}$	**11**	$\dfrac{1}{\sqrt[3]{x}}$	**12**	$\dfrac{1}{\sqrt{x}}$
13	$\dfrac{x^2}{x^4}$	**14**	$\dfrac{x^3}{x^2}$	**15**	$\dfrac{x^6}{x^3}$	**16**	$x^3 \times x^6$
17	$x^2 \times x^3$	**18**	$x \times x^2$				

9.2 You can differentiate a function that is a multiple of powers of x.

You saw that if $y = x^n$, then $\dfrac{dy}{dx} = nx^{n-1}$.

This is true for all real values of n.
It can also be shown that

- **if $y = ax^n$, where a is a constant then $\dfrac{dy}{dx} = anx^{n-1}$.**

Also

- **if $y = f(x) \pm g(x)$ then $\dfrac{dy}{dx} = f'(x) \pm g'(x)$.**

For the IGCSE these standard results can be assumed without proof.

> **Hint:**
> Note that you again reduce the power by 1 and the original power multiplies the expression.

Example 2

Use standard results to differentiate:

a $x^3 + x^2 - x^{\frac{1}{2}}$ **b** $2x^{-3}$ **c** $\frac{1}{3}x^{\frac{1}{2}} + 4x^2$

a $\qquad y = x^3 + x^2 - x^{\frac{1}{2}}$

So $\dfrac{dy}{dx} = 3x^2 + 2x - \frac{1}{2}x^{-\frac{1}{2}}$ — Differentiate each term as you come to it.

First x^3, then x^2, then $-x^{\frac{1}{2}}$.

b $\qquad y = 2x^{-3}$

So $\dfrac{dy}{dx} = -6x^{-4}$ ———————— Differentiate x^{-3}, then multiply the answer by 2.

$\qquad = -\dfrac{6}{x^4}$

c $\qquad x = \frac{1}{3}x^{\frac{1}{2}} + 4x^2$

So $\dfrac{dy}{dx} = \frac{1}{3} \times \frac{1}{2}x^{-\frac{1}{2}} + 8x$ ———————— Take each term as you come to it, and treat each term as a multiple.

$\qquad = \frac{1}{6} \times x^{-\frac{1}{2}} + 8x$

Sometimes you may need to expand or simplify an expression before you can differentiate it.

Example 3

Use standard results to differentiate:

a $\quad \dfrac{1}{4\sqrt{x}}$ $\qquad\qquad$ **b** $\quad x^3(3x + 1)$ $\qquad\qquad$ **c** $\quad \dfrac{x - 2}{x^2}$

a Let $\qquad y = \dfrac{1}{4\sqrt{x}}$ ———— Express the 4 in the denominator as a multiplier of $\frac{1}{4}$ and express the x term as

$\qquad\qquad = \frac{1}{4}x^{-\frac{1}{2}}$ ———— power $-\frac{1}{2}$.

Therefore $\dfrac{dy}{dx} = -\frac{1}{8}x^{-\frac{3}{2}}$ ———— Then differentiate by reducing the power of x and multiplying $\frac{1}{4}$ by $-\frac{1}{2}$.

b Let $\qquad y = x^3(3x + 1)$

$\qquad\qquad = 3x^4 + x^3$ ———— Multiply out the brackets to give a polynomial function.

Therefore $\dfrac{dy}{dx} = 12x^3 + 3x^2$

$\qquad\qquad = 3x^2(4x + 1)$ ———— Differentiate each term.

c Let $\qquad y = \dfrac{x - 2}{x^2}$

$\qquad\qquad = \dfrac{1}{x} - \dfrac{2}{x^2}$ ———— Express the single fraction as two separate fractions, and simplify $\frac{x}{x^2}$ as $\frac{1}{x}$.

$\qquad\qquad = x^{-1} - 2x^{-2}$

Therefore $\dfrac{dy}{dx} = -x^{-2} + 4x^{-3}$ ———— Then express the rational expressions as negative powers of x, and differentiate.

$\qquad\qquad = -\dfrac{1}{x^2} + \dfrac{4}{x^3}$

$\qquad\qquad = \dfrac{-x + 4}{x^3}$ ———— Simplify by using a common denominator.

Example 4

Find the gradient of the curve $y = x^3 - 3x^2 + 2x - 1$ at the point $(3,5)$.

$y = x^3 - 3x^2 + 2x - 1$

$\dfrac{dy}{dx} = 3x^2 - 6x + 2$ ———— First differentiate to determine the gradient of the curve.

When $x = 3$, the gradient is 11. ———— Then substitute for x to calculate the value of the gradient of the curve and of the tangent when $x = 3$.

Exercise 9B

1 Use standard results to differentiate:

   a $x^4 + x^{-1}$ **b** $\frac{1}{2}x^{-2}$ **c** $2x^{-\frac{1}{2}}$

2 Find the gradient of the curve with equation $y = f(x)$ at the point A where:

   a $f(x) = x^3 - 3x + 2$ and A is at $(-1, 4)$ **b** $f(x) = 3x^2 + 2x^{-1}$ and A is at $(2, 13)$

3 Find the point or points on the curve with equation $y = f(x)$, where the gradient is zero:

   a $f(x) = x^2 - 5x$ **b** $f(x) = x^3 - 9x^2 + 24x - 20$

   c $f(x) = x^{\frac{3}{2}} - 6x + 1$ **d** $f(x) = x^{-1} + 4x$

4 Use standard results to differentiate:

   a $2\sqrt{x}$ **b** $\dfrac{3}{x^2}$ **c** $\dfrac{1}{3x^3}$

   d $\frac{1}{3}x^3(x - 2)$ **e** $\dfrac{2}{x^3} + \sqrt{x}$ **f** $\sqrt[3]{x} + \dfrac{1}{2x}$

   g $\dfrac{2x + 3}{x}$ **h** $\dfrac{3x^2 - 6}{x}$ **i** $\dfrac{2x^3 + 3x}{\sqrt{x}}$

   j $x(x^2 - x + 2)$ **k** $3x^2(x^2 + 2x)$ **l** $(3x - 2)\left(4x + \dfrac{1}{x}\right)$

5 Find the gradient of the curve with equation $y = f(x)$ at the point A where:

   a $f(x) = x(x + 1)$ and A is at $(0, 0)$ **b** $f(x) = \dfrac{2x - 6}{x^2}$ and A is at $(3, 0)$

   c $f(x) = \dfrac{1}{\sqrt{x}}$ and A is at $(\frac{1}{4}, 2)$ **d** $f(x) = 3x - \dfrac{4}{x^2}$ and A is at $(2, 5)$

9.3 You can also differentiat e^{ax}, $\sin ax$ and $\cos ax$.

In section 10.1 you will learn about **radians**. Radians are simply an alternative way of measuring angles instead of degrees.

The conversion is simple

• π **radians = 180 degrees**

So for example $60°$ is the same as $\frac{\pi}{3}$ radians and $\frac{\pi}{2}$ radians is equivalent to $90°$.

Your calculator can be set in radian "mode" and you should know how to do this. Try it now and then type in $\cos\left(\frac{\pi}{3}\right)$ and you should get 0.5 since $60°$ is the same as $\frac{\pi}{3}$ radians and $\cos(60°) = 0.5$.

The main reason for using radians is that they make the rules for differentiating $\sin x$ and $\cos x$ much simpler.

You need to learn the following:

• If $y = \sin ax$ then $\dfrac{dy}{dx} = a\cos ax$

• If $y = \cos ax$ then $\dfrac{dy}{dx} = -a\sin ax$

You can also differentiate the exponential function met in chapter 4

• If $y = e^{ax}$ then $\dfrac{dy}{dx} = ae^{ax}$

Example 5

Differentiate

a $y = \sin 3x$ **b** $y = 2 \sin 4x$ **c** $y = 3 \cos 2x$ **d** $y = 3e^{4x}$

a $y = \sin 3x$

$\dfrac{dy}{dx} = 3 \cos 3x$ Use the formula with $a = 3$.

b $y = 2 \sin 4x$

$\dfrac{dy}{dx} = 2 \times 4 \cos 4x$ Remember from section 9.2 if $y = kf(x)$

$= 8 \cos 4x$ then $\dfrac{dy}{dx} = kf'(x)$.

Then use the formula with $a = 4$.

c $y = 3 \cos 2x$

$\dfrac{dy}{dx} = 3 \times (-2) \sin 2x$ Remember the 3 does not change

$= -6 \sin 2x$ and use the formula with $a = 2$.

d $y = 3e^{4x}$

$\dfrac{dy}{dx} = 3 \times 4e^{4x}$ Use the formula with $a = 4$.

$= 12e^{4x}$

Exercise 9C

1. Differentiate

   a e^{2x} **b** e^{-6x}

   c $e^x + 3x^2$ **d** $\sin 2x$

   e $\cos 3x$ **f** $3 \sin 4x + 4 \cos 3x$

2. Find $\dfrac{dy}{dx}$ when

   a $y = \sin 5x$ **b** $y = 2 \sin \frac{1}{2}x$

   c $y = \sin 8x$ **d** $y = 6 \sin \frac{2}{3}x$

   e $y = 2 \cos x$ **f** $y = 6 \cos \frac{5}{6}x$

   g $y = \cos 4x$ **h** $y = 4 \cos\left(\frac{x}{2}\right)$

3. Find the gradient of the curve with equation $y = 2e^{-x}$ at the point $(0, 2)$.

4. Find the gradient of the curve with equation $y = 3 \sin x$ at the point where $x = \dfrac{\pi}{3}$.

5. Find the gradient of the curve with equation $y = 4 \cos 2x$ at the point where $x = \dfrac{\pi}{4}$.

9.4 *You can use the chain rule, product rule and quotient rules to differentiate more complicated functions.*

■ If $y = f(g(x))$ then $\dfrac{dy}{dx} = f'(g(x)) \times g'(x)$

This is called the **chain rule** or differentiating a function of a function.

Example 6

Differentiate the following

a $e^{x^2 + x}$ **b** $\sin(2x^2 + 3)$ **c** $(3x^4 + 2)^5$ **d** $\cos^3 x$

a $y = e^{x^2 + x}$

$\dfrac{dy}{dx} = e^{x^2 + x}(2x + 1)$

Use the chain rule with $f(x) = e^x$ and $g(x) = x^2 + x$.

This comes from differentiating the exponential function $f'(g(x))$ since $\dfrac{d(e^x)}{dx} = e^x$.

This comes from differentiating $g(x)$.

b $y = \sin(2x^2 + 3)$

$\dfrac{dy}{dx} = \cos(2x^2 + 3) \times 4x$

Use chain rule with $f(x) = \sin x$ and $g(x) = 2x^2 + 3$.

The $\cos(...)$ comes from differentiating $\sin(...)$ i.e. $f'(g(x))$.

The $4x$ comes from differentiating $2x^2 + 3$.

c $y = (3x^4 + 2)^5$

$\dfrac{dy}{dx} = 5(3x^4 + 2)^4 \times (12x^3)$

$= 60x^3(3x^4 + 2)^4$

Use the chain rule with $f(x) = x^5$ and $g(x) = 3x^4 + 2$.

This is $f'(g(x))$.

This is $g'(x)$.

d $y = \cos^3 x$

$\dfrac{dy}{dx} = 3\cos^2 x \times (-\sin x)$

$= -3\cos^2 x \sin x$

Use the chain rule with $f(x) = x^3$ and $g(x) = \cos x$.

This is $f'(g(x))$.

The derivative of $\cos x$ is $-\sin x$.

To differentiate a product of two functions you use the **product rule**

■ If $y = uv$ then $\dfrac{dy}{dx} = u\dfrac{dv}{dx} + v\dfrac{du}{dx}$

Example 7

Differentiate

a $y = e^x \sin x$ **b** xe^{x^2} **c** $y = x^2(3 + 2x)^4$

a $y = e^x \sin x$

$\dfrac{dy}{dx} = e^x \cos x + e^x \sin x$ Use the product rule with $u = e^x$ and $v = \sin x$.

b Let $y = xe^{x^2}$

Let $u = x$ and $v = e^{x^2}$

Then $\dfrac{du}{dx} = 1$ and $\dfrac{dv}{dx} = 2xe^{x^2}$ ——— Use the product rule and then use the chain rule to differentiate e^{x^2}.

$\therefore \dfrac{dy}{dx} = x(2xe^{x^2}) + e^{x^2}$

$= e^{x^2}(2x^2 + 1)$ Simplify the answer by factorising.

c $y = x^2(3 + 2x)^4$ Use the product rule with $u = x^2$ and $v = (3 + 2x)^4$.

$\dfrac{dy}{dx} = x^2 \times 4(3 + 2x)^3 \times 2 + 2x \times (3 + 2x)^4$ Use the chain rule to find $\dfrac{dv}{dx}$ where $v = (3 + 2x)^4$.

$= 8x^2(3 + 2x)^3 + 2x(3 + 2x)^4$

$= 2x(3 + 2x)^3[4x + 3 + 2x]$

$= 2x(3 + 2x)^3[6x + 3]$

$= 6x(3 + 2x)^3[2x + 1]$ Simplify your answer if possible.

To differentiate a quotient you can use the **quotient rule**

- If $y = \dfrac{u}{v}$ then $\dfrac{dy}{dx} = \dfrac{v\dfrac{du}{dx} - u\dfrac{dv}{dx}}{v^2}$

Example 8

Differentiate

a $y = \dfrac{x}{2x + 5}$

b $y = \dfrac{e^{2x + 3}}{x}$

c $y = \dfrac{e^x}{\sin x}$

a   Let $u = x$ and $v = 2x + 5$

$\dfrac{du}{dx} = 1$ and $\dfrac{dv}{dx} = 2$

Using $\dfrac{dy}{dx} = \dfrac{v\dfrac{du}{dx} - u\dfrac{dv}{dx}}{v^2}$

$\dfrac{dy}{dx} = \dfrac{(2x + 5) \times 1 - x \times 2}{(2x + 5)^2}$ Recognise that y is a quotient and use the quotient rule.

$= \dfrac{5}{(2x + 5)^2}$ Simplify the numerator of the fraction.

b Let $y = \dfrac{e^{2x+3}}{x}$

then $\dfrac{dy}{dx} = \dfrac{x \times 2e^{2x+3} - e^{2x+3}}{x^2}$ Use the quotient rule, together with the chain rule to differentiate e^{2x+3}.

$= \dfrac{(2x-1)e^{2x+3}}{x^2}$

c $y = \dfrac{e^x}{\sin x}$ Use the quotient rule with $u = e^x$ and $v = \sin x$

$\dfrac{dy}{dx} = \dfrac{\sin x \times e^x - e^x \times \cos x}{\sin^2 x}$

$= \dfrac{e^x(\sin x - \cos x)}{\sin^2 x}$

Exercise 9D

1   Differentiate
    a $(1 + 2x)^4$ **b** $(1 + x^2)^3$ **c** $(3 + 4x)^{\frac{1}{2}}$ **d** $(x^2 + 2x)^3$

2   Differentiate
    a $4e^{3x^2}$ **b** $9e^{3-x}$ **c** e^{-6x} **d** $e^{x^2 + 2x}$

3   Differentiate
    a $\sin(2x + 1)$ **b** $\cos(2x^2 + 4)$ **c** $\sin^3 x$ **d** $\cos^2 2x$

4   Differentiate
    a $x(1 + 3x)^5$ **b** $2x(1 + 3x^2)^3$ **c** $x^3(2x + 6)^4$

5   Differentiate
    a xe^{2x} **b** $(x^2 + 3)e^{-x}$ **c** $(3x - 5)e^{x^2}$

6   Differentiate
    a $x \sin x$ **b** $\sin^2 x \cos x$ **c** $e^x \cos x$

7   Differentiate
    a $\dfrac{5x}{x + 1}$ **b** $\dfrac{2x}{3x - 2}$ **c** $\dfrac{3x^2}{(2x - 1)^2}$

8   Differentiate
    a $\dfrac{x}{e^{2x}}$ **b** $\dfrac{e^x}{x + 1}$ **c** $\dfrac{e^{x^2}}{x}$

9   Differentiate
    a $\dfrac{\sin x}{x}$ **b** $\dfrac{e^x}{\cos x}$ **c** $\dfrac{\sin^2 x}{e^{2x}}$

10   Find the gradient of the following curves at the points indicated
    a $y = x^2(3x - 1)^3$ at the point $(1, 8)$ **b** $y = (2x + 3)e^{2x}$ at the point $(0, 3)$

    c $y = 3 \sin^2 x$ at the point $\left(\dfrac{\pi}{4}, \dfrac{3}{2}\right)$ **d** $y = x \cos x$ at the point $\left(\dfrac{\pi}{2}, 0\right)$

9.5 *You can use differentiation to find the gradient of a tangent to a curve and you can then find the equation of the tangent and normal to that curve at a specified point.*

The tangent at the point A $(a, f(a))$ has gradient $f'(a)$. You can use the formula for the equation of a straight line, $y - y_1 = m(x - x_1)$, to obtain the equation of the tangent at $(a, f(a))$.

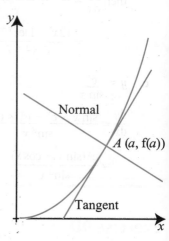

- **The equation of the tangent to a curve at a point $(a, f(a))$ is $y - f(a) = f'(a)(x - a)$.**

The normal to the curve at the point A is defined as being the straight line through A which is perpendicular to the tangent at A (see sketch alongside).

The gradient of the normal is $-\dfrac{1}{f'(a)}$, because the product of the gradients of lines which are at right angles is -1.

- **The equation of the normal at point A is $y - f(a) = -\dfrac{1}{f'(a)}(x - a)$.**

Example 9

Find the equation of the tangent to the curve $y = x^3 - 3x^2 + 2x - 1$ at the point $(3, 5)$.

$$y = x^3 - 3x^2 + 2x - 1$$

$$\frac{dy}{dx} = 3x^2 - 6x + 2$$

First differentiate to determine the gradient of the curve and therefore the gradient of the tangent.

When $x = 3$, the gradient is 11.

So the equation of the tangent at $(3, 5)$ is

Then substitute for x to calculate the value of the gradient of the curve and of the tangent when $x = 3$.

$$y - 5 = 11(x - 3)$$
$$y = 11x - 28$$

You can now use the line equation and simplify.

Example 10

Find the equation of the normal to the curve with equation $y = 3 \cos 2x$ at the point $\left(\dfrac{\pi}{4}, 0\right)$

$$\frac{dy}{dx} = 3(-\sin 2x) \times 2$$

Using the chain rule.

$$= -6 \sin 2x$$

Remember x is in radians.

Gradient of curve $= -6$

Substitute $x = \dfrac{\pi}{4}$ to find the gradient of the curve.

So gradient of normal $= \dfrac{1}{6}$

The normal is perpendicular to the tangent so use the perpendicular gradient rule.

So equation of the normal is

$$y - 0 = \frac{1}{6}\left(x - \frac{\pi}{4}\right)$$

i.e. $\quad y = \dfrac{1}{6}\left(x - \dfrac{\pi}{4}\right)$

Exercise 9E

1 Find the equation of the tangent to the curve:

  a $y = x^2 - 7x + 10$ at the point $(2, 0)$ **b** $y = x + \dfrac{1}{x}$ at the point $(2, 2\frac{1}{2})$

  c $y = \dfrac{2x - 1}{x}$ at the point $(1, 1)$

2 Find the equation of the normal to the curves:

  a $y = x^2 - 5x$ at the point $(6, 6)$ **b** $y = x^2 - \dfrac{8}{\sqrt{x}}$ at the point $(4, 12)$

3 For $f(x) = 12 - 4x + 2x^2$, find an equation of the tangent and normal at the point where $x = -1$ on the curve with equation $y = f(x)$.   © Edexcel Limited

4 Find the equation of the tangent to the curve $y = xe^{2x}$ at the point $(\frac{1}{2}, \frac{1}{2}e)$.

5 Find the equation of the tangent to the curve $y = \dfrac{e^{\frac{x}{3}}}{x}$ at the point $(3, \frac{1}{3}e)$.

6 Find the equation of the tangent to the curve with equation $y = x \sin x$ at the point $(\pi, 0)$.

7 Find the equation of the normal to the curve with equation $y = 2\cos^2 x$ at the point $\left(\dfrac{\pi}{4}, 1\right)$.

9.6   *You can reverse the process of differentiation by integration.*

You have seen that

if $y = x^2$ then $\dfrac{dy}{dx} = 2x$ and if $y = x^2 + 3$ then $\dfrac{dy}{dx} = 2x$ as well.

So if you were asked to find y given that $\dfrac{dy}{dx} = 2x$ you cannot give a unique answer but can say that $y = x^2 + c$ where c is some constant.

We call this process **integration** and write

$$\int 2x \, dx = x^2 + c$$

This symbol, which is an elongated "S" means integrate.	$2x$ is the expression to be integrated.	The dx tells you which letter is the variable to integrate: "dx" says integrate x.

The rules for integration that you need for IGCSE are:

- $\displaystyle\int x^n \, dx = \dfrac{x^{n+1}}{n+1} + c \qquad (n \neq -1)$

- $\displaystyle\int e^{ax} \, dx = \dfrac{1}{a}e^{ax} + c$

- $\displaystyle\int \sin ax \, dx = -\dfrac{1}{a}\cos ax + c$

- $\displaystyle\int \cos ax \, dx = \dfrac{1}{a}\sin ax + c$

Example 11

Find:

a $\displaystyle\int (x^{\frac{1}{2}} + 2x^3)\,dx$

b $\displaystyle\int (x^{-\frac{3}{2}} + 2)\,dx$

c $\displaystyle\int (3x^2 + p^2 x^{-2} + q)\,dx$

d $\displaystyle\int (4t^2 + 6)\,dt$

e $\displaystyle\int x\left(x^2 + \frac{2}{x}\right)dx$

a $\displaystyle\int (x^{\frac{1}{2}} + 2x^3)\,dx$

$= \dfrac{x^{\frac{3}{2}}}{\frac{3}{2}} + \dfrac{2x^4}{4} + c$

First apply the rule term by term.

$= \frac{2}{3}x^{\frac{3}{2}} + \frac{1}{2}x^4 + c$

Then simplify each term.

b $\displaystyle\int (x^{-\frac{3}{2}} + 2)\,dx$

$= \dfrac{x^{-\frac{1}{2}}}{-\frac{1}{2}} + 2x + c$

Remember $\dfrac{-3}{2} + 1 = -\dfrac{1}{2}$ and the integral of a constant like 2 is $2x$.

$= -2x^{-\frac{1}{2}} + 2x + c$

c $\displaystyle\int (3x^2 + p^2 x^{-2} + q)\,dx$

$= \dfrac{3x^3}{3} + \dfrac{p^2}{-1}x^{-1} + qx + c$

The dx tells you to integrate with respect to the variable x, so any other letters must be treated as constants.

$= x^3 - p^2 x^{-1} + qx + c$

d $\displaystyle\int (4t^2 + 6)\,dt$

$= \dfrac{4t^3}{3} + 6t + c$

The dt tells you that this time you must integrate with respect to t.

e $\displaystyle\int x\left(x^2 + \frac{2}{x}\right)dx$

First multiply out the bracket.

$= \displaystyle\int (x^3 + 2)\,dx$

Then apply the rule to each term.

$= \dfrac{x^4}{4} + 2x + c$

Example 12

Find $\int (2 \cos x + 3e^{-x} - \sin 2x)\,dx$

Let $I = \int (2 \cos x + 3e^{-x} - \sin 2x)\,dx$

Then using the standard formulae integrate term by term

$\int 2 \cos x\,dx = 2 \sin x$

$\int 3e^{-x}\,dx = -3e^{-x}$

Integrate each term using the above rules.
You only need one $+c$ for the whole integral
so this is best added at the end.

$\int \sin 2x\,dx = -\frac{1}{2}\cos 2x$

So $I = 2 \sin x - 3e^{-x} + \frac{1}{2}\cos 2x + c$ Add the $+c$ at the end.

Exercise 9F

Find the following integrals.

1 $\int (x^3 + 2x)\,dx$ **2** $\int (2x^{-2} + 3)\,dx$

3 $\int (5x^{\frac{3}{2}} - 3x^2)\,dx$ **4** $\int (2x^{\frac{1}{2}} - 2x^{-\frac{1}{2}} + 4)\,dx$

5 $\int (4x^3 - 3x^{-4} + r)\,dx$ **6** $\int (3t^2 - t^{-2})\,dt$

7 $\int (2t^2 - 3t^{-\frac{3}{2}} + 1)\,dt$ **8** $\int (x + x^{-\frac{1}{2}} - \frac{3}{2})\,dx$

9 $\int (px^4 + 2t + 3x^{-2})\,dx$ **10** $\int (pt^3 + q^2 + px^3)\,dt$

11   Find the following integrals:

   a $\int (2x + 3)x^2\,dx$ **b** $\int \dfrac{(2x^2 + 3)}{x^2}\,dx$ **c** $\int (2x + 3)^2\,dx$

   d $\int (2x + 3)(x - 1)\,dx$ **e** $\int (2x + 3)\sqrt{x}\,dx$

12   Integrate
   a $2 \sin 3x$ **b** $3e^{4x}$ **c** $2 \cos 3x$ **d** $2e^{-x}$

13   Integrate the following with respect to x:

   a $5e^x - 4 \sin x + 2x^3$ **b** $2(\sin x - \cos x + x)$

   c $5e^x + 4 \cos x - \dfrac{2}{x^2}$ **d** $e^x + \sin x + \cos x$

9.7   *You can apply calculus to problems involving displacement, velocity and acceleration.*

- **Displacement is represented by s and is a measure of distance: $+$ or $-$ indicates direction.**

- **Velocity is represented by v and is a measure of speed: $+$ or $-$ indicates direction.**

- **Acceleration is represented by a and is a measure of change in speed: $+$ means the object is getting faster and $-$ means it is getting slower.**

The important relationships between these variables are:

$$v = \frac{ds}{dt}$$

$$a = \frac{dv}{dt} \quad \text{which can also be written as } a = \frac{d^2s}{dt^2}$$ — This means take displacement and differentiate it twice.

where t represents time.

Example 13

The velocity of a ball, v m/s, after t seconds is given by $v = 8 + 10t - t^2$.

a Find the acceleration after t seconds.

b Work out when the acceleration is zero.

c Hence find the maximum velocity.

a $a = \frac{dv}{dt} = 10 - 2t$

b $0 = 10 - 2t$
$2t = 10$
$t = 5$ seconds

c The maximum velocity occurs when $a = 0$, when $t = 5$.
$v \text{(max)} = 8 + 50 - 25 = 33$ m/s

Example 14

The velocity of a particle, v m/s, after t seconds is given by

$$v = 12t - 8t^3 \qquad (t \geqslant 0)$$

Given that the initial displacement is 10 m, find

a an expression for s in terms of t,

b the displacement when $t = 2$.

a $s = \int v\,dt$

$s = 6t^2 - 2t^4 + c$

$t = 0$, $s = 10$ so $10 = 0 + 0 + c$ so $c = 10$

$s = 6t^2 - 2t^4 + 10$

To find the displacement you have to integrate the velocity.

Use the given information about $t = 0$, $s = 10$
i.e. the "initial" conditions.

b When $t = 2$
$s = 24 - 32 + 10$
$= 2$

Exercise 9G

1 The displacement, s metres, of a particle after t seconds is given by $s = 100 + 5t^2$.
Find an expression for the velocity, $v = \frac{ds}{dt}$.

2 The displacement, s metres, of a particle after t seconds is given by $s = 30 + 48t - 16t^2$.
Find an expression for the velocity, $v = \frac{ds}{dt}$.

3 The displacement, s metres, of a particle after t seconds is given by $s = 20 + 40t + 5t^2$.

    a Find an expression for the velocity, v.

    b Work out the velocity in m/s, after 3 seconds.

4 The displacement, s metres, of a particle after t seconds is given by $s = 20 + 30t - 5t^2$.

    a Find an expression for the velocity, v.

    b Work out the velocity in m/s, after 3 seconds.

5 The velocity, v m/s, of a particle after t seconds is given by $v = 32t + 100$.

    a Find an expression for the acceleration, $a = \dfrac{dv}{dt}$.

    Given that when $t = 0$ the displacement is 0

    b find an expression for the displacement s.

6 The velocity, v m/s, of a particle after t seconds is given by $v = 160 - 32t$.

    a Find an expression for the acceleration, $a = \dfrac{dv}{dt}$.

    Given that when $t = 0$ the displacement is 384 m from the origin, find

    b an expression for the displacement s,

    c the time when the particle passes through the origin.

7 The displacement, s metres, of a particle after t seconds is given by $s = t^3 + 4t^2 - 5t + 2$.

    a Find an expression for v.

    b Find an expression for a.

    c Work out, giving the correct units, the velocity and acceleration of the particle after one second.

8 The displacement, s metres, of a particle after t seconds is given by $s = t^3 - 2t^2 + 3t + 1$.

    a Find an expression for v.

    b Find an expression for a.

    c Work out, giving the correct units, the velocity and acceleration of the particle after two seconds.

9 The velocity, v m/s, of a particle after t seconds is given by $v = t^2 + 10t + 5$.

    a Find an expression for the acceleration, a.

    b Work out the acceleration, in m/s^2, after 2 seconds.

    The displacement $s = 0$ when $t = 0$.

    c Find the displacement when $t = 2$.

10 The velocity, v m/s, of a particle after t seconds is given by $v = 24 + 6t - t^2$.

    a Find an expression for the acceleration, a.

    b Work out the acceleration, in m/s^2, after 2 seconds.

    The displacement $s = 100$ when $t = 3$.

    c Find the expression for s in terms of t.

9.8 *You need to be able to find the coordinates of a stationary point on a curve and work out whether it is a minimum point or a maximum point.*

- Points of **zero gradient** are called **stationary points** and stationary points may be maximum points, minimum points or neither.

Hint:
A is a maximum point.

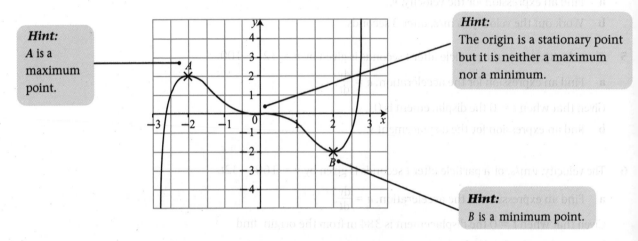

Hint:
The origin is a stationary point but it is neither a maximum nor a minimum.

Hint:
B is a minimum point.

- **To find the coordinates of a stationary point:**
  ① Find $\dfrac{dy}{dx}$, i.e. $f'(x)$, and solve the equation $f'(x) = 0$ to find the value, or values, of x.
  ② Substitute the value(s) of x which you have found into the equation $y = f(x)$ to find the corresponding value(s) of y.
  ③ This gives the coordinates of any stationary points.

- You can also find out whether stationary points are maximum points or minimum points by finding the value of $\dfrac{d^2y}{dx^2}$ at the stationary point. This is because $\dfrac{d^2y}{dx^2}$ measures the change in gradient.

Hint:
$\dfrac{d^2y}{dx^2}$ is the second derivative of y with respect to x.
You find $\dfrac{d^2y}{dx^2}$ by differentiating $\dfrac{dy}{dx}$ again with respect to x.

If you imagine the diagram above shows a roller coaster and imagine yourself sitting in a carriage at one of the points *A*, *O* or *B*. At each of these points you could remain stationary (hence the name **stationary points**)

Now imagine you are travelling along the roller coaster and think about your acceleration (you saw that this was given by the second derivative in section 9.7)

As you approach *A* you are getting slower so your acceleration $a < 0$.

As you approach *B* you are getting faster so your acceleration $a > 0$.

This gives rise to the following tests for a maximum and a minimum point:

- If $\dfrac{dy}{dx} = 0$ and $\dfrac{d^2y}{dx^2} < 0$, the point is a **maximum point**.

- If $\dfrac{dy}{dx} = 0$ and $\dfrac{d^2y}{dx^2} > 0$, the point is a **minimum point**.

You may see the notation: $f''(x)$ used for the second derivative of $f(x)$.

Example 15

Find the stationary points on the curve with equation $y = 2x^3 - 15x^2 + 24x + 6$ and determine, by finding the second derivative, whether the stationary points are maximum or minimum.

$y = 2x^3 - 15x^2 + 24x + 6$

$\dfrac{dy}{dx} = 6x^2 - 30x + 24$

Differentiate and put the derivative equal to zero.

Putting $6x^2 - 30x + 24 = 0$
$\qquad\quad 6(x - 4)(x - 1) = 0$

Solve the equation to obtain the values of x for the stationary points.

So $x = 4$ or $x = 1$

When $x = 1$,

$y = 2 - 15 + 24 + 6 = 17$

When $x = 4$,

$y = 2 \times 64 - 15 \times 16 + 24 \times 4 + 6 = -10$

Substitute $x = 4$ and $x = 1$ into the original equation of the curve to obtain the values of y which correspond to these values.

So the stationary points are at $(1, 17)$ and $(4, -10)$

$\dfrac{d^2y}{dx^2} = 12x - 30$

Differentiate again to obtain the second derivative.

When $x = 1$, $\dfrac{d^2y}{dx^2} = -18$ which is <0

So $(1, 17)$ is a maximum point.

When $x = 4$, $\dfrac{d^2y}{dx^2} = 18$ which is >0

So $(4, 1)$ is a minimum point

Substitute $x = 1$ and $x = 4$ into the second derivative expression. If the second derivative is negative then the point is a maximum point, whereas if it is positive then the point is a minimum point.

Hint:
You may be told whether a stationary value is a maximum or a minimum, in which case it will not be necessary for you to check.

Exercise 9H

1   Find the least value of each of the following functions:

 a $f(x) = x^2 - 12x + 8$ b $f(x) = x^2 - 8x - 1$ c $f(x) = 5x^2 + 2x$

2   Find the greatest value of each of the following functions:

 a $f(x) = 10 - 5x^2$ b $f(x) = 3 + 2x - x^2$ c $f(x) = (6 + x)(1 - x)$

3 Find the coordinates of the points where the gradient is zero on the curves with the given equations. Establish whether these points are maximum points or minimum points, by considering the second derivative in each case.

a $y = 4x^2 + 6x$

b $y = 9 + x - x^2$

c $y = x^3 - x^2 - x + 1$

d $y = x(x^2 - 4x - 3)$

e $y = x + \dfrac{1}{x}$

f $y = x^2 + \dfrac{54}{x}$

4 The maximum point on the curve with equation $y = x\sqrt{\sin x}$, $0 < x < \pi$, is the point A. Show that the x-coordinate of point A satisfies the equation $2\tan x + x = 0$.

© Edexcel Limited

Hint:
Remember in questions **4** and **5** that x will be measured in radians.

5 $f(x) \equiv e^{2x}\sin 2x$, $0 \leqslant x \leqslant \pi$

a Use calculus to find the coordinates of the turning points on the graph of $y = f(x)$.

b Show that $f''(x) = 8e^{2x}\cos 2x$.

c Hence, or otherwise, determine which turning point is a maximum and which is a minimum.

© Edexcel Limited

9.9 *You can use integration to find areas and volumes..*

- **Area of region between $y = f(x)$, the x-axis and $x = a$ and $x = b$ is given by:**

$$\text{Area} = \int_a^b y \, dx$$

This area can be thought of as a limit of a sum of approximate rectangular strips of width δx and length y.

Hint:
Since the strip is roughly rectangular the area is approximately y δ x.

Thus the area is the limit of $\sum y\delta x$ as $\delta x \to 0$. The integration symbol $\int$ is an elongated 'S' to represent this idea of a sum.

If each strip is now revolved through 2π radians (or 360 degrees) about the x-axis, it will form a shape that is approximately cylindrical. The volume of each cylinder will be $\pi y^2 \delta x$ since the radius is y and the height is δx.

The limit of the sum $\sum \pi y^2 \delta x$, as $\delta x \to 0$, is given by $\pi \int y^2 \, dx$ and this formula can be used to find the volume of the solid formed when the region R is rotated through 2π radians about the x-axis.

- **Volume of revolution formed when $y = f(x)$ is rotated about the x-axis between $x = a$ and $x = b$ is given by:**

$$\text{Volume} = \pi \int_a^b y^2 \, dx$$

Example 16

Find the area of the region R bounded by the curve with equation $y = (4 - x)(x + 2)$ and the positive x- and y-axes.

When $x = 0$, $y = 8$

When $y = 0$, $x = 4$ or -2

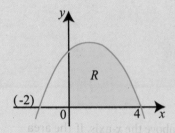

A sketch of the curve will often help in this type of question.

The area of R is given by

$$A = \int_0^4 (4 - x)(x + 2)\, dx$$

Multiply out the brackets.

So $A = \int_0^4 (8 + 2x - x^2)\, dx$

$$A = \left[8x + x^2 - \frac{x^3}{3} \right]_0^4$$

Integrate.

$$A = \left(32 + 16 - \frac{64}{3} \right) - (0)$$

Use limits of 4 and 0.

So the area is $26\frac{2}{3}$

Example 17

The region R is bounded by the curve with equation $y = \sin 2x$, the x-axis and the lines $x = 0$ and $x = \frac{\pi}{2}$.

a   Find the area of R.

b   Find the volume of the solid formed when the region R is rotated through 2π radians about the x-axis.

a   Area $= \int_0^{\frac{\pi}{2}} \sin 2x\, dx$

$$= \left[-\tfrac{1}{2} \cos 2x \right]_0^{\frac{\pi}{2}}$$

$$= \left(-\tfrac{1}{2}(-1) \right) - \left(-\tfrac{1}{2} \right)$$

$$= 1$$

b   Volume $= \pi \int_0^{\frac{\pi}{2}} \sin^2 2x \, dx$ Use $\cos 2A = 1 - 2\sin^2 A$.
                                                                Rearrange to give $\sin^2 A = \ldots$

$= \pi \int_0^{\frac{\pi}{2}} \frac{1}{2}(1 - \cos 4x) \, dx$ Note that $2 \times 2x$ gives $4x$ in the cos term.

$= \pi \left[\frac{1}{2}x - \frac{1}{8}\sin 4x \right]_0^{\frac{\pi}{2}}$ Multiply out and integrate.

$= \left(\frac{\pi^2}{4} - 0 \right) - (0)$

$= \frac{\pi^2}{4}$

In the examples so far the area that you were calculating was above the x-axis. If the area between a curve and the x-axis lies below the x-axis, then $\int y \, dx$ will give a negative answer.

Example 18

Find the area of the finite region bounded by the curve $y = x(x - 3)$ and the x-axis.

When $x = 0$, $y = 0$
When $y = 0$, $x = 0$ or 3

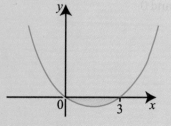

First sketch the curve.
It is U-shaped. It crosses the x-axis at 0 and 3.

Area $= \int_0^3 x(x - 3) \, dx$ The limits on the integral will therefore be 0 and 3.

$= \int_0^3 x(x^2 - 3x) \, dx$ Multiply out the bracket.

$= \left[\frac{x^3}{3} - \frac{3x^2}{2} \right]_0^3$ Integrate as usual.

$= \left(\frac{27}{3} - \frac{27}{2} \right) - (0)$

$= -\frac{27}{6}$ or $-\frac{9}{2}$ or -4.5

So the area is 4.5   State the area as a positive quantity.

The following example shows that great care must be taken if you are trying to find an area which straddles the x-axis such as the shaded region below, bounded by the curve with equation $y = (x + 1)(x - 1)x = x^3 - x$.

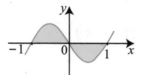

Notice that:

$$\int_{-1}^{1}(x^3 - x)\,dx = \left[\frac{x^4}{4} - \frac{x^2}{2}\right]_{-1}^{1}$$

$$= \left(\frac{1}{4} - \frac{1}{2}\right) - \left(\frac{1}{4} - \frac{1}{2}\right)$$

$$= 0$$

This is because:

$$\int_{0}^{1}(x^3 - x)\,dx = \left[\frac{x^4}{4} - \frac{x^2}{2}\right]_{0}^{1}$$

$$= \left(\frac{1}{4} - \frac{1}{2}\right) - (0) = -\frac{1}{4}$$

and $$\int_{-1}^{0}(x^3 - x)\,dx = \left[\frac{x^4}{4} - \frac{x^2}{2}\right]_{-1}^{0}$$

$$= -\left(\frac{1}{4} - \frac{1}{2}\right) = \frac{1}{4}$$

So the area of the shaded region is actually $\frac{1}{4} + \frac{1}{4} = \frac{1}{2}$.

For examples of this type you need to draw a sketch, unless one is given in the question.

Example 19

Sketch the curve with equation $y = x(x - 1)(x + 3)$ and find the area of the finite region bounded by the curve and the x-axis.

When $x = 0, y = 0$ ⎤ Find out where the curve intercepts
When $y = 0, x = 0, 1$ or -3 ⎦ the axes.

$x \to \infty, y \to \infty$ ⎤ Find out what happens to y when x is large
$x \to -\infty, y \to -\infty$ ⎦ and positive or large and negative.

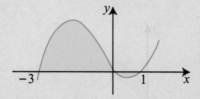

Since the area between $x = 0$ and 1 is below the axis, the integral between these points will give a negative answer.

The area is given by $\int_{-3}^{0} y\,dx + -\int_{0}^{1} y\,dx$

Now $\int y\, dx = \int (x^3 + 2x^2 - 3x)\, dx$ Multiply out the brackets.

$$= \left[\frac{x^4}{4} + \frac{2x^3}{3} - \frac{3x^2}{2} \right]$$

So $\displaystyle\int_{-3}^{0} y\, dx = (0) - \left(\frac{81}{4} - \frac{2}{3} \times 27 - \frac{3}{2} \times 9 \right)$

$$= 11.25$$

and $\displaystyle\int_{0}^{1} y\, dx = \left(\frac{1}{4} + \frac{2}{3} - \frac{3}{2} \right) - (0)$

$$= -\frac{7}{12}$$

So the area required is $11.25 + \dfrac{7}{12} = 11\dfrac{5}{6}$

Sometimes you may wish to find an area between a curve and a line. (The method also applie
to finding the area between two curves.)

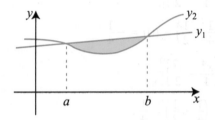

You find the area of the shaded region by calculating $\displaystyle\int_{a}^{b} (y_1 - y_2)\, dx$. This is because $\displaystyle\int_{a}^{b} y_1\, dx$

gives the area below the line (or curve) with equation y_1, and $\displaystyle\int_{a}^{b} y_2\, dx$ gives the area below y_2

So the shaded region is simply $\displaystyle\int_{a}^{b} y_1\, dx - \int_{a}^{b} y_2\, dx = \int_{a}^{b} (y_1 - y_2)\, dx$.

- **The area between a line (equation y_1) and a curve (equation y_2) is given by**

$$\text{Area} = \int_{a}^{b} (y_1 - y_2)\, dx$$

Example 20

The diagram shows a sketch of part of the curve with equation $y = x(4 - x)$ and the line
with equation $y = x$.

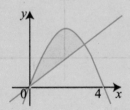

Find the area of the region bounded by the curve and the line.

Method 1

$$x = x(4 - x)$$
$$x = 4x - x^2$$
$$x^2 - 3x = 0$$
$$x(x - 3) = 0$$

So $x = 0$ or 3

First find where the line and the curve cross.

Find y-coordinates by substituting back in one of the equations. The line $y = x$ is the simplest.

So the line cuts the curve at
$(0, 0)$ and $(3, 3)$

The area is given by $\int_0^3 [x(4 - x) - x]\,dx$

Use the formula with 'curve − line' since the curve is above the line.

$$\text{Area} = \int_0^3 (3x - x^2)\,dx$$

Simplify the expression to be integrated.

$$= \left[\frac{3}{2}x^2 - \frac{x^3}{3}\right]_0^3$$

$$= \left(\frac{27}{2} - 9\right) - (0) = 4.5$$

Method 2

Area beneath curve   minus   Area of triangle

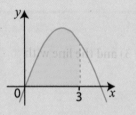   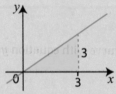

You should notice that you could have found this area by first finding the area beneath the curve between $x = 0$ and $x = 3$, and then subtracting the area of a triangle.

$$\int_0^3 (4x - x^2)\,dx \qquad - \qquad \frac{1}{2} \times 3 \times 3$$

$$= \left[2x^2 - \frac{x^3}{3}\right]_0^3 \qquad - \qquad 4.5$$

$$= \left(18 - \frac{27}{3}\right) - (0) \qquad - \qquad 4.5$$

$$= 9 - 4.5$$

$$= 4.5$$

The $\int_a^b (y_1 - y_2)\,dx$ formula can be applied even if part of the region is below the x-axis.

Consider the following:

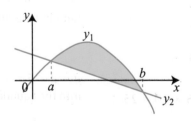

If both the curve and the line are translated upwards by $+k$, where k is sufficiently large to ensure that the required area is totally above the x-axis, the diagram will look like this:

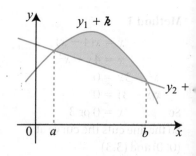

You should notice that since the translation is in the y-direction only, then the x-coordinates of the points of intersection are unchanged and so the limits of the integral will remain the same.

So the area in this case is given by $\int_a^b [y_1 + k - (y_2 + k)]\,dx$

$$= \int_a^b (y_1 - y_2)\,dx$$

Notice that the value of k does not appear in the final formula so you can always use this approach for questions of this type.

Sometimes you will need to add or subtract an area found by integration to the area of a triangle, trapezium or other similar shape as the following example shows.

Example 21

The diagram shows a sketch of the curve with equation $y = x(x - 3)$ and the line with equation $y = 2x$.

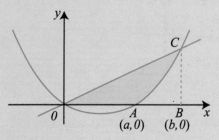

Find the area of the shaded region OAC.
The required area is given by:

$$\text{Area of triangle } OBC - \int_a^b x(x - 3)\,dx$$

The curve cuts the x-axis at $x = 3$
(and $x = 0$) so $a = 3$
The curve meets the line $y = 2x$ when

$2x = x(x - 3)$	Line = curve.
So $\quad 0 = x^2 - 5x$	Simplify the equation.
$0 = x(x - 5)$	
$x = 0$ or 5, so $b = 5$	

The point C is $(5, 10)$ $\qquad\qquad\qquad\qquad$ $y = 2 \times 5 = 10$, substituting $x = 5$
Area of triangle $OBC = \frac{1}{2} \times 5 \times 10 = 25$ $\qquad$ into the equation of the line.

Area between curve, x-axis and the line $x = 5$ is

$$\int_3^5 x(x - 3)\,dx = \int_3^5 (x^2 - 3x)\,dx$$

$$= \left[\frac{x^3}{3} - \frac{3x^2}{2}\right]_3^5$$

$$= \left(\frac{125}{3} - \frac{75}{2}\right) - \left(\frac{27}{3} - \frac{27}{2}\right)$$

$$= \left(\frac{25}{6}\right) - \left(-\frac{27}{6}\right)$$

$$= \frac{52}{6} \text{ or } \frac{26}{3}$$

Shaded region is therefore $= 25 - \frac{26}{3} = \frac{49}{3}$ or $16\frac{1}{3}$

Exercise 9I

Sketch the following and find the area of the finite region or regions bounded by the curves and the x-axis.

1   $y = x(x + 2)$ 2 $y = (x + 1)(x - 4)$

3   $y = (x + 3)x(x - 3)$ 4 $y = x^2(x - 2)$

5   $y = x(x - 2)(x - 5)$

6   Find the area between the curve with equation $y = f(x)$, the x-axis and the lines $x = a$ and $x = b$ in each of the following cases:

   a $f(x) = 3x^2 - 2x + 2$; $a = 0, b = 2$

   b $f(x) = x^3 + 4x$; $a = 1, b = 2$

   c $f(x) = \sqrt{x} + 2x$; $a = 1, b = 4$

   d $f(x) = 7 + 2x - x^2$; $a = -1, b = 2$

   e $f(x) = \frac{8}{x^3} + \sqrt{x}$; $a = 1, b = 4$

7   The diagram shows part of the curve with equation $y = x^2 + 2$ and the line with equation $y = 6$. The line cuts the curve at the points A and B.

   a   Find the coordinates of the points A and B.

   b   Find the area of the finite region bounded by AB and the curve.

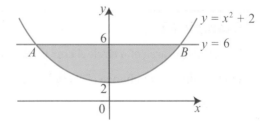

8   The diagram shows the finite region, R, bounded by the curve with equation $y = 4x - x^2$ and the line $y = 3$. The line cuts the curve at the points A and B.

   a   Find the coordinates of the points A and B.

   b   Find the area of R.

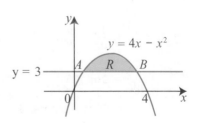

9 The diagram shows a sketch of part of the curve with equation $y = 9 - 3x - 5x^2 - x^3$ and the line with equation $y = 4 - 4x$. The line cuts the curve at the points $A(-1, 8)$ and $B(1, 0)$.
Find the area of the shaded region between AB and the curve.

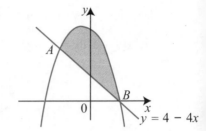

10 The diagram shows the finite region, R, bounded by the curve with equation $y = x(4 + x)$, the line with equation $y = 12$ and the y-axis.
   a Find the coordinate of the point A where the line meets the curve.
   b Find the area of R.

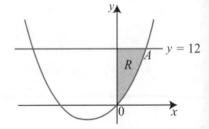

11 The diagram shows part of a sketch of the curve with equation $y = \dfrac{2}{x^2} + x$.
The points A and B have x-coordinates $\frac{1}{2}$ and 2 respectively. Find the area of the finite region between AB and the curve.

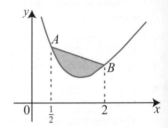

9.10 *You can relate one rate of change to another.*

You can use the chain rule once, or several times, to connect the rates of change in a question involving more than two variables.

Example 22

Given that the area of a circle A cm^2 is related to its radius r cm by the formula $A = \pi r^2$, and that the rate of change of its radius in cm s^{-1} is given by $\dfrac{dr}{dt} = 5$, find $\dfrac{dA}{dt}$ when $r = 3$.

$A = \pi r^2$

$\therefore \quad \dfrac{dA}{dr} = 2\pi r$ As A is a function of r, find $\dfrac{dA}{dr}$.

Using $\dfrac{dA}{dt} = \dfrac{dA}{dr} \times \dfrac{dr}{dt}$ You should use the chain rule, giving the derivative which you need to find in terms of known derivatives.

$\dfrac{dA}{dt} = 2\pi r \times 5$

$= 30\pi$, when $r = 3$.

Example 23

The volume of a hemisphere V cm^3 is related to its radius r cm by the formula $V = \frac{2}{3}\pi r^3$ and the total surface area S cm^2 is given by the formula $S = \pi r^2 + 2\pi r^2 = 3\pi r^2$. Given that the rate of increase of volume (in cm^3 s^{-1}) $\frac{dV}{dt} = 6$, find the rate of increase of surface area $\frac{dS}{dt}$.

$V = \frac{2}{3}\pi r^3$ and $S = 3\pi r^2$ ————— This is area of circular base plus area of curved surface.

$\frac{dV}{dr} = 2\pi r^2$ and $\frac{dS}{dr} = 6\pi r$ ————— As V and S are functions of r, find $\frac{dV}{dr}$ and $\frac{dS}{dr}$.

Now $\frac{dS}{dt} = \frac{dS}{dr} \times \frac{dr}{dV} \times \frac{dV}{dt}$

$\qquad = 6\pi r \times \dfrac{1}{2\pi r^2} \times 6$ ————— Use an extended chain rule together with the property that $\frac{dr}{dV} = 1 \div \frac{dV}{dr}$.

$\qquad = \dfrac{18}{r}$

- **You can use the following formula for finding approximations**

$$\delta y \approx \frac{dy}{dx} \times \delta x$$

This formula shows an approximate relationship between a small change in the variable x (δx) and the equivalent small change in the variable y (δy).

Example 24

Given $y = 4x^3$ find the approximate percentage change in y for a 1% change in x

$\dfrac{dy}{dx} = 12x^2$ \qquad\qquad First find $\frac{dy}{dx}$.

So \quad $\delta y \approx 12x^2 \times \dfrac{x}{100}$ \qquad δx is 1% of $x = \dfrac{x}{100}$.

$\delta y \approx \dfrac{12x^3}{100}$

The percentage change in y will be $\dfrac{\delta y}{y} \times 100$ \qquad Using the usual definition of percentage change.

Percentage change $= \dfrac{12x^3}{4x^3 \times 100} \times 100$

$\qquad\qquad = 3\%$

Exercise 9J

1   Given that $V = \frac{1}{3}\pi r^3$ and that $\frac{dV}{dt} = 8$, find $\frac{dr}{dt}$ when $r = 3$.

2   Given that $A = \frac{1}{4}\pi r^2$ and that $\frac{dr}{dt} = 6$, find $\frac{dA}{dt}$ when $r = 2$.

3 Given that $y = xe^x$ and that $\dfrac{dx}{dt} = 5$, find $\dfrac{dy}{dt}$ when $x = 2$.

4 If $y = 5x^4$, find the approximate percentage change in y due to a change of 0.5% in the value of x.

5 If $y = 3x^2$, find the approximate percentage change in y for a 1% change in x.

6 If the radius of a spherical bubble increases from 1 cm to 1.02 cm, find (to 2 significant figures) the approximate increase in the volume of the bubble.

9.11 *You need to be able to apply what you have learned about turning points to solve problems.*

Example 25

The diagram shows a minor sector OMN of a circle with centre O and radius r cm. The perimeter of the sector is 100 cm and the area of the sector is A cm^2.

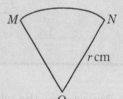

a Show that $A = 50r - r^2$.

Given that r varies, find:

b The value of r for which A is a maximum and show that A is a maximum.

c The value of $\angle MON$ for this maximum area.

d The maximum area of the sector OMN.

a Let the perimeter of the sector be P, so

$$P = 2r + r\theta$$ ———— This is the sum of two radii ($2r$) and an arc length MN ($r\theta$)

Rearrange and substitute $P = 100$ to give

$$\theta = \frac{100 - 2r}{r} \qquad ①$$

The area of the sector, $A = \frac{1}{2}r^2\theta \qquad ②$

Substitute ① in ② ———— The area formula is in terms of two variables r and θ, so you need to substitute for θ so that the formula is in terms of one variable r.

$$A = \frac{1}{2}r^2\left(\frac{100 - 2r}{r}\right)$$

So $A = 50r - r^2$

b $\dfrac{dA}{dr} = 50 - 2r$

When $\dfrac{dA}{dr} = 0$, $r = 25$ ———— Use the method which you learned to find stationary values: put the first derivative equal to zero, then check the sign of the second derivative.

Also $\dfrac{d^2A}{dr^2} = -2$, which is negative

So the area is a maximum when $r = 25$.

c Substitute $r = 25$ into

$$\theta = \frac{100 - 50}{25} = 2$$

So angle $MON = 2$ radians

d The maximum value of the area is

$50 \times 25 - 25^2 = 625 \, \text{cm}^2$ ——— Use $A = 50r - r^2$.

① Answer the final two parts of the question by using the appropriate equations and give the units in your answer.

Example 26

A large tank in the shape of a cuboid is to be made from $54 \, \text{m}^2$ of sheet metal. The tank has a horizontal base and no top. The height of the tank is x metres. Two of the opposite vertical faces are squares.

a Show that the volume, $V \, \text{m}^3$, of the tank is given by $V = 18x - \frac{2}{3}x^3$.

b Given that x can vary, use differentiation to find the maximum or minimum value of V.

c Justify that the value of V you have found is a maximum.

a Let the length of the tank be y metres.

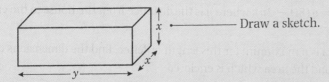 ——— Draw a sketch.

Total area, $\quad A = 2x^2 + 3xy$

So $\qquad 54 = 2x^2 + 3xy$

$$y = \frac{54 - 2x^2}{3x}$$ ——— Rearrange to find y in terms of x.

But $\qquad V = x^2 y$

So $\qquad V = x^2\left(\dfrac{54 - 2x^2}{3x}\right)$ ——— Substitute into the equation the expression for y.

$$= \frac{x}{3}(54 - 2x^2)$$

So $\qquad V = 18x - \frac{2}{3}x^3$ ——— Simplify.

b So $\quad \dfrac{dV}{dx} = 18 - 2x^2$

Put $\dfrac{dV}{dx} = 0$

Differentiate V with respect to x and put $\dfrac{dV}{dx} = 0$

$0 = 18 - 2x^2$

So $\quad x^2 = 9$

$x = -3$ or 3

Rearrange to find x.

But x is a length so $x = 3$

When $x = 3$, $V = 18 \times 3 - \frac{2}{3} \times 3^3$ —— Substitute value of x into expression for V.

$$= 54 - 18$$
$$= 36$$

$V = 36$ is a maximum or minimum value of V.

c $\dfrac{\mathrm{d}^2V}{\mathrm{d}x^2} = -4x$ —————— Find the second derivative of V.

When $x = 3$, $\dfrac{\mathrm{d}^2V}{\mathrm{d}x^2} = -4 \times 3 = -12$

This is negative, so $V = 36$ is the maximum value of V.

Exercise 9K

1 A rectangular garden is fenced on three sides, and the house forms the fourth side of the rectangle.

Given that the total length of the fence is 80 m show that the area, A, of the garden is given by the formula $A = y(80 - 2y)$, where y is the distance from the house to the end of the garden.

Given that the area is a maximum for this length of fence, find the dimensions of the enclosed garden, and the area which is enclosed.

2 A closed cylinder has total surface area equal to 600π. Show that the volume, $V\,\mathrm{cm}^3$, of this cylinder is given by the formula $V = 300\pi r - \pi r^3$, where $r\,\mathrm{cm}$ is the radius of the cylinder. Find the maximum volume of such a cylinder.

3 A sector of a circle has area $100\,\mathrm{cm}^2$. Show that the perimeter of this sector is given by the formula $P = 2r + \dfrac{200}{r}, r > \sqrt{\dfrac{100}{\pi}}$.

Find the minimum value for the perimeter of such a sector.

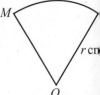

4 A shape consists of a rectangular base with a semicircular top, as shown. Given that the perimeter of the shape is 40 cm, show that its area, $A\,\mathrm{cm}^2$, is given by the formula

$$A = 40r - 2r^2 - \frac{\pi r^2}{2}$$

where $r\,\mathrm{cm}$ is the radius of the semicircle. Find the maximum value for this area.

The shape shown is a wire frame in the form of a large rectangle split by parallel lengths of wire into 12 smaller equal-sized rectangles.

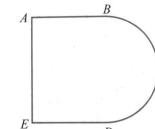

Given that the total length of wire used to complete the whole frame is 1512 mm, show that the area of the whole shape is A mm^2, where $A = 1296x - \dfrac{108x^2}{7}$, where x mm is the width

of one of the smaller rectangles.
Find the maximum area which can be enclosed in this way.

Mixed Exercise 9L

1 Given that: $y = x^{\frac{3}{2}} + \dfrac{48}{x} \; (x > 0)$

   a Find the value of x and the value of y when $\dfrac{dy}{dx} = 0$.

   b Show that the value of y which you found in **a** is a minimum. © Edexcel Limited

2 A curve has equation $y = x^3 - 5x^2 + 7x - 14$. Determine, by calculation, the
   coordinates of the stationary points of the curve C. © Edexcel Limited

3 The function f, defined for $x \in R, x > 0$, is such that:

   $$f'(x) = x^2 - 2 + \frac{1}{x^2}$$

   a Find the value of $f''(x)$ at $x = 4$.
   b Given that $f(3) = 0$, find $f(x)$.
   c Prove that f is an increasing function. © Edexcel Limited

4 A curve has equation $y = x^3 - 6x^2 + 9x$.
   Find the coordinates of its maximum turning point. © Edexcel Limited

5 A wire is bent into the plane shape $ABCDEA$ as shown.
   Shape $ABDE$ is a rectangle and BCD is a semicircle with
   diameter BD. The area of the region enclosed by the wire
   is R m^2, $AE = x$ metres. $AB = ED = y$ metres. The total
   length of the wire is 2 m.
   a Find an expression for y in terms of x.
   b Prove that $R = \dfrac{x}{8}(8 - 4x - \pi x)$
   c Given that x can vary, using calculus and showing
      your working, find the maximum value of R.
      (You do not have to prove that the value you obtain is a maximum.) © Edexcel Limited

6 A cylindrical biscuit tin has a close-fitting lid which overlaps the tin by 1 cm, as shown. The radii of the tin and the lid are both x cm. The tin and the lid are made from a thin sheet of metal of area 80π cm^2 and there is no wastage. The volume of the tin is V cm^3.

    a Show that $V = \pi(40x - x^2 - x^3)$.

Given that x can vary:

    b use differentiation to find the positive value of x for which V is stationary.

    c Prove that this value of x gives a maximum value of V.

    d Find this maximum value of V.

    e Determine the percentage of the sheet metal used in the lid when V is a maximum.

© Edexcel Limited

7 The diagram shows part of the curve with equation $y = f(x)$, where:

$$f(x) \equiv 200 - \frac{250}{x} - x^2, \ x > 0$$

The curve cuts the x-axis at the points A and C.
The point B is the maximum point of the curve.

    a Find $f'(x)$.

    b Use your answer to part **a** to calculate the coordinates of B.

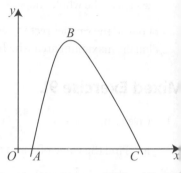

© Edexcel Limited

8 The diagram shows the part of the curve with equation $y = 5 - \frac{1}{2}x^2$ for which $y \geq 0$.
The point $P(x, y)$ lies on the curve and O is the origin.

    a Show that $OP^2 = \frac{1}{4}x^4 - 4x^2 + 25$.

Taking $f(x) \equiv \frac{1}{4}x^4 - 4x^2 + 25$:

    b find the values of x for which $f'(x) = 0$.

    c Hence, or otherwise, find the minimum distance from O to the curve, showing that your answer is a minimum.

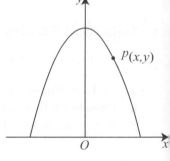

© Edexcel Limited

9 The diagram shows part of the curve with equation $y = 3 + 5x + x^2 - x^3$.
The curve touches the x-axis at A and crosses the x-axis at C.
The points A and B are stationary points on the curve.

    a Show that C has coordinates $(3, 0)$.

    b Using calculus and showing all your working, find the coordinates of A and B.

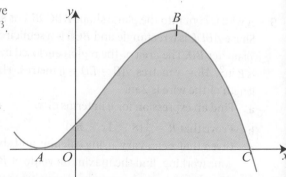

10 Differentiate with respect to x: $x^2 \sin 3x$

11 Given that $2y = x - \sin x \cos x$, show that $\dfrac{dy}{dx} = \sin^2 x$.

12 Differentiate, with respect to x, $\dfrac{\sin x}{x}$, $x > 0$.

13 Differentiate $e^{2x} \cos x$ with respect to x.
The curve **C** has equation $y = e^{2x} \cos x$.
  a Show that the turning points on **C** occur when $\tan x = 2$.
  b Find an equation of the tangent to **C** at the point where $x = 0$.

14

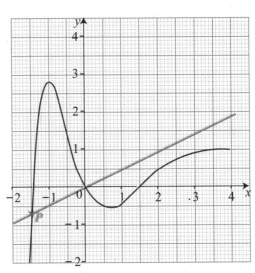

The figure shows part of the curve **C** with equation $y = f(x)$, where $f(x) = (x^3 - 2x)e^{-x}$
  a Find $f'(x)$.
The normal to **C** at the origin O intersects **C** at a point **P**, as shown in the figure.
  b Show that the x-coordinate of **P** is the solution of the equation
$$2x^2 = e^x + 4.$$

15 The diagram shows the finite shaded region
bounded by the curve with equation
$y = x^2 + 3$, the lines $x = 1$, $x = 0$ and the x-axis.
This region is rotated through $360°$ about the x-axis.

Find the volume generated.

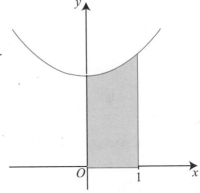

1 Differentiation

You should know, and be able to use, the following standard formulae.

function	derivative
x^n	nx^{n-1}
$\sin ax$	$a\cos ax$
$\cos ax$	$-a\sin ax$
e^{ax}	ae^{ax}
$f(x)g(x)$	$f'(x)g(x) + f(x)g'(x)$
$\dfrac{f(x)}{g(x)}$	$\dfrac{f'(x)g(x) - f(x)g'(x)}{(g(x))^2}$
$f(g(x))$	$f'(g(x))g'(x)$

2 Integration

You should know, and be able to use, the following standard formulae.

function	integral
x^n	$\dfrac{1}{n+1}x^{n+1} + c \quad n \neq -1$
$\sin ax$	$-\dfrac{1}{a}\cos ax + c$
$\cos ax$	$\dfrac{1}{a}\sin ax + c$
e^{ax}	$\dfrac{1}{a}e^{ax} + c$

3 Areas and volumes

Area between a curve and x-axis $= \displaystyle\int_a^b y\,dx,\ y \geqslant 0$

Area between a curve and y-axis $= \displaystyle\int_c^d x\,dy,\ x \geqslant 0$

Volume of revolution (360° about x-axis) $= \pi\displaystyle\int_a^b y^2\,dx$

Volume of revolution (360° about y-axis) $= \pi\displaystyle\int_c^d x^2\,dy$

4 A turning point is a point where $\dfrac{dy}{dx} = 0$

If $\dfrac{dy}{dx} = 0$ and $\dfrac{d^2y}{dx^2} > 0$ then the point is a **minimum**.

If $\dfrac{dy}{dx} = 0$ and $\dfrac{d^2y}{dx^2} < 0$ then the point is a **maximum**.

10.1 You can measure angles in radians.

In your previous IGCSE you worked with angles in degrees, where one degree is $\frac{1}{360}$th of a complete revolution. This convention dates back to the Babylonians. It has the advantage that 360 has a great number of factors making division of the circle that much easier, but it is only a convention. Another, and perhaps initially stranger, measure of an angle is the radian.

- **If the arc AB has length r, then $\angle AOB$ is 1 radian (1^c or 1 rad).**

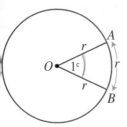

Hint:
The symbol for radians is ^{c}, so $\emptyset^c$ means that $\emptyset$ is in radians. If there is no symbol with an angle you should assume that it is in radians, unless the context makes it clear that it is in degrees.

You can put this into words.

- **A radian is the angle subtended at the centre of a circle by an arc whose length is equal to that of the radius of the circle.**

As an arc of length r subtends 1 radian at the centre of the circle, it follows that the circumference (an arc of length $2\pi r$) subtends 2π radians at the centre.

As the circumference subtends an angle of $360°$ at the centre.

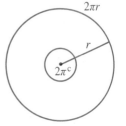

2π radians $= 360°$
so π radians $= 180°$

It follows that 1 rad $= 57.295\ldots°$.

- **1 radian $= \dfrac{180°}{\pi}$ or $180° = \pi$ radians**

Example 1

Convert the following angles into degrees:

a $\dfrac{7\pi}{8}$ rad   **b** $\dfrac{4\pi}{15}$ rad

a $\dfrac{7\pi}{8}$ rad   **b** $\dfrac{4\pi}{15}$ rad

$= \dfrac{7}{8} \times 180°$ $= 4 \times \dfrac{180°}{15}$ Remember that π rad $= 180°$.
Check using your calculator.

$= 157.5°$ $= 48°$

Caution:
If you have been working in radian mode on your calculator make sure you return to degree mode when working with questions involving degrees.

Example 2

Convert the following angles into radians:

a 150°   **b** 110°

a $150° = 150 \times \dfrac{\pi}{180}$ rad ———— Since $180° = \pi$ rad, $1° = \dfrac{\pi}{180}$ rad.

$= \dfrac{5\pi}{6}$ rad ———— It is worth remembering that $30° = \dfrac{\pi}{6}$ rad.

b $110° = 110 \times \dfrac{\pi}{180}$ rad

$= \dfrac{11}{18}\pi$ rad ———— Your calculator will give the decimal answer 1.919 86 ...
These answers, in terms of π, are exact.

Exercise 10A

1 Convert the following angles in radians to degrees:

a $\dfrac{\pi}{20}$ **b** $\dfrac{\pi}{15}$ **c** $\dfrac{5\pi}{12}$

d $\dfrac{\pi}{2}$ **e** $\dfrac{7\pi}{9}$ **f** $\dfrac{7\pi}{6}$

g $\dfrac{5\pi}{4}$ **h** $\dfrac{3\pi}{2}$ **i** 3π

2 Use your calculator to convert the following angles to degrees, giving your answer to the nearest 0.1°:

a 0.46^c **b** 1^c **c** 1.135^c **d** $\sqrt{3}^c$

e 2.5^c **f** 3.14^c **g** 3.49^c

3 Use your calculator to write down the value, to 3 significant figures, of the following trigonometric functions.

a $\sin 0.5^c$ **b** $\cos \sqrt{2}^c$ **c** $\tan 1.05^c$

d $\sin 2^c$ **e** $\cos 3.6^c$

4 Convert the following angles to radians, giving your answers as multiples of π:

a 8°   **b** 10°   **c** 22.5°   **d** 30°

e 45°   **f** 60°   **g** 75°   **h** 80°

i 112.5°   **j** 120°   **k** 135°   **l** 200°

m 240°   **n** 270°   **o** 315°   **p** 330°

5 Use your calculator to convert the following angles to radians, giving your answers to 3 significant figures:

a 50°   **b** 75°   **c** 100°

d 160°   **e** 230°   **f** 320°.

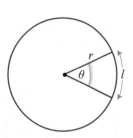

- To find the arc length l of a circle use the formula $l = r\theta$, where r is the radius of the circle and θ is the angle, in radians, contained by the sector.

Example 3

Show that the length of an arc is $l = r\theta$.

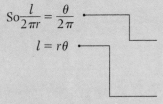

The circle has centre O and radius r.
The arc AB has length l.

So $\dfrac{l}{2\pi r} = \dfrac{\theta}{2\pi}$

$l = r\theta$

$\dfrac{\text{Length of arc}}{\text{Circumference}} = \dfrac{\text{angle } AOB}{\text{total angle around } O}$

(both angles are in radians).

Multiply throughout by $2\pi r$.
If you know two of r, θ and l, the third can be found.

Example 4

Find the length of the arc of a circle of radius 5.2 cm, given that the arc subtends an angle of 0.8 rad at the centre of the circle.

Arc length $= 5.2 \times 0.8$ cm   Use $l = r\theta$, with $r = 5.2$ and $\theta = 0.8$.

$\qquad\quad = 4.16$ cm

Example 5

An arc AB of a circle, with centre O and radius r cm, subtends an angle of θ radians at O. The perimeter of the sector AOB is P cm. Express r in terms of θ.

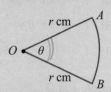

Draw a diagram to display the data.

$P = r\theta + 2r$

$\quad = r(2 + \theta)$

So $r = \dfrac{P}{(2 + \theta)}$

The perimeter $= $ arc $AB + OA + OB$, where arc $AB = r\theta$.

Factorising.

Example 6

The border of a garden pond consists a straight edge AB of length 2.4 m, and a curved part C, as shown in the diagram below. The curved part is an arc of a circle, centre O and radius 2 m. Find the length of C.

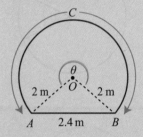

C subtends the reflex angle θ at O, so length of $C = 2\theta$.

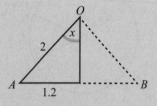

You can use the isosceles triangle AOB to find the angle AOB inside the triangle.
(*Use your calculator in radian mode.*)

$\sin x = \dfrac{1.2}{2}$

$x = 0.6435 \text{ rad}$

Acute $\angle AOB = 2x$ rad

$\qquad\qquad = 2(0.6435)$

$\qquad\qquad = 1.287 \text{ rad}$

So $\theta = (2\pi - 1.287) \text{ rad}$ $\qquad\qquad \theta + $ acute $\angle AOB = 2\pi$ rad.

$\qquad = 4.996 \text{ rad}$

So length of $C = 9.99 \text{ m}$ (3 s.f.) $\qquad\qquad C = 2\theta$

Exercise 10B

1   An arc AB of a circle, centre O and radius r cm, subtends an angle θ radians at O.
   The length of AB is l cm.

   a   Find l when   **i** $r = 6, \theta = 0.45$ **ii** $r = 4.5, \theta = 0.45$ **iii** $r = 20, \theta = \frac{3}{8}\pi$

   b   Find r when   **i** $l = 10, \theta = 0.6$ **ii** $l = 1.26, \theta = 0.7$ **iii** $l = 1.5\pi, \theta = \frac{5}{12}\pi$

   c   Find θ when   **i** $l = 10, r = 7.5$ **ii** $l = 4.5, r = 5.625$ **iii** $l = \sqrt{12}, r = \sqrt{3}$

2   A minor arc AB of a circle, centre O and radius 10 cm, subtends an angle x at O.
   The major arc AB subtends an angle $5x$ at O. Find, in terms of π, the length of the minor arc AB.

3   An arc AB of a circle, centre O and radius 6 cm, has length l cm. Given that the chord AB has length 6 cm, find the value of l, giving your answer in terms of π.

4 The sector of a circle of radius $\sqrt{10}$ cm contains an angle of $\sqrt{5}$ radians, as shown in the diagram. Find the length of the arc, giving your answer in the form $p\sqrt{q}$ cm, where p and q are integers.

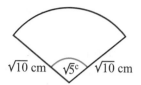

$\sqrt{10}$ cm $\quad \sqrt{5}^c \quad \sqrt{10}$ cm

5 Referring to the diagram, find:
    a The perimeter of the shaded region when $\theta = 0.8$ radians.
    b The value of θ when the perimeter of the shaded region is 14 cm.

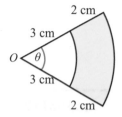

6 A sector of a circle of radius r cm contains an angle of 1.2 radians. Given that the sector has the same perimeter as a square of area $36\ \text{cm}^2$, find the value of r.

7 A sector of a circle of radius 15 cm contains an angle of θ radians. Given that the perimeter of the sector is 42 cm, find the value of θ.

8 In the diagram AB is the diameter of a circle, centre O and radius 2 cm. The point C is on the circumference such that $\angle COB = \frac{2}{3}\pi$ radians.

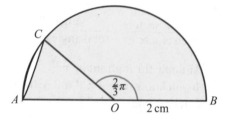

    a State the value, in radians, of $\angle COA$.

The shaded region enclosed by the chord AC, arc CB and AB is the template for a brooch.

    b Find the exact value of the perimeter of the brooch.

9 The points A and B lie on the circumference of a circle with centre O and radius 8.5 cm. The point C lies on the major arc AB. Given that $\angle ACB = 0.4$ radians, calculate the length of the minor arc AB.

0 In the diagram OAB is a sector of a circle, centre O and radius R cm, and $\angle AOB = 2\theta$ radians. A circle, centre C and radius r cm, touches the arc AB at T, and touches OA and OB at D and E respectively, as shown.

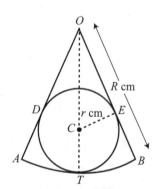

    a Write down, in terms of R and r, the length of OC.
    b Using $\triangle OCE$, show that $R \sin \theta = r(1 + \sin \theta)$.
    c Given that $\sin \theta = \frac{3}{4}$ and that the perimeter of the sector OAB is 21 cm, find r, giving your answer to 3 significant figures.

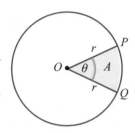

- **To find the area A of a sector of a circle use the formula $A = \frac{1}{2}r^2\theta$, where r is the radius of the circle and θ is the angle, in radians, contained by the sector.**

Example 7

Show that the area of the sector of a circle with radius r is $A = \frac{1}{2}r^2\theta$.

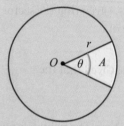

The circle has centre O and radius r.

The sector POQ has area A.

So $\dfrac{A}{\pi r^2} = \dfrac{\theta}{2\pi}$ $\dfrac{\text{area of sector}}{\text{area of circle}} = \dfrac{\text{angle } POQ}{\text{total angle around } O}$

$A = \frac{1}{2}r^2\theta$ Multiply throughout by πr^2.
If you know two of r, θ and A, the third can be found.

Example 8

In the diagram, the area of the minor sector AOB is 28.9 cm^2.
Given that $\angle AOB = 0.8$ radians, calculate the value of r.

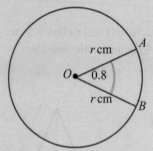

$28.9 = \frac{1}{2}r^2(0.8) = 0.4r^2$ Let area of sector be $A \text{ cm}^2$, and use $A = \frac{1}{2}r^2\theta$.

So $r^2 = \dfrac{28.9}{0.4} = 72.25$ Find r^2 and then take the square root.

$r = 8.5$

Example 9

A plot of land is in the shape of a sector of a circle of radius 55 m. The length of fencing that is erected along the edge of the plot to enclose the land is 176 m. Calculate the area of the plot of land.

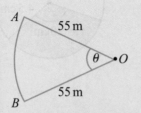

Draw a diagram to include all the data and let the angle of the sector be θ.

$$\text{Arc } AB = 176 - (55 + 55)$$
$$= 66 \text{ m}$$

As the perimeter is given, first find length of arc AB.

$$66 = 55\theta$$

Use the formula for arc length, $l = r\theta$.

So $\theta = 1.2$ radians

$$\text{Area of plot} = \tfrac{1}{2}(55)^2(1.2)$$

Use the formula for area of a sector, $A = \tfrac{1}{2}r^2\theta$.

$$= 1815 \text{ m}^2$$

Exercise 10C

(*Note:* give non-exact answers to 3 significant figures.)

1   Find the area of the shaded sector in each of the following circles with centre C.
    Leave your answer in terms of π, where appropriate.

a

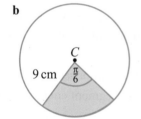

b

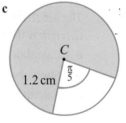

c

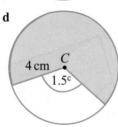

d

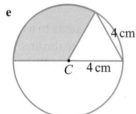

e

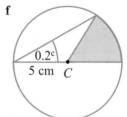

f

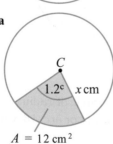

a

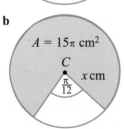

b

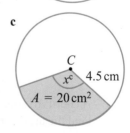

c

2 For the following circles with centre C, the area A of the shaded sector is given. Find the value of x in each case.

a

A circle with centre C. A sector marked 1.2^c with x cm and $A = 12$ cm².

b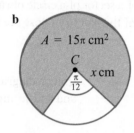

$A = 15\pi$ cm², centre C, sector angle $\frac{\pi}{12}$, x cm.

c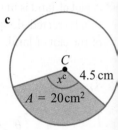

Circle with centre C, x^c, 4.5 cm, $A = 20$ cm².

3 The arc AB of a circle, centre O and radius 6 cm, has length 4 cm.
Find the area of the minor sector AOB.

4 The chord AB of a circle, centre O and radius 10 cm, has length 18.65 cm and subtends an angle of θ radians at O.
  a Show that $\theta = 2.40$ (to 3 significant figures).
  b Find the area of the minor sector AOB.

5 The area of a sector of a circle of radius 12 cm is 100 cm².
Find the perimeter of the sector.

6 The arc AB of a circle, centre O and radius r cm, is such that $\angle AOB = 0.5$ radians.
Given that the perimeter of the minor sector AOB is 30 cm:
  a Calculate the value of r.
  b Show that the area of the minor sector AOB is 36 cm².
  c Calculate the area of the segment enclosed by the chord AB and the minor arc AB.

7 In the diagram, AB and AC are tangents to a circle, centre O and radius 3.6 cm. Calculate the area of the shaded region, given that $\angle BOC = \frac{2}{3}\pi$ radians.

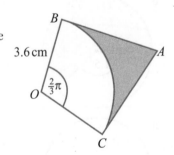

8 A chord AB subtends an angle of θ radians at the centre O of a circle of radius 6.5 cm.
Find the area of the segment enclosed by the chord AB and the minor arc AB, when:

  a $\theta = 0.8$ **b** $\theta = \frac{2}{3}\pi$ **c** $\theta = \frac{4}{3}\pi$

9 An arc AB subtends an angle of 0.25 radians at the *circumference* of a circle, centre O and radius 6 cm. Calculate the area of the minor sector OAB.

10 In the diagram, AD and BC are arcs of circles with centre O, such that $OA = OD = r$ cm, $AB = DC = 8$ cm and $\angle BOC = \theta$ radians.

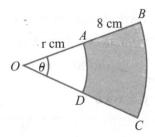

    a Given that the area of the shaded region is 48 cm^2, show that $r = \dfrac{6}{\theta} - 4$.

    b Given also that $r = 10\theta$, calculate the perimeter of the shaded region.

11 A sector of a circle of radius 28 cm has perimeter P cm and area A cm^2. Given that $A = 4P$, find the value of P.

12 The diagram shows a triangular plot of land. The sides AB, BC and CA have lengths 12 m, 14 m and 10 m respectively. The lawn is a sector of a circle, centre A and radius 6 m.

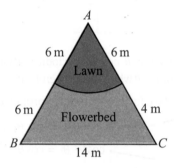

    a Show that $\angle BAC = 1.37$ radians, correct to 3 significant figures.

    b Calculate the area of the flowerbed.

10.4 *You can use sin x, cos x and tan x for angles of any magnitude.*

You should be familiar with the shapes of the graphs of the basic trigonometric functions and some of their properties.

$y = \sin \theta$

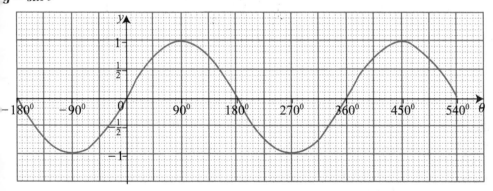

Functions that repeat themselves after a certain interval are called periodic functions, and the interval is called the period of the function. You can see that sin θ is periodic with a period of $360°$.

Hint:
The graph of sin θ, where θ is in radians, has period 2π.

There are many symmetry properties of sin θ but you can see from the graph that

Hint:
Because it is periodic.

$\sin(\theta + 360°) = \sin \theta$ and $\sin(\theta - 360°) = \sin \theta$

$\sin(90° - \theta) = \sin(90° + \theta)$

Hint:
Symmetry about $\theta = 90°$.

$y = \cos \theta$

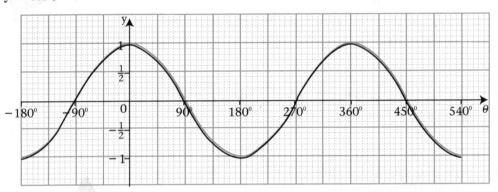

Like sin θ, cos θ is periodic with a period of $360°$. In fact, the graph of cos θ is the same as that of sin θ when it has been translated by $90°$ to the left.

Two further symmetry properties of cos θ are

Hint:
Because it is periodic.

$\cos(\theta + 360°) = \cos \theta$ and $\cos(\theta - 360°) = \cos \theta$

$\cos(-\theta) = \cos \theta$

Hint:
Symmetry about $\theta = 0°$.

$y = \tan \theta$

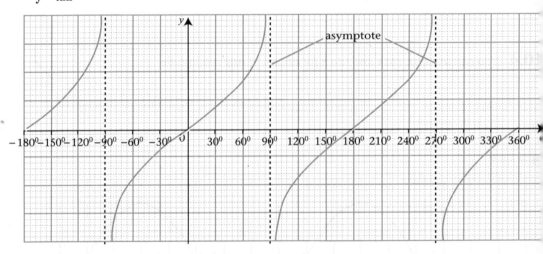

Hint:
The dotted lines on the graph are called asymptotes, lines to which the curve approaches but never reaches; these occur at $\theta = (2n + 1)90°$ where n is an integer.

This function behaves very differently from the sine and cosine functions but it is still periodic, it repeats itself in cycles of $180°$ so its period is $180°$.

The period symmetry properties of tan θ are

$\tan(\theta + 180°) = \tan \theta$
$\tan(\theta - 180°) = \tan \theta$

You can find the trigonometrical ratios of angles 30°, 45° and 60° exactly.

Consider an equilateral triangle ABC of side 2 units.

If you drop a perpendicular from A to meet BC at D, then $BD = DC = 1$ unit, $\angle BAD = 30°$ and $\angle ABD = 60°$.

Using Pythagoras' theorem in $\triangle ABD$

$$AD^2 = 2^2 - 1^2 = 3$$

So $AD = \sqrt{3}$ units

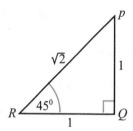

Using $\triangle ABD$, $\sin 30° = \dfrac{1}{2}$, $\cos 30° = \dfrac{\sqrt{3}}{2}$, $\tan 30° = \dfrac{1}{\sqrt{3}} = \dfrac{\sqrt{3}}{3}$,

and $\sin 60° = \dfrac{\sqrt{3}}{2}$, $\cos 60° = \dfrac{1}{2}$, $\tan 60° = \sqrt{3}$.

If you now consider an isosceles right-angled triangle PQR, in which $PQ = QR = 1$ unit, then the ratios for 45° can be found.

Using Pythagoras' theorem

$$PR^2 = 1^2 + 1^2 = 2$$

So $PR = \sqrt{2}$ units

Then $\sin 45° = \cos 45° = \dfrac{1}{\sqrt{2}} = \dfrac{\sqrt{2}}{2}$ and $\tan 45° = 1$

Example 10

Find the exact values of
a $\cos 405°$ **b** $\tan 120°$ **c** $\sin 300°$

a $\cos 405 = \cos(360 + 45)$ This can be seen from the graph, using the fact
            $= \cos(45)$ that $\cos x$ has a period of 360°.

            $= \dfrac{1}{\sqrt{2}}$ Using the above triangle PRQ.

b $\tan 120 = \tan(180 - 60)$ This can be seen from the graph, using the
            $= \tan(-60)$ fact that $\tan x$ has a period of 180°.

            $= -\tan(60)$

            $= -\sqrt{3}$ Using the above triangle ABD.

c $\sin 300 = \sin(360 - 60)$ See the graph, using the fact that the period
            $= \sin(-60)$ of $\sin x$ is 360°. Then use triangle ABD.

            $= -\sin(60)$

            $= -\dfrac{\sqrt{3}}{2}$

Exercise 10D

1 Express the following as trigonometric ratios of either 30°, 45° or 60°, and hence find their exact values.

    a $\sin 135°$ **b** $\sin(-60°)$ **c** $\sin 330°$

    d $\sin 420°$ **e** $\sin(-300°)$ **f** $\cos 120°$

    g $\cos 300°$ **h** $\cos 225°$ **i** $\cos(-210°)$

    j $\cos 495°$ **k** $\tan 135°$ **l** $\tan(-225°)$

    m $\tan 210°$ **n** $\tan 300°$ **o** $\tan(-120°)$

10.5   *You can use the sine and cosine rules.*

You should have met these rules in your previous IGCSE.

- **sine rule**   is $\dfrac{a}{\sin A} = \dfrac{b}{\sin B} = \dfrac{c}{\sin C}$

- **cosine rule**   is $a^2 = b^2 + c^2 - 2bc \cos A$

- **area of a triangle**   is $\frac{1}{2}ab \sin C$

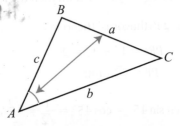

Hint:
Note that side a is opposite angle A.

Example 11

In $\triangle ABC$, $AB = 8$ cm, $\angle BAC = 30°$ and $\angle BCA = 40°$. Find BC.

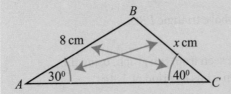

Always draw a diagram and carefully add the data. Here $c = 8$ (cm), $C = 40°$, $A = 30°$, $a = x$ (cm)

In a triangle, the larger an angle is, the larger the opposite side is. Here, as $C > A$, then $c > a$, so you know that $8 > x$.

$\dfrac{x}{\sin 30°} = \dfrac{8}{\sin 40°}$ Using the sine rule, $\dfrac{a}{\sin A} = \dfrac{c}{\sin C}$.

So $x = \dfrac{8 \sin 30°}{\sin 40°}$ Multiply throughout by $\sin 30°$.

     $= 6.22$ Give answer to 3 significant figures.

Example 12

In $\triangle ABC$, $AB = 4$ cm, $AC = 12$ cm and $\angle ABC = 64°$. Find $\angle ACB$.

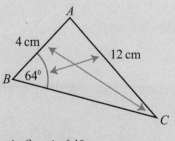

Here $b = 12$ cm, $c = 4$ cm, $B = 64°$.

$$\frac{\sin C}{4} = \frac{\sin 64°}{12}$$

As you need to find angle C, use the sine rule $\frac{\sin C}{c} = \frac{\sin B}{b}$.

So $\sin C = \frac{4 \sin 64°}{12}$

$C = 17.4°$

As $4 < 12$, you know that $C < 64°$.

$$C = \sin^{-1}\left(\frac{4 \sin 64°}{12}\right).$$

Sometimes the sine rule will lead to two possible values for an angle.

Example 13

In $\triangle ABC$, $AB = 4$ cm, $AC = 3$ cm and $\angle ABC = 44°$. Work out the two possible values of $\angle ACB$.

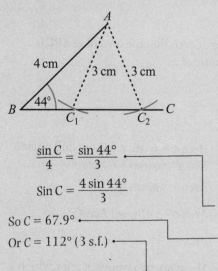

$$\frac{\sin C}{4} = \frac{\sin 44°}{3}$$

$$\text{Sin } C = \frac{4 \sin 44°}{3}$$

So $C = 67.9°$

Or $C = 112°$ (3 s.f.)

Here $\angle ACB > \angle ABC$, as $AB > AC$, and so there will be two possible results. The diagram shows why.

With $\angle ABC = 44°$ and $AB = 4$ cm drawn, imagine putting a pair of compasses at A, then drawing an arc with centre A and radius 3 cm. This will intersect BC at C_1 and C_2 showing that there are two triangles ABC_1 and ABC_2 where $b = 3$ cm, $c = 4$ cm and $B = 44°$.
(This would not happen if $AC > 4$ cm.)

Use $\frac{\sin C}{c} = \frac{\sin B}{b}$, where $b = 3$, $c = 4$, $B = 44°$.

This is the value your calculator will give to 3 s.f., which corresponds to $\triangle ABC_2$.

As $\sin(180 - x)° = \sin x°$, $C = 180 - 67.9°$ $= 112.1°$ is another possible answer. This corresponds to $\triangle ABC_1$.

You can rearrange the cosine rule formula to help you find an angle.

Rearrange the equation $a^2 = b^2 + c^2 - 2bc \cos A$ in the form $\cos A = \ldots$

$$a^2 = b^2 + c^2 - 2bc \cos A$$

So $\quad 2bc \cos A = b^2 + c^2 - a^2$

So $\qquad \cos A = \dfrac{b^2 + c^2 - a^2}{2bc}$ $\qquad$ Divide throughout by $2bc$.

Example 14

In $\triangle PQR$, $PQ = 5.9$ cm, $QR = 8.2$ cm and $PR = 10.6$ cm.
Calculate the size of $\angle PQR$.

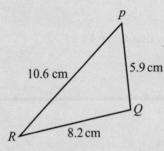

Here $p = 8.2$ cm, $r = 5.9$ cm, $q = 10.6$ cm, and you have to find angle Q.

$$\cos Q = \dfrac{8.2^2 + 5.9^2 - 10.6^2}{2 \times 8.2 \times 5.9}$$

Use the cosine rule $\cos Q = \dfrac{p^2 + r^2 - q^2}{2pr}$

$$= -0.1065\ldots$$

$$Q = 96.1°$$

$$Q = \cos^{-1}(-0.1065\ldots)$$

$$\angle PQR = 96.1°$$

Example 15

In $\triangle ABC$, $AB = 5$ cm, $BC = 6$ cm and $\angle ABC = x°$. Given that the area of $\triangle ABC$ is 12 cm^2 and that AC is the longest side, find the value of x.

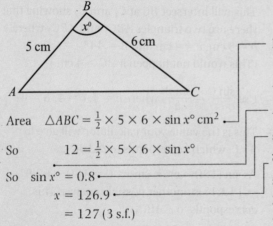

Here $a = 6$ cm, $c = 5$ cm and angle $B = x°$, so use:

Area $= \frac{1}{2}ac \sin B$.

Area $\triangle ABC = \frac{1}{2} \times 5 \times 6 \times \sin x°$ cm^2

Area of $\triangle ABC$ is 12 cm^2.

So $\qquad 12 = \frac{1}{2} \times 5 \times 6 \times \sin x°$

$\sin x° = \frac{12}{15}$.

So $\quad \sin x° = 0.8$

$$x = 126.9$$

$$= 127 \text{ (3 s.f.)}$$

There are two values of x for which $\sin x° = 0.8$, 53.1 and 126.9, but here you know B is the largest angle because AC is the largest side.

Exercise 10E

1 In each of the following triangles calculate the values of x and y.

a
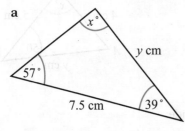

b
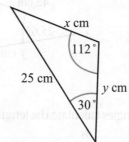

c
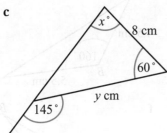

d
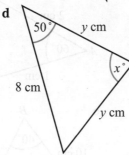

e
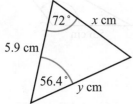

f
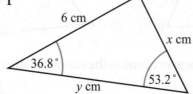

2 In each of the diagrams shown below, work out the value of x:

a
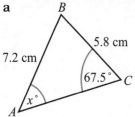

b
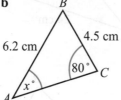

c
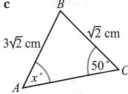

d
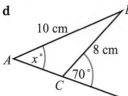

e
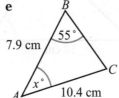

f
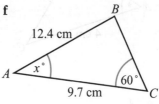

3 In each of the diagrams shown below, calculate the possible values of x and the corresponding values of y:

a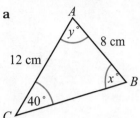

b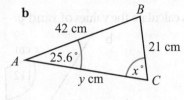

c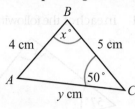

4 In each of the following triangles calculate the length of the third side:

a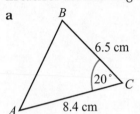

b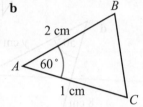

c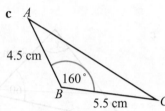

d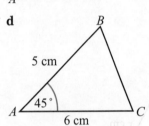

e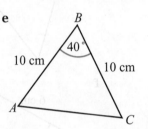

f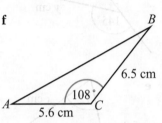

5 In the following triangles calculate the size of the angle marked *:

a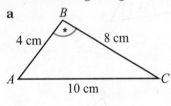

b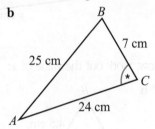

c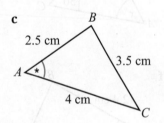

d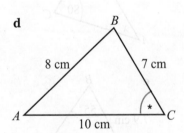

e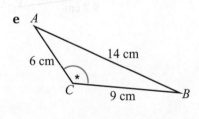

f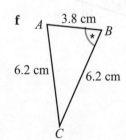

6 Calculate the area of the following triangles:

a

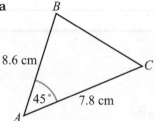

b

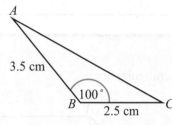

c

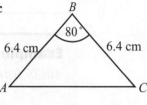

7 The area of a triangle is $10\,\text{cm}^2$. The angle between two of the sides, of length 6 cm and 8 cm respectively, is obtuse. Work out:
   a The size of this angle.
   b The length of the third side.

8 In each triangle below, find the value of x and the area of the triangle:

a

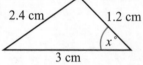

b

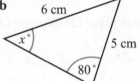

c

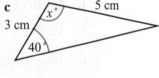

9 The sides of a triangle are 3 cm, 5 cm and 7 cm respectively. Show that the largest angle is 120°, and find the area of the triangle.

10 In each of the figures below calculate the total area:

a

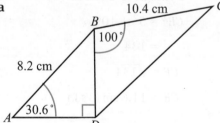

b

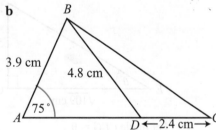

Example 16

ABCDEFGH is a rectangular box.

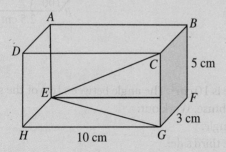

Find to 3 significant figures:

a   length *EG*

b   length *CE*

c   the angle *CE* makes with plane *EFGH* (angle *CEG*).

a   Draw triangle *EGH* in 2D.

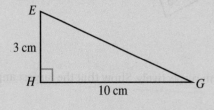

Pythagoras' Theorem

$EG^2 = 3^2 + 10^2$

$= 109$

$EG = \sqrt{109}$

$EG = 10.4 \text{ cm (3 s.f.)}$

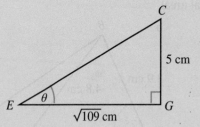

Pythagoras' Theorem

$CE^2 = 5^2 + 109$

$= 134$

$CE = \sqrt{134}$

$CE = 11.6 \text{ cm (3 s.f.)}$

c   Let angle *CEG* = θ

$\tan \theta = \dfrac{5}{\sqrt{109}} \Rightarrow \theta = \text{angle } CEG = 25.6° \text{ (3 s.f.)}$

Sometimes you may be asked to find the angle between two planes. To do this you need to do the following:

i   identify the line of intersection of the two planes

ii   find a point *X* on this line and points *A* and *B* on the two planes so that *AX* and *BX* are both perpendicular to the line

iii find the angle *AXB* which is the angle between the two planes.

Example 17

VWXYZ is a solid regular pyramid on a rectangular base *WXYZ* where *WX* = 8 cm and *XY* = 6 cm The vertex of the pyramid *V* is 12 cm directly above the centre of the base.

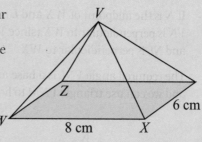

Find:

a *VX*

b the angle between *VX* and the base *WXYZ* (angle *VXZ*)

c the area of pyramid face *VWX*.

d the angle between the plane *VWX* and the plane *WXYZ*.

a Let M be the mid-point *ZX*.

Draw *WXYZ* in 2D.
Pythagoras' Theorem on triangle *ZWX*:

$$ZX^2 = 6^2 + 8^2$$
$$= 100$$
$$ZX = 10 \text{ cm} \Rightarrow MX = 5 \text{ cm}$$

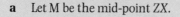

Draw triangle *VMX* in 2D.
Pythagoras' Theorem on triangle *VMX*:

$$VX^2 = 5^2 + 12^2$$
$$= 169$$
$$VX = 13 \text{ cm}$$

b Angle *VXZ* = Angle *VXM* = θ

$$\tan \theta = \frac{12}{5} \Rightarrow \theta = 67.4° \text{ (3 s.f.)}$$
$$\Rightarrow \text{Angle } VXZ = 67.4° \text{ (3 s.f.)}$$

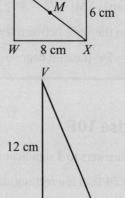

c Let *N* be the mid-point of *WX*.

Area of triangle *VWX* = $\frac{1}{2}$ × base × perpendicular height

$$= \frac{1}{2} \times WX \times VN$$
$$= \frac{1}{2} \times 8 \times VN$$

Draw triangle *VNX* in 2D.

Pythagoras' Theorem on triangle *VNX*:

$$13^2 = 4^2 + VN^2$$
$$VN^2 = 13^2 - 4^2$$
$$= 153$$
$$VN = \sqrt{153} \Rightarrow \text{Area of } VWX = \frac{1}{2} \times 8 \times \sqrt{153}$$
$$= 49.5 \text{ cm}^2 \text{ (3 s.f.)}$$

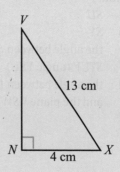

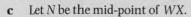

d The line of intersection of the two planes is *WX*.

If *N* is the midpoint of *WX* and *L* is the midpoint of *YZ* then *VN* is perpendicular to *WX* (since *VWX* is an isosceles triangle) and *NL* is perpendicular to *WX*.

The required angle *VNL* is a base angle of an isosceles triangle and we can use triangle *VNM* to find it.

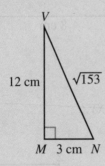

$\tan(VNM) = \frac{12}{3} = 4$

so the angle between the planes is $\arctan(4) = 75.96...$

$= 76°$ (nearest degree)

Exercise 10F

Give all answers to 3 significant figures.

1 *ABCDEFGH* is a rectangular box.
Find:
  a *EG*
  b *AG*
  c the angle between *AG* and plane *EFGH* (angle *AGE*)
  d the angle between the plane *DCFE* and the plane *EFGH*.

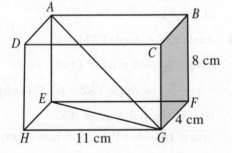

2 *STUVWXYZ* is a rectangular box.
Find:
  a *SU*
  b *SY*
  c the angle between *SY* and plane *STUV* (angle *YSU*)
  d the angle between the plane *TUZW* and the plane *VSWZ*.

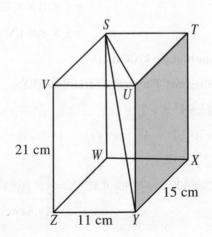

3 *LMNOPQRS* is a cube of side 10 cm.
Find:

a *PR*

b *LR*

c the angle between *LR* and plane *PQRS*
(angle *LRP*).

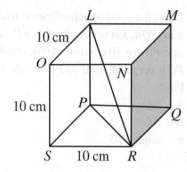

4 *ABCDEFGH* is a cube of side 20 cm.
Find:

a *CF*

b *DF*

c the angle between *DF* and plane *BCGF*
(angle *DFC*)

d the angle *MHA*, if *M* is the mid-point of *AB*.

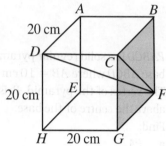

5 *ABCDEF* is a small ramp where *ABCD* and
CDEF are both rectangles and perpendicular
to each other.
Find:

a *AC*

b *AF*

c angle *FAB*

d the angle between *AF* and plane *ABCD* (angle *FAC*).

e the angle between the plane *ABFE* and the plane *ABCD*.

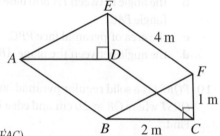

6 *PQRSTU* is an artificial ski-slope where
PQRS and *RSTU* are both rectangles and
perpendicular to each other.
Find:

a *UP*

b *PR*

c the angle between *UP* and plane *PQRS*
(angle *UPR*)

d the angle between *MP* and plane *PQRS*,
if *M* is the mid-point of *TU*.

e the angle between the plane *RSTU* and the plane *PQUT*.

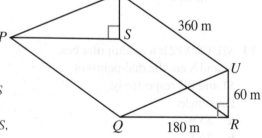

7 *ABCD* is a solid on a horizontal triangular base
ABC. Edge *AD* is 25 cm and vertical. *AB* is
perpendicular to *AC*. Angles *ABD* and *ACD* are
equal to 30° and 20° respectively.
Find:

a *AB*

b *AC*

c *BC*.

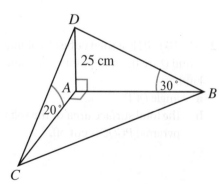

8 *PQRS* is a solid on a horizontal triangular base *PQR*. *S* is vertically above *P*. Edges *PQ* and *PR* are 50 cm and 70 cm respectively. *PQ* is perpendicular to *PR*. Angle *SQP* is 30°. Find:

a *SP*

b *RS*

c angle *PRS*.

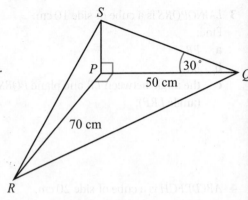

9 *PABCD* is a solid regular pyramid on a rectangular base *ABCD* where *AB* = 10 cm and *BC* = 7 cm. The vertex of the pyramid, *P*, is 15 cm directly above the centre of the base. Find:

a *PA*

b the angle between *PA* and base *ABCD* (angle *PAC*)

c the area of pyramid face *PBC*.

d the angle between the plane *ABCD* and the plane *PBC*.

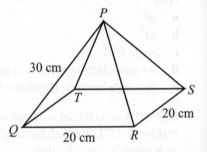

10 *PQRST* is a solid regular pyramid on a square base *QRST* where *QR* = 20 cm and edge *PQ* = 30 cm. Find:

a the height of *P* above base *QRST*

b the angle *PS* makes with the base *QRST*

c the total external area of the pyramid including the base.

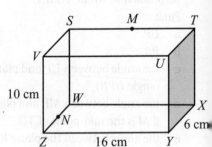

11 *STUVWXYZ* is a rectangular box. *M* and *N* are the mid-points of *ST* and *WZ* respectively. Find angle:

a *SYW*

b *TNX*

c *ZMY*.

12 *ABCDEFGH* is a solid cube of volume 1728 cm³. *P* and *Q* are the mid-points of *FG* and *GH* respectively. Find:

a angle *QCP*

b the total surface area of the solid remaining after pyramid *PGQC* is cut off.

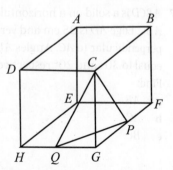

13 A church is made from two solid rectangular blocks with a regular pyramidal roof above the tower, with V being 40 m above ground level. Find:

  a VA

  b   the angle of elevation of V from E

  c   the cost of tiling the tower roof if the church is charged €250/m².

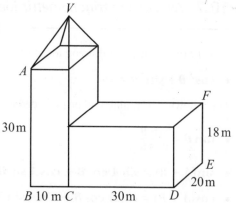

14 A hemispherical lampshade of diameter 40 cm is hung from a point by four chains, each of length 50 cm. If the chains are equally spaced on the rim of the hemisphere, find:

  a   the angle each chain makes with the horizontal

  b   the angle between two adjacent chains.

15 The angle of elevation to the top of a church tower is measured from A and from B

From A, due South of the church tower VC, the angle of elevation $\angle VAC = 15°$.

From B, due East of the church, the angle of elevation $\angle VBC = 25°$. $AB = 200$ m.

Find the height of the tower.

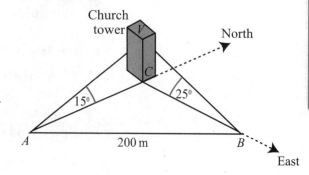

16 An aircraft is flying at a constant height of 2000 m. It is flying due East at a constant speed. At T, the plane's angle of elevation from O is 25°, and on a bearing from O of 310°. One minute later, it is at R and due North of O.

$RSWT$ is a rectangle and the points O, W and S are on horizontal ground. Find:

  a   the lengths OW and OS

  b   the angle of elevation of the aircraft, $\angle ROS$

  c   the speed of the aircraft in km/h.

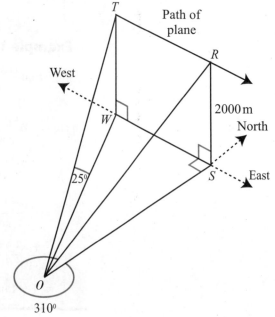

You should know the following identity

- $\cos^2 \theta + \sin^2 \theta = 1$

The following formulae will be provided if required:

- $\tan \theta = \dfrac{\sin \theta}{\cos \theta}$

- $\sin(A + B) = \sin A \cos B + \cos A \sin B$

- $\cos(A + B) = \cos A \cos B - \sin A \sin B$

- $\tan(A + B) = \dfrac{\tan A + \tan B}{1 - \tan A \tan B}$

Example 18

Simplify the following expressions:

a $\sin^2 3\theta + \cos^2 3\theta$

b $5 - 5\sin^2 \theta$

c $\dfrac{\sin 2\theta}{\sqrt{1 - \sin^2 2\theta}}$

a $\sin^2 3\theta + \cos^2 3\theta = 1$ $\sin^2 \theta + \cos^2 \theta \equiv 1$, with θ replaced by 3θ.

b $5 - 5\sin^2 \theta = 5(1 - \sin^2 \theta)$ Always look for factors.

           $= 5\cos^2 \theta.$ $\sin^2 \theta + \cos^2 \theta \equiv 1$, so $1 - \sin^2 \theta \equiv \cos^2 \theta.$

c $\dfrac{\sin 2\theta}{\sqrt{1 - \sin^2 2\theta}} = \dfrac{\sin 2\theta}{\sqrt{\cos^2 2\theta}}$ $\sin^2 2\theta + \cos^2 2\theta \equiv 1$, so $1 - \sin^2 2\theta \equiv \cos^2 2\theta.$

           $= \dfrac{\sin 2\theta}{\cos 2\theta}$ $\tan \theta \equiv \dfrac{\sin \theta}{\cos \theta}$, so $\dfrac{\sin 2\theta}{\cos 2\theta} \equiv \tan 2\theta.$

           $= \tan 2\theta$

Example 19

Show that $\dfrac{\cos^4 \theta - \sin^4 \theta}{\cos^2 \theta} \equiv 1 - \tan^2 \theta$

When you have to prove an identity like this you may quote the basic identities like '$\sin^2 \theta + \cos^2 \theta \equiv 1$'.

$\text{LHS} = \dfrac{\cos^4 \theta - \sin^4 \theta}{\cos^2 \theta}$

Usually the best strategy is to start with the more complicated side (here the left-hand side, LHS) and try to produce the expression on the other side.

$= \dfrac{(\cos^2 \theta + \sin^2 \theta)(\cos^2 \theta - \sin^2 \theta)}{\cos^2 \theta}$

The numerator can be factorised as the 'difference of two squares'.
$\sin^2 \theta + \cos^2 \theta \equiv 1.$

$= \dfrac{(\cos^2 \theta - \sin^2 \theta)}{\cos^2 \theta}$

$= \dfrac{\cos^2 \theta}{\cos^2 \theta} - \dfrac{\sin^2 \theta}{\cos^2 \theta}$

Divide through by $\cos^2 \theta$ and note that $\dfrac{\sin^2 \theta}{\cos^2 \theta} = \left(\dfrac{\sin \theta}{\cos \theta}\right)^2 = \tan^2 \theta.$

$= 1 - \tan^2 \theta = \text{RHS}$

Example 20

a Use the formulae for $\sin(A + B)$ and $\cos(A + B)$ to prove that

$$\tan(A + B) \equiv \frac{\tan A + \tan B}{1 - \tan A \tan B}$$

b Hence show that $\tan(A - B) \equiv \dfrac{\tan A - \tan B}{1 + \tan A \tan B}$

a $\tan(A + B) \equiv \dfrac{\sin(A + B)}{\cos(A + B)}$

$\equiv \dfrac{\sin A \cos B + \cos A \sin B}{\cos A \cos B - \sin A \sin B}$

Dividing the 'top and bottom' by $\cos A \cos B$ gives
$\tan(A + B)$

$\equiv \dfrac{\dfrac{\sin A \cancel{\cos B}}{\cos A \cancel{\cos B}} + \dfrac{\cancel{\cos A} \sin B}{\cancel{\cos A} \cos B}}{\dfrac{\cancel{\cos A}\cancel{\cos B}}{\cancel{\cos A}\cancel{\cos B}} - \dfrac{\sin A \sin B}{\cos A \cos B}}$

Cancel terms, as shown, and use the result $\tan \theta = \dfrac{\sin \theta}{\cos \theta}$

$\equiv \dfrac{\tan A + \tan B}{1 - \tan A \tan B}$

b Replace B by $-B$ in the result above:

$\tan(A - B) \equiv \dfrac{\tan A + \tan(-B)}{1 - \tan A \tan(-B)}$

Use the result $\tan(-\theta) = -\tan \theta$ which can be seen from the graph in section 10.4.

$\equiv \dfrac{\tan A - \tan B}{1 + \tan A \tan B}$

Example 21

Show, using the formula for $\sin(A - B)$, that $\sin 15° = \dfrac{\sqrt{6} - \sqrt{2}}{4}$

$\sin 15° = \sin(45 - 30)°$

$= \sin 45° \cos 30° - \cos 45° \sin 30°$

$= (\tfrac{1}{2}\sqrt{2})(\tfrac{1}{2}\sqrt{3}) - (\tfrac{1}{2}\sqrt{2})(\tfrac{1}{2})$

$= \tfrac{1}{4}(\sqrt{3}\sqrt{2} - \sqrt{2})$

$= \tfrac{1}{4}(\sqrt{6} - \sqrt{2})$

You know the exact form of sin and cos for many angles, e.g. 30°, 45°, 60°, 90°, 180°..., so write 15° using two of these angles.
[You could equally use $\sin(60 - 45)°$.]

Example 22

Given that $2\sin(x + y) = 3\cos(x - y)$, express $\tan x$ in terms of $\tan y$.

Expanding $\sin(x + y)$ and $\cos(x - y)$ gives
$2 \sin x \cos y + 2 \cos x \sin y$
$= 3 \cos x \cos y + 3 \sin x \sin y$

so $\dfrac{2 \sin x \cos y}{\cos x \cos y} + \dfrac{2 \cos x \sin y}{\cos x \cos y}$

$= \dfrac{3 \cos x \cos y}{\cos x \cos y} + \dfrac{3 \sin x \sin y}{\cos x \cos y}$

This is similar to the expression seen in deriving $\tan(A + B)$. A good strategy is to divide both sides by $\cos x \cos y$.

$$2 \tan x + 2 \tan y = 3 + 3 \tan x \tan y$$
$$2 \tan x - 3 \tan x \tan y = 3 - 2 \tan y \qquad \text{Collect all terms in } \tan x \text{ on one side.}$$
$$\tan x (2 - 3 \tan y) = 3 - 2 \tan y \qquad \text{Factorise.}$$

So
$$\tan x = \frac{3 - 2 \tan y}{2 - 3 \tan y}$$

Exercise 10G

1   Simplify each of the following expressions:

a $1 - \cos^2 \tfrac{1}{2}\theta$
b $5 \sin^2 3\theta + 5 \cos^2 3\theta$
c $\sin^2 A - 1$

d $\dfrac{\sin \theta}{\tan \theta}$
e $\dfrac{\sqrt{1 - \cos^2 x}}{\cos x}$
f $\dfrac{\sqrt{1 - \cos^2 3A}}{\sqrt{1 - \sin^2 3A}}$

g $(1 + \sin x)^2 + (1 - \sin x)^2 + 2 \cos^2 x$

h $\sin^4 \theta + \sin^2 \theta \cos^2 \theta$

i $\sin^4 \theta + 2 \sin^2 \theta \cos^2 \theta + \cos^4 \theta$

2   Using the identities $\sin^2 A + \cos^2 A \equiv 1$ and/or $\tan A \equiv \dfrac{\sin A}{\cos A}$ $(\cos A \neq 0)$, prove that:

a $(\sin \theta + \cos \theta)^2 \equiv 1 + 2 \sin \theta \cos \theta$

b $\dfrac{1}{\cos \theta} - \cos \theta \equiv \sin \theta \tan \theta$

c $\tan x + \dfrac{1}{\tan x} \equiv \dfrac{1}{\sin x \cos x}$

d $\cos^2 A - \sin^2 A \equiv 2 \cos^2 A - 1 \equiv 1 - 2 \sin^2 A$

e $(2 \sin \theta - \cos \theta)^2 + (\sin \theta + 2 \cos \theta)^2 \equiv 5$

f $2 - (\sin \theta - \cos \theta)^2 \equiv (\sin \theta + \cos \theta)^2$

g $\sin^2 x \cos^2 y - \cos^2 x \sin^2 y = \sin^2 x - \sin^2 y$

3   Express the following as a single sine, cosine or tangent:

a $\sin 15° \cos 20° + \cos 15° \sin 20°$
b $\sin 58° \cos 23° - \cos 58° \sin 23°$

c $\cos 130° \cos 80° - \sin 130° \sin 80°$
d $\dfrac{\tan 76° - \tan 45°}{1 + \tan 76° \tan 45°}$

e $\cos 2\theta \cos \theta + \sin 2\theta \sin \theta$
f $\cos 4\theta \cos 3\theta - \sin 4\theta \sin 3\theta$

g $\sin \tfrac{1}{2}\theta \cos 2\tfrac{1}{2}\theta + \cos \tfrac{1}{2}\theta \sin 2\tfrac{1}{2}\theta$
h $\dfrac{\tan 2\theta + \tan 3\theta}{1 - \tan 2\theta \tan 3\theta}$

i $\sin(A + B) \cos B - \cos(A + B) \sin B$

j $\cos\left(\dfrac{3x + 2y}{2}\right) \cos\left(\dfrac{3x - 2y}{2}\right) - \sin\left(\dfrac{3x + 2y}{2}\right) \sin\left(\dfrac{3x - 2y}{2}\right)$

4   Calculate, without using your calculator, the exact value of:

a $\sin 30° \cos 60° + \cos 30° \sin 60°$
b $\cos 110° \cos 20° + \sin 110° \sin 20°$

c $\sin 33° \cos 27° + \cos 33° \sin 27°$
d $\cos\dfrac{\pi}{8} \cos\dfrac{\pi}{8} - \sin\dfrac{\pi}{8} \sin\dfrac{\pi}{8}$

e $\sin 60° \cos 15° - \cos 60° \sin 15°$
f $\cos 70°(\cos 50° - \tan 70° \sin 50°)$

g $\dfrac{\tan 45° + \tan 15°}{1 - \tan 45° \tan 15°}$

h $\dfrac{1 - \tan 15°}{1 + \tan 15°}$

Hint:

$\tan 45° = 1.$

i $\dfrac{\tan\left(\dfrac{7\pi}{12}\right) - \tan\left(\dfrac{\pi}{3}\right)}{1 + \tan\left(\dfrac{7\pi}{12}\right) \tan\left(\dfrac{\pi}{3}\right)}$

j $\sqrt{3} \cos 15° - \sin 15°$

$\dfrac{}{4}$

Hint:

Look at e.

5 Prove the identities

a $\sin(A + 60°) + \sin(A - 60°) \equiv \sin A$

b $\dfrac{\cos A}{\sin B} - \dfrac{\sin A}{\cos B} \equiv \dfrac{\cos(A + B)}{\sin B \cos B}$

c $\dfrac{\sin(x + y)}{\cos x \cos y} \equiv \tan x + \tan y$

d $\cos\left(\theta + \dfrac{\pi}{3}\right) + \sqrt{3} \sin \theta \equiv \sin\left(\theta + \dfrac{\pi}{6}\right)$

10.8 *You can solve simple trigonometric equations.*

You can use your calculator to find a solution to an equation such as

$\sin \theta = 0.4$

giving $\quad \theta = 23.6°$

In section 10.4 you saw that there are other possible solutions to this equation namely:
$\theta = 180° - 23.6° = 156.4°$ or $\theta = 23.6° + 360° = 383.6°$ and so on.

The following table summarises the situation:

Equation	1ˢᵗ Solution (calc)	2 ⁿᵈ Solution	3ʳᵈ Solution	4ᵗʰ Solution
$\sin x = k$	a	$180 - a$	All cases are $a \pm 360$	All cases are 2ⁿᵈ sol. ± 360
$\cos x = k$	a	$360 - a$		
$\tan x = k$	a	$180 + a$		

The shaded column is the key part to learn.

Example 23

Solve, in the interval $0 \leqslant x < 360$, giving your answers to the nearest degree.

a $\sin x° = 0.5$ **b** $\quad 4 \sin x° = -3$ **c** $\quad 2 \tan x° + 1 = 0$

a $\sin x° = 0.5$

so $x = 30$ Using a calculator.

or $x = 180 - 30 = 150$ Using the formula in the table.

So $x = 30°$ or $150°$

b $4 \sin x° = -3$

so $\sin x° = -\frac{3}{4}$ First rearrange into the form $\sin x = k$ and then use a calculator.

giving $x = -48.6$

This is outside of the range so find the second solution:

$$x = 180 - (-48.6) = 228.6$$ Using the formula in the table.

or $x = -48.6 + 360 = 311.4$ Since you only have one solution in range, check the

so $x = 229°$ or $311°$ (to nearest degree) 3rd solution as well using the formula in the table.

c $2 \tan x° + 1 = 0$

$\tan x° = -\frac{1}{2}$ Rearrange into the form $\tan x = k$.

so $x = -26.6$ Use a calculator to find the first solution.

or $x = -26.6 + 180 = 153.4$ Use formula in the table to find the second solution.

$x = -26.6 + 360 = 333.4$

so $x = 153°$ or $333°$ (to nearest degree)   Since you only have one solution in range, find the third solution.

You can easily adapt this method to solve more complicated equations.

Example 24

Solve, in the interval $0 \leqslant x < 360°$, giving your answers to 1 decimal place.

a $\cos(x - 25)° = 0.4$ **b** $\tan 2x° = 3$

a $\cos(x - 25)° = 0.4$ Think of the equation as $\cos y = 0.4$ and first solve this equation to find y.

Let $y = x - 25$

then $y = 66.4$ Find the first solution from a calculator and the second using the

or $y = 360 - 66.4 = 293.6$ formula in the table.

so $x - 25 = 66.4$ or 293.6

so $x = 91.4°$ or $318.6°$ Then use $x = y + 25$ and add 25 to obtain x values.

b $\tan 2x = 3$ First solve the equation $\tan y = 3$.

Let $y = 2x$ then

$y = 71.6, 251.6, 431.6, 611.6$ Use a calculator to find the first solution and then the formulae in the table for

so $x = 35.8, 125.8, 215.8, 305.8$ the second, third and fourth.
Use $y = 2x$ and divide your answers by 2 to obtain x.

NB An equation of the form $\tan x = k$ usually has 2 solutions in the interval $(0, 360)$ and so an equation of the form $\tan 2x = k$ will usually have $2 \times 2 = 4$ solutions in this interval.

Sometimes you may have to work in radians.

Example 25

Solve $2\cos 2x + 1 = 0$ for $-\pi < x \leqslant \pi$.
Give your answers as multiples of π.

$2\cos 2x + 1 = 0$	First rearrange into the form $\cos 2x = k$.
so $\quad \cos 2x = -\frac{1}{2}$	Solve $\cos y = -\frac{1}{2}$ and then use $y = 2x$ to get x values.
so $\quad 2x = \frac{2\pi}{3}$	Using a calculator in degree mode gives $120°$ which is easily converted into $\frac{2\pi}{3}$ radians.
or $\quad 2x = 2\pi - \frac{2\pi}{3}$ or $\frac{2\pi}{3} - 2\pi$ or $\left(2\pi - \frac{2\pi}{3}\right) - 2\pi$	Use the formulae for 2nd, 3rd and 4th solutions from the table.
so $\quad 2x = \frac{2\pi}{3}, \frac{4\pi}{3}, -\frac{4\pi}{3}, -\frac{2\pi}{3}$	
and $\quad x = \frac{\pi}{3}, \frac{2\pi}{3}, -\frac{2\pi}{3}, -\frac{\pi}{3}$	Finally divide by 2 to get x.

You may have obtained these solutions more quickly by noticing that if $\cos y = -\frac{1}{2}$
then $y = \pm\frac{2\pi}{3}$ or $\pm\frac{4\pi}{3}$ from the graph in Section 10.4.

Exercise 10H

1 Solve the following equations for θ, in the interval $0 < \theta \leqslant 360°$:

  a $\sin\theta = -1$ **b** $\tan\theta = \sqrt{3}$

  c $\cos\theta = \frac{1}{2}$ **d** $\sin\theta = \sin 15°$

  e $\cos\theta = -\cos 40°$ **f** $\tan\theta = -1$

  g $\cos\theta = 0$ **h** $\sin\theta = -0.766$

  i $7\sin\theta = 5$ **j** $2\cos\theta = -\sqrt{2}$

2 Solve the following equations for x, giving your answers to 3 significant figures where appropriate, in the intervals indicated:

  a $\sin x° = -\frac{\sqrt{3}}{2}$, $-180 \leqslant x \leqslant 540$

  b $2\sin x° = -0.3$, $-180 \leqslant x \leqslant 180$

  c $\cos x° = -0.809$, $-180 \leqslant x \leqslant 180$

  d $\cos x° = 0.84$, $-360 < x < 0$

  e $\tan x° = \frac{\sqrt{3}}{3}$, $0 \leqslant x \leqslant 720$

  f $\tan x° = 2.90$, $80 \leqslant x \leqslant 440$

3 Solve, in the intervals indicated, the following equations for θ, where θ is measured in radians. Give your answer in terms of π or 2 decimal places.

  a $\sin\theta = 0, -2\pi < \theta \leqslant 2\pi$ **b** $\cos\theta = -\frac{1}{2}, -2\pi < \theta \leqslant \pi$

  c $\sin\theta = \frac{1}{\sqrt{2}}, -2\pi < \theta \leqslant \pi$ **d** $2(1 + \tan\theta) = 1 - 5\tan\theta, -\pi < \theta \leqslant 2\pi$

4 Find the values of θ, in the interval $0 \leqslant \theta \leqslant 360°$, for which:

a $\sin 4\theta = 0$ **b** $\cos 3\theta = -1$ **c** $\tan 2\theta = 1$ **d** $\cos 2\theta = \frac{1}{2}$

e $\tan \frac{1}{2}\theta = -\frac{1}{\sqrt{3}}$ **f** $\sin(-\theta) = \frac{1}{\sqrt{2}}$ **g** $\tan(45° - \theta) = -1$

h $2\sin(\theta - 20°) = 1$ **i** $\tan(\theta + 75°) = \sqrt{3}$

5 Solve, in the intervals indicated, the following equations for θ, where θ is measured in radians. Give your answer in terms of π or 2 decimal places.

a $\sin\theta = 0, -2\pi < \theta \leqslant 2\pi$ **b** $\sin\theta = \tan\theta, 0 < \theta \leqslant 2\pi$

10.9 *You can use trigonometric formulae to solve equations.*

Example 26

Solve the following equations for $0 \leqslant x < 360$

a $2\sin x = \tan x$ **b** $\sin^2(x - 30) = \frac{1}{2}$

a $2\sin x = \frac{\sin x}{\cos x}$ Use $\tan x = \frac{\sin x}{\cos x}$.

$2\sin x \cos x = \sin x$ Multiply by $\cos x$ and collect terms on one side.

$2\sin x \cos x - \sin x = 0$

$\sin x(2\cos x - 1) = 0$ Factorise.

so $\sin x = 0$ $\Rightarrow x = 0, 180$ Find all the solutions using the formulae to find second solutions.

or $\cos x = \frac{1}{2}$ $\Rightarrow x = 60, 300$

so $x = 0, 60°, 180°, 300°$ NB Some students "cancel" $\sin x$ at the "factorise" stage and they will lose the answer 0 and 180. Cancelling should be avoided – factorise instead.

b $\sin^2(x - 30) = \frac{1}{2}$ Square root to get in the form $\sin(x - 30) = k$. Don't forget the $\pm$.

$\sin(x - 30) = \pm\frac{1}{\sqrt{2}}$

$+\frac{1}{\sqrt{2}}$ gives $x - 30 = 45, 180 - 45$ Consider both cases separately, remembering $\sin 45 = \frac{1}{\sqrt{2}}$ from section 10.4.

so $x = 75, 165$ Solve for $x - 30$ and then add 30 to get x.

$-\frac{1}{\sqrt{2}}$ gives $x - 30 = -45; 180 - -45; -45 + 360$

so $x = (-15), 255, 345$ Since the first solution is outside the range you will need the second and third solutions in this case.

Therefore $x = 75°, 165°, 255°, 345°$

Sometimes you may have to solve a quadratic equation.

Example 27

Find the values of x, in the interval $-\pi < x \leqslant \pi$, satisfying the equation.

$$2\cos^2 x + 9\sin x = 3\sin^2 x$$

Give your answers in radians correct to 3 significant figures.

$2\cos^2 x + 9\sin x = 3\sin^2 x$	Since the equation has a $\sin x$ term you can use $\cos^2 x + \sin^2 x = 1$ to replace $\cos^2 x$ with $1 - \sin^2 x$.
$2(1 - \sin^2 x) + 9\sin x = 3\sin^2 x$	
$2 - 2\sin^2 x + 9\sin x = 3\sin^2 x$	
$0 = 5\sin^2 x - 9\sin x - 2$	This is a quadratic in $\sin x$.
$0 = (5\sin x + 1)(\sin x - 2)$	Factorise.

so $\sin x = 2$ or $-\frac{1}{5}$ $\sin x = 2$ has no solutions.

$\sin x = -\frac{1}{5} \Rightarrow x = -0.20135...$

or $x = \pi - -0.20135... = 3.342...$ (outside range) Use a calculator in "rad" mode to get 1st solution, and the formula for 2nd.

or $x = 3.342 - 2\pi = -2.940$ To find further solutions you need to consider $-0.201 \pm 2\pi$ and $3.342 \pm 2\pi$ selecting values in range.

so $x = -0.201, -2.94$

Exercise 10I

1 Solve the following equations for θ, in the interval $0 < \theta \leqslant 360°$:

   a $\sqrt{3}\sin\theta = \cos\theta$ **b** $\sin\theta + \cos\theta = 0$

2 Solve, in the intervals indicated, the following equations for θ, where θ is measured in radians. Give your answer in terms of π or 2 decimal places.

   a $\sin\theta = \tan\theta, 0 < \theta \leqslant 2\pi$ **b** $2\cos\theta = 3\sin\theta, 0 < \theta \leqslant 2\pi$

3 Solve for θ, in the interval $0 \leqslant \theta \leqslant 360°$, the following equations.
Give your answers to 3 significant figures where they are not exact.

   a $4\cos^2\theta = 1$ **b** $3\sin^2\theta + \sin\theta = 0$

   c $2\cos^2\theta - 5\cos\theta + 2 = 0$ **d** $\tan^2 2\theta = 3$

   e $\sin\theta + 2\cos^2\theta + 1 = 0$ **f** $3\sin^2\theta = \sin\theta\cos\theta$

   g $4\cos^2\theta - 5\sin\theta - 5 = 0$

4 Solve for x, in the interval $0 \leqslant x \leqslant 2\pi$, the following equations.
Give your answers to 3 significant figures unless they can be written in the form $\frac{a}{b}\pi$, where a and b are integers.

   a $2\sin^2\left(x + \frac{\pi}{3}\right) = 1$ **b** $6\sin^2 x + \cos x - 4 = 0$

   c $\cos^2 x - 6\sin x = 5$

Mixed Exercise 10J

1 Simplify the following expressions:

  a $\cos^4 \theta - \sin^4 \theta$

  b $\sin^2 3\theta - \sin^2 3\theta \cos^2 3\theta$

  c $\cos^4 \theta + 2 \sin^2 \theta \cos^2 \theta + \sin^4 \theta$

2 **a** Given that $2(\sin x + 2 \cos x) = \sin x + 5 \cos x$, find the exact value of $\tan x$.

  b Given that $\sin x \cos y + 3 \cos x \sin y = 2 \sin x \sin y - 4 \cos x \cos y$, express $\tan y$ in terms of $\tan x$.

3 Given that $2 \sin 2\theta = \cos 2\theta$:

  a show that $\tan 2\theta = 0.5$.

  b Hence find the value of θ, to one decimal place, in the interval $0 \le \theta < 360°$ for which $2 \sin 2\theta° = \cos 2\theta°$.

4 Find all the values of θ in the interval $0 \le \theta < 360$ for which:

  a $\cos(\theta + 75)° = 0.5$,

  b $\sin 2\theta° = 0.7$, giving your answers to one decimal place.

5 Find, giving your answers in terms of π, all values of θ in the interval $0 < \theta < 2\pi$, for which:

  a $\tan\left(\theta + \dfrac{\pi}{3}\right) = 1$

  b $\sin 2\theta = -\dfrac{\sqrt{3}}{2}$

6 Find, in degrees, the values of θ in the interval $0 \le \theta < 360°$ for which

$$2 \cos^2 \theta - \cos \theta - 1 = \sin^2 \theta$$

Give your answers to 1 decimal place, where appropriate.

7 Solve the following equation in the interval given in brackets:

$$\sin 3\theta \cos 2\theta = \sin 2\theta \cos 3\theta \quad \{0 \le \theta \le 2\pi\}$$

8 Without using calculus, find the maximum and minimum value of the following expressions. In each case give the smallest positive value of θ at which each occurs.

  a $\sin \theta \cos 10° - \cos \theta \sin 10°$

  b $\cos 30° \cos \theta - \sin 30° \sin \theta$

9 **a** Without using a calculator, find the values of:

  i $\sin 40° \cos 10° - \cos 40° \sin 10°$ **ii** $\dfrac{1}{\sqrt{2}} \cos 15° - \dfrac{1}{\sqrt{2}} \sin 15°$ **iii** $\dfrac{1 - \tan 15°}{1 + \tan 15°}$

  b Find, to 1 decimal place, the values of x, $0 \le x \le 360°$, which satisfy the equation

$$2 \sin x = \cos(x - 60)$$

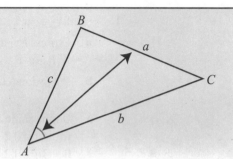

1 The sine rule is

$$\frac{a}{\sin A} = \frac{b}{\sin B} = \frac{c}{\sin C} \quad \text{or} \quad \frac{\sin A}{a} = \frac{\sin B}{b} = \frac{\sin C}{c}$$

2 The cosine rule is

$$a^2 = b^2 + c^2 - 2bc \cos A \quad \text{or} \quad b^2 = a^2 + c^2 - 2ac \cos B$$
$$\text{or} \quad c^2 = a^2 + b^2 - 2ab \cos C$$

3 You can find an unknown angle using a rearranged form of the cosine rule:

$$\cos A = \frac{b^2 + c^2 - a^2}{2bc} \quad \text{or} \quad \cos B = \frac{a^2 + c^2 - b^2}{2ac} \quad \text{or} \quad \cos C = \frac{a^2 + b^2 - c^2}{2ab}$$

4 You can find the area of a triangle using the formula

$$\text{area} = \tfrac{1}{2}ab \sin C$$

if you know the length of two sides (a and b) and the value of the angle C between them.

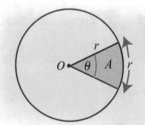

5 1 radian $= \dfrac{180°}{\pi}$.

6 The length of an arc of a circle is $l = r\theta$.

7 The area of a sector is $A = \tfrac{1}{2}r^2\theta$.

8 The addition (or compound angle) formulae are
- $\sin(A + B) \equiv \sin A \cos B + \cos A \sin B$ $\sin(A - B) \equiv \sin A \cos B - \cos A \sin B$
- $\cos(A + B) \equiv \cos A \cos B - \sin A \sin B$ $\cos(A - B) \equiv \cos A \cos B + \sin A \sin B$

- $\tan(A + B) \equiv \dfrac{\tan A + \tan B}{1 - \tan A \tan B}$ $\tan(A - B) \equiv \dfrac{\tan A - \tan B}{1 + \tan A \tan B}$

9 $\tan \theta = \dfrac{\sin \theta}{\cos \theta}$ (providing $\cos \theta \neq 0$, when $\tan \theta$ is not defined)

10 $\sin^2 \theta + \cos^2 \theta = 1$

11 A first solution of the equation $\sin \alpha = k$ is your calculator value, $\alpha = \sin^{-1} k$. A second solution is $(180° - \alpha)$, or $(\pi - \alpha)$ if you are working in radians. Other solutions are found by adding or subtracting multiples of $360°$ or 2π radians.

12 A first solution of the equation $\cos \alpha = k$ is your calculator value of $\alpha = \cos^{-1} k$. A second solution is $(360° - \alpha)$, or $(2\pi - \alpha)$ if you are working in radians. Other solutions are found by adding or subtracting multiples of $360°$ or 2π radians.

13 A first solution of the equation $\tan \alpha = k$ is your calculator value $\alpha = \tan^{-1} k$. A second solution is $(180° + \alpha)$, or $(\pi + \alpha)$ if you are working in radians. Other solutions are found by adding or subtracting multiples of $360°$ or 2π radians.

Review exercise

1     $f(x) = 5x^2 - 25x + 3.$

    a   Express $f(x)$ in the form $f(x) = A(x + B)^2 + C$, giving the values of the constants A, B and C.

    b   Write down the minimum value of $f(x)$ and the value of x for which it occurs.

2   **a**   On the same axes, sketch and label the graphs of the lines with equations

       i $4y = 12 - 3x$,

       ii $3y = 12 - 4x$,

       iii $y = 2 - x$.

    b   Show clearly the region for which

$$3y + 4x \leqslant 12, \;\; 4y + 3x \leqslant 12, \;\; y + x \geqslant 2, \;\; x \geqslant 0, \;\; y \geqslant 0.$$

3   The sum of the first n terms of an arithmetic series is $\frac{5}{4}n^2 + \frac{7}{4}n$. Find

    a   the first term of the series,

    b   the common difference of the series,

    c   the 50th term of the series.

4   The finite region enclosed by the curve with equation $y = 9 - x^2$ and the x-axis is rotated through $360°$ about the x-axis. Find, to 3 significant figures, the volume of the solid generated.

5   The points P, Q and R have coordinates $(2, 4)$, $(4, 8)$ and $(4, 0)$ respectively.

    a   Show that $\triangle PQR$ is isosceles.

    b   Calculate the size of each angle of $\triangle PQR$.

6

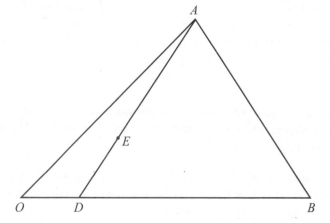

In the diagram, $\overrightarrow{OA} = \mathbf{a}$ and $\overrightarrow{OB} = \mathbf{b}$. The point D on OB is such that $OD : OB = 1 : 4$ and the point E divides DA in the ratio $1 : 2$.

    a   Find, in terms of $\mathbf{a}$ and $\mathbf{b}$,

       i $\overrightarrow{AD}$.   **ii** $\overrightarrow{OE}$.   **iii** $\overrightarrow{BE}$.

The point F lies on OA such that $\overrightarrow{OF} = \mu\overrightarrow{OA}$. Given that F, E and B are collinear,

b find the value of μ.

The point G lies on AB such that $\overrightarrow{AG} = \lambda\overrightarrow{AB}$. Given that EG is parallel to DB,

c find the value of λ.

7 Use $\tan\theta \equiv \dfrac{\sin\theta}{\cos\theta}$

    a to show that $\dfrac{d}{d\theta}(\tan\theta) = \dfrac{1}{\cos^2\theta}$.

    b to solve, in degrees to one decimal place, the equation $5\sin\theta = 7\cos\theta$, $0 \leqslant \theta \leqslant 360°$.

8 A particle P moves in a straight line. Initially P is at rest at a fixed point O of the line. At time t seconds after leaving O the velocity, v m/s, of P is given by $v = 3t - t^2$. Find the distance P moves before coming to rest again.

9 The lengths of the sides of a triangle are in the ratios $3 : 5 : 7$. Find, in degrees to 3 significant figures, the three angles of this triangle.

10 **a** Copy and complete the following table for $y = \frac{1}{2}e^x + 3$, giving your values to 2 decimal places.

x	-2	-1	0	1	2	3
y	3.07		3.5	4.36		

    b Using a scale of 2 cm to 1 unit on the x-axis and 1 cm to 1 unit on the y-axis, draw the graph of $y = \frac{1}{2}e^x + 3$ for $-2 \leqslant x \leqslant 3$.

    c Use your graph to estimate, to 2 significant figures, the solution of the equation $e^x = 10$, showing your method clearly.

    d By drawing a straight line on your graph, estimate, to 1 decimal place, the solution of the equation $x = \ln 4(1 - x)$.

11 Find the first three terms in the expansion of $\left(x - \dfrac{3}{x}\right)^6$ as a series of descending powers of x, simplifying each term as far as possible.

12 Given that the equation $(p - 6)x^2 + 4px - 4 = 0$ has no real roots, find the set of possible values of p.

13 **a** Show that $\displaystyle\sum_{r=1}^{n} r = \frac{n}{2}(n + 1)$.

    b Show that $a^3 - (a - 1)^3 \equiv 3a^2 - 3a + 1$.

    c Hence show that $\displaystyle\sum_{r=1}^{n} \{r^3 - (r - 1)^3\} = 3\sum_{r=1}^{n} r^2 - \frac{1}{2}(3n^2 + n)$.

    d Show that $\displaystyle\sum_{r=1}^{n} \{r^3 - (r - 1)^3\} = n^3$.

    e Hence deduce that $\displaystyle\sum_{r=1}^{n} r^2 = \frac{1}{6}n(n + 1)(2n + 1)$.

14 a Find the coordinates of the points of intersection of the curve with equation $y = x^2 - 3x + 14$ and the line with equation $y = 5x - 1$.

b Find the area of the finite region bounded by the curve and the line.

15

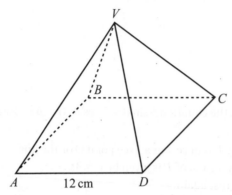

The diagram shows a right pyramid with vertex V and square base $ABCD$, of side 12 cm. The size of angle AVC is 90°.

a Show that the height of the pyramid is $6\sqrt{2}$ cm.

b Find, in cm, the length of VA.

c Find, in cm, the exact length of the perpendicular from D to VA. Give your answer in the form $p\sqrt{q}$, where p and q are integers and q is prime.

Find, in degrees to 1 decimal place, the size of

d the angle between the plane VAB and the base $ABCD$,

e the angle between the plane VAB and the plane VAD.

16 Oil is dripping from a leaking pipe and forms a circular pool. Find an estimate of the percentage increase in the radius of the pool when the area has increased by $x\%$, where x is small.

17 The line l passes through the points with coordinates $(5, 5)$ and $(11, 10)$.

a Show that an equation for l is $6y = 5x + 5$.

The curve C with equation $xy = 5$ intersects the line l in two points.

b Find the coordinates of these two points.

The line L passes through $(1, 0)$ and is perpendicular to l.

c Find an equation for L.

d Show, using algebra, that L never meets C.

18 Solve, to 3 significant figures, for $0 \leqslant \theta \leqslant \pi$,

a $(4 \sin \theta - 1)(2 \sin \theta + 5) = 0$,

b $\tan(2\theta - \frac{1}{3}\pi) = 2.4$,

c $9 \sin^2 \theta - 9 \cos \theta = 11$.

19 Solve

a $\log_5 p = 4$,

b $2\log_m 8 + 3\log_8 m = 7$

c Solve the equations $\quad 5\log_x 16 - 2\log_9 y = 19$

$\qquad\qquad\qquad\qquad\qquad 3\log_x 16 - 4\log_9 y = 14$

20 Prove that the line with equation $y = 2x + 12$ is a tangent to the curve with equation $y = 8 - 2x - x^2$.

21 The lengths of the sides of a triangle are 4 cm, 5 cm and 6 cm. Find, in degrees to one decimal place, the size of the largest angle of the triangle.

22 Referred to a fixed origin O, the position vectors of the points P and Q are $(6\mathbf{i} - 5\mathbf{j})$ and $(10\mathbf{i} + 3\mathbf{j})$ respectively. The midpoint of PQ is R.

  a Find the position vector of R.

The midpoint of OP is S.

  b Prove that SR is parallel to OQ.

23 The region enclosed by the curve $y = 2x^2 + 5$, the x-axis, the y-axis and the line $x = 3$ is rotated through $360°$ about the x-axis. Find, in terms of π, the volume of the solid generated.

24 $\quad\sin(A + B) \equiv \sin A \cos B + \cos A \sin B$

$\quad\cos(A + B) \equiv \cos A \cos B - \sin A \sin B$

  a Obtain an expression for $\cos 2\theta$ in terms of $\cos^2 \theta$.

  b Write down an expression for $\sin 2\theta$ in terms of $\sin \theta$ and $\cos \theta$.

  c Show that $\cos 3\theta \equiv 4\cos^3 \theta - 3\cos \theta$.

  d Solve, for $0 < \theta < \pi$, the equation $9\cos \theta - 12\cos^3 \theta = 2$, giving your answers to 3 significant figures.

  e Find $\displaystyle\int_0^{\frac{\pi}{2}} (3\cos^3 \theta + 2\sin \theta)\,d\theta$.

25 The fourth term of an arithmetic series is four times the eighth term. The sum of the first four terms is 164. Find

  a the common difference of the series.

  b the first term of the series.

The sum of the first n terms of the series is S_n.

  c Find the greatest value of n for which S_n is positive.

26 **a** Find the coordinates of the points where the curve with equation $y = x^2 - 3x + 6$ meets the line with equation $y = 4x - 4$.

  b Find the set of values of x for which $x^2 - 3x + 6 \geqslant 4x - 4$.

27 The position vectors of points P and Q are $(3\mathbf{i} + 4\mathbf{j})$ and $(2\mathbf{i} - 7\mathbf{j})$ respectively, referred to a fixed origin O. The point R divides PQ internally in the ratio $2 : 3$.

Find, in terms of $\mathbf{i}$ and $\mathbf{j}$,

  a $\overrightarrow{PQ}$,

  b $\overrightarrow{OR}$.

28 A right pyramid has a horizontal square base of side 16 cm. The length of each sloping edge is 30 cm. Calculate, in degrees to the nearest $0.1°$, the size of the angle between a triangular face and the horizontal.

29 A water tank is in the shape of a right circular cylinder with no lid. The base of the cylinder is a circle of radius r cm and the height is h cm. The total external surface area of the tank is A cm^2. The capacity of the tank is $50\,000\pi$ cm^3.

   a Show that $A = \left(\dfrac{100\,000}{r} + r^2\right)\pi$.

   b Find, to the nearest whole number, the minimum value of A. Verify that the value you have found is a minimum.

30 Find the sum of all the integers from 5 to 195 inclusive which are **not** multiples of 5.

31 The sum of the first and third terms of a geometric series is 50. The sum of the second and third terms is 30.

   a Find the two possible values of the common ratio of the series.

   Given that the series is convergent,

   b find the least number of terms of the series for which the sum exceeds 79.9.

32 In $\triangle ABC$, $AB = 6.3$ cm, $BC = 4.6$ cm and $\angle BAC = 32°$. Find, to one decimal place, the two possible sizes of $\angle ACB$.

33 Solve the equation $\log_2(2x + 3) - \log_2 x = 3$.

34 The point P has coordinates $(-5, 0)$ and the point Q has coordinates $(1, 12)$.

   a Find an equation of the line l through Q which is perpendicular to PQ.

   The line l meets the x-axis at R.

   b Find the coordinates of R.

   The points P, Q and R lie on a circle.

   c Write down the coordinates of the centre of the circle.

35 A particle P moves in a straight line. At time t seconds, the velocity, v m/s, of P is given by $v = 5 - 2t + t^2$. Find

   a the acceleration, in m/s^2, of P when $t = 3$,

   b the distance, in metres, travelled by P in the interval $0 \leqslant t \leqslant 4$.

36

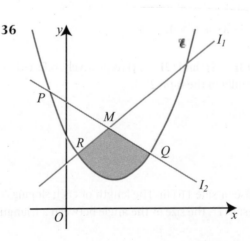

The diagram shows the curve $\mathscr{C}$ with equation $y = x^2 - 6x + 11$. The three points P, Q and R lie on $\mathscr{C}$. The point R has coordinates $(1, 6)$ and the gradient of $\mathscr{C}$ at R is -4. The line l_1 is the normal to the curve at R.

a Find an equation, with integer coefficients, for l_1.

The line l_2 passes through the point with coordinates $(4, 10)$ and is perpendicular to the line l_1.

b Find an equation for l_2.

The line l_2 also passes through the points P and Q.

c Show that the coordinates of Q are $(5, 6)$ and find the coordinates of P.

The lines l_1 and l_2 intersect at M.

d Find the y-coordinate of M.

e Find the area of the shaded region.

37 $\quad$ $f(x) = x^3 - 5x^2 + px + q$, $p, q \in \mathbb{R}$.

Given that $(x + 2)$ and $(x - 3)$ are factors of $f(x)$,

a form a pair of simultaneous equations in p and q,

b find the value of p and the value of q,

c factorise $f(x)$ completely,

d sketch the curve with equation $y = f(x)$.

The curve with equation $y = f(x)$ meets the curve with equation $y = x^3$ in two points.

e Find the x-coordinates of the two points of intersection.

f Find the area of the finite region bounded by the curve with equation $y = f(x)$, the curve with equation $y = x^3$ and the positive x-axis.

38

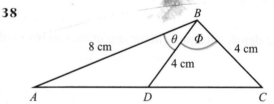

The diagram shows $\triangle ABC$ with $AB = 8$ cm, $BC = 4$ cm, $\angle ABD = \theta$ and $\angle DBC = \phi$. The mid-point of AC is D. By considering $\cos ADB$ and $\cos BDC$, or otherwise,

a show that $AC = 4\sqrt{6}$ cm.

By considering the areas of triangles ABC and DBC, or otherwise,

b show that $\sin(\theta + \phi) = \sin \phi$.

c Hence show that $\theta + 2\phi = 180°$.

39 $\quad$ A curve has equation $16y = x^2$. The x-coordinate of point P of the curve is 12.

a Find an equation, with integer coefficients, for the tangent to the curve at P.

b Find an equation, with integer coefficients, for the normal to the curve at P.

c Find the area of the triangle formed by the tangent at P, the normal at P and the y-axis.

The finite region bounded by the curve, the tangent at P and the y-axis is rotated through $360°$ about the y-axis.

d Find, in terms of π, the volume of the solid generated.

40 a Expand $\left(1 + \frac{x}{p}\right)^{\frac{1}{2}}$, where $p \neq 0$, in ascending powers of x, up to and including the term in x^3, simplifying your terms as far as possible.

Given that the coefficient of x is twice the coefficient of x^3,

b find the possible values of p.

41 A solid rectangular block has volume 486 cm^3. The width of the block is x cm, the length is $3x$ cm and the height is h cm.

a Show that $x^2 h = 162$.

The total surface area of the block is $A \text{ cm}^2$.

b Show that $A = 6x^2 + \dfrac{1296}{x}$.

c Find, to 3 significant figures, the value of x such that $\dfrac{dA}{dx} = 0$.

d Show that this value of x gives a minimum value of A.

e Find, to 3 significant figures, the minimum value of A.

42 a Show that $\displaystyle\sum_{r=1}^{n} r = \frac{n(n+1)}{2}$.

b Hence, or otherwise, find the sum of all the integers from 1 to 99 inclusive which are not multiples of 5.

43 a Expand $(1 - 6x)^{\frac{1}{3}}$ in ascending powers of x up to and including the term in x^2, simplifying each term.

b By substituting $x = \dfrac{1}{27}$ into your expansion, obtain an approximation, to 6 significant figures, for $\sqrt[3]{21}$.

c Calculate the percentage error, to 2 significant figures, in the approximation obtained in part **b**.

Given that $\dfrac{(1 - 6x)^{\frac{1}{3}}}{(1 + x)^3} \equiv a + bx + cx^2 + \dots$

d find the values of a, b and c,

e state the range of values for x which the series $a + bx + cx^2 + \dots$ converges.

44 Find an equation, with integer coefficients, for the perpendicular bisector of the line joining the points $(5, 9)$ and $(11, -3)$.

45 The region enclosed by the curve with equation $y = e^{2x} + 4$, the x-axis, the y-axis and the line $x = 2$ is rotated through $360°$ about the x-axis. Find, in terms of e and π, the volume of the solid generated.

46 Using $\cos(A + B) \equiv \cos A \cos B - \sin A \sin B$,

a show that $\cos^2 \theta \equiv \frac{1}{2}(\cos 2\theta + 1)$.

$$f(\theta) = 8 \cos^4 \theta - 4 \cos^2 \theta - 1.$$

b Show that $f(\theta) = \cos 4\theta + 2 \cos 2\theta$.

c Solve the equation

$$8 \cos^4 \theta° - 4 \cos^2 \theta° - 2 \cos 2\theta° = 1.5. \text{ for } 0 \leqslant \theta \leqslant 180.$$

Given that $\int_0^{\frac{\pi}{3}} f(\theta)d\theta = k\sqrt{3}.$

d find the value of k.

47 A curve has equation $y = 2 + \dfrac{1}{x + 1}, x \neq -1.$

   a Find an equation of the asymptote to the curve which is parallel to
       i the x-axis.   **ii** the y-axis.

   b Find the coordinates of the points where the curve crosses the coordinate axes.

   c Sketch the curve, showing clearly the asymptotes and the coordinates of the points where the curve crosses the coordinate axes.

48 A particle P moves in a straight line. At time t seconds, the velocity v m/s, of P is given by $v = t^2 - 2t + 9$. Find

   a the acceleration of P, in m/s^2, when $t = 3$.

   b the distance P travels in the interval $0 \leqslant t \leqslant 6$.

49

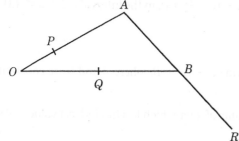

In the diagram $\overrightarrow{OA} = \mathbf{a}$ and $\overrightarrow{OB} = \mathbf{b}$. The point P divides OA in the ratio $1 : 2$. and Q is the midpoint of OB.

   a Find $\overrightarrow{PQ}$, in terms of $\mathbf{a}$ and $\mathbf{b}$.

R is the point on AB produced such that $OR = 2\mathbf{b} - \mathbf{a}$.

   b Find $\overrightarrow{PR}$, in terms of $\mathbf{a}$ and $\mathbf{b}$.

   c Hence show that P, Q and R are collinear.

50 Differentiate with respect to x.

   a $y = 5x^2 \cos 3x.$

   b $y = \dfrac{e^{3x}}{x^2 + 3}.$

51 The volume of a right conical pile of sand is increasiong at a constant rate of 0.75 m^3/s. The height. h metres. of the cone is always equal to the diameter of the base of the cone. Find. to 3 significant figures. the rate of increase of the radius of the base when $h = 1.5$.

52 In $\triangle ABC$, $AB = 2x$ cm, $BC = 5$ cm, $AC = (2x + 3)$ cm and $\angle BAC = 60°$.

    a Find, to 3 significant figures, the value of x.

    Using your value of x,

    b find, in degrees to 1 decimal place, the size of $\angle ACB$.

53 Find the set of values of p for which the equation $x^2 + 2px + (10 - 3p) = 0$ has real, unequal roots.

54 **a** Copy and complete the table for $y = 2x - \dfrac{1}{x^2}$, giving the values of y to 3 significant figures where appropriate

x	0.5	1.0	1.5	2.0	2.5	3.0	3.5	4.0
y	-3		2.56		4.84			7.94

    b Using a scale of 4 cm to 1 unit on the x-axis and 2 cm to 1 unit on the y-axis, draw the graph of $y = 2x - \dfrac{1}{x^2}$ for $0.5 \leqslant x \leqslant 4.0$.

    c Express $2x - \dfrac{1}{x^2}$ as a single fraction, and hence use your graph to estimate, to 2 significant figures, the value of $\sqrt[3]{0.5}$.

    d By drawing a suitable straight line on your graph, find an estimate, to 2 significant figures, of the root of the equation $3x - 6 - \dfrac{1}{x^2} = 0$, in the interval $0.5 \leqslant x \leqslant 4.0$.

55 $f(x) = x^2 - 7x + 10$.

    Given that $f(x)$ can be expressed in the form $(x + A)^2 + B$, where A and B are constants,

    a find the value of A and the value of B.

    b Hence, or otherwise, determine the value of x for which $f(x)$ has its least value and state this least value.

    The curve C has equation $y = x^2 - 7x + 10$. The line l with equation $y = x + 3$ intersects the curve C at two points.

    c Find the coordinates of each of these two points.

    d Find the coordinates of the points where the curve intersects the x-axis.

    e Sketch, on the same axes, the curve C and the line l.

    f Find the area of the region bounded by the curve C, the line l and the lines $x = 2$ and $x = 5$.

56 Solve the equations

$$y - 2x = 5,$$
$$2x^2 + 2xy + y^2 = 5.$$

57 $f(x) = 2x^2 + px - 6$.

    The equation $f(x) = 0$ has roots α and β. Without solving the equation,

    a find, in terms of p,

      i $\alpha^2 + \beta^2$,   **ii** $\alpha^2\beta^2$.

Given that $\alpha - \beta = 4$,

b find the possible values of p.

Given that p is positive,

c form an equation with roots α^2 and β^2.

58 The third, fourth and fifth terms of a geometric series are $(5x - 9)$, $(7x - 3)$ and $(12x + 4)$ respectively.

a Determine the two possible values of x.

Given that all the terms of the series are positive, find, for the series,

b the common ratio,

c the first term,

d the sum of the first 12 terms.

59 Differentiate, with respect to x,

a $y = (5x^2 - 2)e^{2x}$,

b $y = \dfrac{x^3 + 2}{x - x^2}$, simplifying your answer.

60 Find the exact solution of the equation
$$\frac{32}{e^x} - e^x = 4.$$

61 Triangle LMN has $LM = 5$ cm, $LN = 8.2$ cm and $MN = 6.4$ cm. Calculate, in degrees to the nearest $0.1°$, the size of $\angle LMN$.

62 A curve has equation $y = 3x^2 - 7x + 5$. The point P on the curve has x-coordinate 2. The tangent and the normal to the curve at P meet the x-axis at A and B respectively. Find the area of $\triangle APB$.

63 a Expand $(1 + \frac{1}{4}x)^{\frac{1}{3}}$ in ascending powers of x, up to and including the term in x^2, simplifying each term as far as possible.

b Expand $(1 - \frac{1}{4}x)^{-\frac{1}{3}}$ in ascending powers of x, up to and including the term in x^2, simplifying each term as far as possible.

c State the range of values of x for which both of your expansions are valid.

Using your answers to parts **a** and **b**,

d expand $\left(\dfrac{4 + x}{4 - x}\right)^{\frac{1}{3}}$ in ascending powers of x, up to and including the term in x^2, simplifying each term as far as possible.

e Hence obtain an estimate, to 3 significant figures, of $\displaystyle\int_{0}^{0.3} \left(\dfrac{4 + x}{4 - x}\right)^{\frac{1}{3}} dx$.

64 Using the identities
$$\cos(A + B) \equiv \cos A \cos B - \sin A \sin B$$
$$\sin(A + B) \equiv \sin A \cos B + \cos A \sin B,$$
express

a $\cos 2A$ in terms of $\cos A$,

b $\sin 2A$ in terms of $\sin A$ and $\cos A$, simplifying your answer.

c Hence show that $\cos 3A \equiv 4\cos^3 A - 3\cos A$.

d Solve, for $0 \leqslant x \leqslant 180°$, the equation $4\cos^3 x - 3\cos x = 0.6$, giving your solutions to one decimal place.

e Evaluate $\int_0^{\frac{\pi}{7}} \cos^3 \theta \, d\theta$, giving your answer in the form $\frac{a}{b}\sqrt{c}$, where a, b and c are integers.

65 Find the coordinates of the points of intersection of the curve with equation $y = x^2 - 8x + 11$ and the line with equation $x + y = 5$.

66 a Expand $(p + qx)^5$, simplifying each term as far as possible.

In the expansion of $(p + qx)^5$, $p \neq 0$, $q \neq 0$, the coefficient of x^4 is twice the coefficient of x^2. Also, when $x = 2$, the value of $(p + qx)^5$ is 7776.

b Find the possible pairs of values of p and q.

67 Solve the equation

a $\log_p 243 = 5$,

b $\log_4(3q + 4) = 3$.

$$f(x) = 2x\log_x 3 - 5\log_x 9 - x + 5$$

c Find the value of a and the value of b so that $f(x) = (x - 5)(a\log_x 3 - b)$.

d Hence solve the equation $f(x) = 0$.

68 The points A, B and C have coordinates $(2, 6)$, $(6, 8)$ and $(4, 2)$ respectively.

a Find the exact lengths of

    i AB,   **ii** BC,   **iii** AC.

b Find the size of each angle of $\triangle ABC$.

A circle is drawn to pass through the points A, B and C. Find

c the coordinates of the centre of the circle,

d the exact length of the radius of the circle.

69 Solve, for $-180° \leqslant \theta < 180°$, $6\sin^2 \theta - 7\cos \theta = 1$

70 A right pyramid $ABCDE$ has a square base $ABCD$ of side 5 cm. The height of the pyramid is 6 cm. Find, in degrees to 1 decimal place, the angle between the plane ABE and the base.

71 The third and fifth terms of an arithmetic series are given by $\log pq^4$ and $\log pq^8$ respectively, $q \neq 1$.

The common difference of the series is $b \log q$, where b is a constant. Find

a the value of b,

b the first term of the series.

The sum of the first n terms of the series can be written in the form $s \log pq^r$.

c Express r and s in terms of n.

Given that the sum of the first 16 terms of the series is 10 times the sum of the first 4 terms of the series,

d   show that $\log p = 5 \log q$.

72 $f(x) = 3x^2 - 6x + p$.

The equation $f(x) = 0$ has roots α and β. Without solving the equation $f(x) = 0$,

a   form a quadratic equation, with integer coefficients, which has roots $(\alpha + \beta)$ and

$\dfrac{1}{\alpha + \beta}$.

b   form a quadratic equation which has roots $\dfrac{\alpha + \beta}{\alpha}$ and $\dfrac{\alpha + \beta}{\beta}$.

Given that 3 is a root of the equation found in part **b**, find

c   the value of p,

d   the other root of the equation.

73   Find the set of values of p for which the equation $x^2 - 2px + (12 - p) = 0$ has no real roots.

(All questions © Edexcel Limited)

Revision tips and techniques

Revision tips

We all learn differently, so some of these revision tips will suit you and others may not. Try them out and see if they work for you.

Revision guidelines

- Start your revision early! You should start your revision at least three months before the IGCSE Further Pure Mathematics examinations.
- Plan your revision.
- Split the work into chunks.
- Go through the chunks to ensure you understand each piece of work. If you do not understand something, ask for help. You can ask your teacher or a friend who is also studying Further Pure Mathematics, but do not delay and hope the problem will go away. It won't. You will never learn anything really well unless you understand it.
- Summarise the work in a form you can go through easily the next time.
- Ensure that you have completed the summarising of the entire course at least a month before your exams start.
- Go through each summary at least twice more, referring back to more detailed notes where necessary. You could summarise your summaries!
- Make your revision active – do not just sit and read the textbook or your notes. Find activities to make yourself think about what you are doing.
- Remember that your two exam papers will test your skills as well as your knowledge and understanding. Practising past exam questions will help you to make sure you know what the examiner wants you to do.

Revision aims

When you revise, you are trying to:

1. Improve your memory
   You are trying to increase your knowledge and understanding of mathematics, but your brain quickly forgets. Most of what you try to learn by heart you will forget over the next few days. Nevertheless, you can help your brain to remember by using different revision techniques.

2. Organise what you have studied
   If you organise what you have studied so that it all makes better sense, you will be able to remember more of it. You can organise it by linking together the main ideas. Remembering one idea will help you remember another.

3. Improve your understanding
   If you can improve your understanding of mathematics, you will find that your skills also improve.

Splitting the work into chunks

It is very much up to you how you do this. For example, you might like to split all of your Further Pure Mathematics work up according to the arrangement of your notes – the chunks in which you were taught. Or you might like to do it using groups of chapters in your textbook. Just doing this exercise will help you to learn, because it makes you think about the subject as a whole and how each part relates to other parts.

It is also worth making a list of individual topics with minimal detail under each heading: simply key words and key equations.

The process of doing these summaries is a really good way of getting your brain to think hard about what you need to know, which in itself is very useful revision. It's much better than just learning things from a revision guide, where someone else has done the summarising.

How long should I spend revising?

You are far better off doing a sensible amount of quality revision rather than hour after hour of meaningless reading. Lots of people find they cannot concentrate for periods of much more than 20 minutes. If that is you, then take a short break every 20 minutes – make a cup of coffee or get some fresh air for a few minutes before going back to your work.

After about an hour and a half take a longer break of at least fifteen minutes, and do something completely different. Other people find they work best by settling down to concentrate for a longer period – say 45 minutes – when they think only about their work and nothing else, and then take a longer break.

If you have done the preparatory work described above, you should not need to spend hours cramming the night before. All you should need to do is a quick run through the basics and a check on anything that you are unsure of. That way, you can get to bed early and arrive at the examination room refreshed and ready to demonstrate your knowledge, skills and understanding.

Where should I do my revision?

Ideally you should have your own private space where you can work undisturbed. If you are unable to find your own private space, find somewhere without any immediate distractions (such as a television). Some people like to play music as they work – others don't. If you do, make sure you are concentrating on your work, not the music!

Some important points to remember

- Make your revision active. You should always be doing something active to force your brain to work. Just staring at notes or the textbook is no good.
- Keep fit. Take exercise. Eat healthily. Take breaks to do things you enjoy. Try not to worry.

Revision techniques

You need to make your revision active. In order to break the course down into chunks that you can usefully revise, you really need to think about the subject material. When you come to summarise the chunks, you have to think about it again. By the time you are one month away from your examination, you should have already gone through the work at least twice. Now comes the intensive learning, so here are some suggestions to help you do this.

Sticky notes

Do you have difficulty remembering formulae? One way is to write the formulae on sticky notes (or small cards) and stick them on your bedroom or bathroom mirror, so that you see them every time you look in the mirror. If they are on your bathroom mirror, you can test yourself while you are brushing your teeth!

Answering practice questions

It is a good idea to answer practice questions on a topic when you revise it. You will need the help of your teacher to mark it and provide you with feedback very soon afterwards. It is also helpful, during the early part of the revision period, to work through some questions with your teacher to show you how to plan a good answer in the time allowed.

How to revise using this book

The topics in this book have been arranged in a logical sequence so you can work your way through them from beginning to end. However, how you work on them depends on how much time there is between now and your examination.

If you have plenty of time before the examination, you can work through each topic in turn, reading the examples and trying the questions from the mixed exercises.

If you are short of time, you should look at the summary of key points at the end of each chapter and then try some of the mixed exercise questions. However much time you have you should always allow some time to answer some past examination papers

Make sure you break your revision into short blocks of about 40 minutes, separated by five- or ten-minute breaks. Nobody can study effectively for hours without a break.

Exam advice

In this section you will find some key points to watch out for in your Further Pure Mathematics exam. They are based on common errors made by students in the past.

Chapter 1
Make sure you know the rules of logarithms and apply them carefully.

Don't make the classic error and write:

$$\log(x + 3) = \log x + \log 3$$

Chapter 3
When solving quadratic inequalities, remember to draw a sketch or use a table to make sure you get the correct interval.

Chapter 4
Make sure you know the graphs of the basic shapes.

Use a simple point on the graph to check you've not made a silly mistake (e.g if $x = 1$ is y positive or negative?).

Chapters 7 and 8
Remember that drawing a diagram often helps with vector questions and those involving coordinate geometry.

Chapter 9

Don't confuse the rules for integration and differentiation.

Don't forget the $+c$ when integrating.

Remember if you are differentiating $\sin x/3x$ it is not $\cos x/3$ but you must use the quotient rule.

Chapter 10

Always check the mode of your calculator for degrees or radians.

Remember there is a special formula for $\sin(x + y)$ – it is not equal to $\sin x + \sin y$.

Practice examination papers

You are expected to have an electronic calculator when answering these papers.

Paper 1

Time: 2 hours

1 In $\triangle ABC$, $AB = 5.7$ cm, $BC = 8.4$ cm and $\angle ACB$ is $42°$.
Find, to the nearest $0.1°$, the two possible sizes of $\angle BAC$. (4

(Total 4 marks

2 $$f(x) = x^3 + px^2 + qx - 36, \ p \text{ and } q \in \mathbb{Z}^+$$

The three roots of the equation $f(x) = 0$ are α, α and 4, where $\alpha \in \mathbb{Z}^+$.

a Show that $\alpha = 3$ (2

b Hence find the value of p and the value of q. (3

(Total 5 marks

3 The volume of a sphere is increasing at a rate of $25\ \text{cm}^3/\text{s}$.
Find the rate of increase of the surface area of the sphere when the radius is 2.5 cm. (6

(Total 6 marks

4 Solve the equations $xy = 6$,
$$xy + x + y = 11$$ (6

(Total 6 marks

5 Relative to a fixed origin O, the position vector of the point A is $3\mathbf{i} + 8\mathbf{j}$ and the position vector of the point B is $12\mathbf{i} + q\mathbf{j}$.

The point C divides AB internally in the ratio $1 : 2$ and $\overrightarrow{OC} = p\mathbf{i} + 4\mathbf{j}$.

a Find the value of p and the value of q. (5

The point D lies on OB and the line DC is parallel to OA. The mid-point of DC is M.

b Find, in terms of $\mathbf{i}$ and $\mathbf{j}$, the position vector of M. (3

(Total 8 marks

6

The figure shows the curve C_1 with equation $y^2 = 8x + 4$ and the curve C_2 with equation $y^2 = 8 - 4x$.

The curves C_1 and C_2 intersect at the points A and B.

a   Find the exact coordinates of A.   (3)

The shaded region enclosed by C_1, C_2 and the x-axis is rotated through $360°$ about the x-axis.

b   Find, in terms of π, the volume of the solid generated.   (6)

(Total 9 marks)

7   The sum, S_n, of the first n terms of an arithmetic series is given by $S_n = \frac{n}{4}(13 + 7n)$.
Find

a   the first term of the series.   (1)

b   the rth term of the series.   (3)

c   the common difference of the series.   (2)

The pth term of the series is a multiple of the first term.

b   Given that $p \neq 1$, find the least value of p.   (3)

(Total 9 marks)

8   **a**   Expand fully $(a + bx)^6$, simplifying each term as far as possible.   (4)

In the expansion of $(a + bx)^6$, $a \neq 0$, $b \neq 0$, the coefficient of x^3 is twice the coefficient of x^4. When $x = 3$ the value of $(a + bx)^6$ is $46\,656$.

b   Find the possible pairs of values of a and b.   (6)

(Total 10 marks)

9   Solve the equation

a $\log_x 125 = 3$ (2)

b $\log_4 (9y + 4) = 4$ (3)

c $3 - \log_3 p = \log_p 9$ (6)

(Total 11 marks)

10   The curve C_1, with equation $y = x^2$, meets the curve C_2, with equation $y = \dfrac{x^2}{x - 1}$, at the origin and at the point A.

Find

a   the coordinates of A.   (4)

b   an equation of the tangent to C_1 at A.   (4)

c   an equation of the tangent to C_2 at A.   (4)

The tangent to C_1 at A meets the y-axis at the point B and the tangent to C_2 at A meets the y-axis at the point D.

d   Find the area of $\triangle BAD$.   (3)

(Total 15 marks)

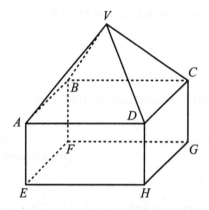

The figure shows a solid *VABCDEFGH* which consists of a cuboid *ABCDEFGH* and a right pyramid *VABCD*.

AB = 5 cm, *BC* = 12 cm, *EC* = 17 cm.

The height of the pyramid is 10 cm.

Calculate, in cm to 3 significant figures, the length of

a   *AE*,   (3)

b   *VA*.   (3)

Find, in degrees to the nearest 0.1°, the size of the angle between

c   *EC* and the plane *ABCD*,   (3)

d   the plane *VAB* and the plane *ABGH*,   (4)

e   the plane *VAB* and the plane *VCD*.   (4)

(Total 17 marks)

TOTAL FOR PAPER: 100 MARKS

Paper 2

Time: 2 hours

1   Differentiate with respect to x, $e^{2x} \sin 3x$. (3)

(Total 3 marks)

2   In $\triangle ABC$, $AB = 5\,\text{cm}$, $BC = 8.3\,\text{cm}$ and $AC = 6.9\,\text{cm}$.

   a   Find, in degrees, to the nearest $0.1°$, the size of $\angle ACB$. (3)

   b   Find, in cm^2, to 3 significant figures, the area of $\triangle ABC$. (3)

(Total 6 marks)

3   A curve has equation $y = 3 - \dfrac{2}{x - 2}$, $x \neq 2$

   a   Write down an equation of the asymptote to the curve which is parallel to
      i   the x-axis,   **ii**   the y-axis. (2)

   b   Calculate the coordinates of the point where the curve crosses
      i   the x-axis,   **ii**   the y-axis. (2)

   c   Sketch the curve, showing clearly the asymptotes and the coordinates of the
      points where the curve crosses the coordinate axes. (3)

(Total 7 marks)

4   **a**   Copy and complete the table for $y = e^x - 4x^2$, giving your values of y to 3 significant
      figures.

x	0	0.5	1.0	1.5	2.0	2.5	3.0	3.5	4.0
y	1	0.649		−4.52		−12.8		−15.9	

(2)

   b   Draw the graph of $y = e^x - 4x^2$ for $0 \leqslant x \leqslant 4.0$ (2)

   c   For each of the following equations, use your graph to obtain an estimate, to one
      decimal place, for the root between $x = 0$ and $x = 4$
      i $x^2 = \frac{1}{4}e^x + 2$
      ii $x = \ln(4x^2 - 3)$ (5)

(Total 9 marks)

5   A particle moves along a straight line.

   At time t seconds the velocity, $v\,\text{ms}^{-1}$, of the particle is given by $v = t^3 - 7t^2 + 12t$, $t \geqslant 0$

   a   Find the values of t for which the particle is instantaneously at rest. (3)

   b   Sketch the graph of $v = t^3 - 7t^2 + 12t$, $t \geqslant 0$ (2)

   c   Find, to 3 significant figures, the total distance travelled by the particle in the
      interval $0 \leqslant t \leqslant 4$ (4)

(Total 9 marks)

6   The sum to infinity of a convergent geometric series is $80x$, $x > 0$, and the sum
   of the first four terms is $75x$.

   a   Find the possible values of the common ratio of the series. (4)

Given that the first term of the series is greater than $100x$,

   b   find, in terms of x, the first term of the series.   (3)

Given that the fifth term of the series is 30

   c   find the value of x.   (3)

(Total 10 marks)

7   The curve with equation $y = 4e^{2x}$ meets the curve with equation $y = (e^{2x} - 3)^2$
at the points A and B.

   a   Find the coordinates of A and the coordinates of B.   (6)

   b   Find, to 4 significant figures, the length of AB.   (2)

The point C has coordinates $(5, 0)$.

   c   Find, to 3 significant figures, the area of $\triangle ABC$.   (4)

(Total 12 marks)

8   A solid metal cube of side 5 cm is melted down and all the metal is used to make
a right cylinder.
The radius of the cylinder is r cm and the height is h cm.
The total surface area of the cylinder is A cm^2.

   a   Show that $A = \dfrac{250}{r} + 2\pi r^2$ (4)

   b   Find, to 3 significant figures, the value of r for which $\dfrac{dA}{dr} = 0$ (3)

   c   Show that the value of r found in part **b** gives a minimum value of A.   (3)

   d   Find, to 3 significant figures, the minimum value of A.   (2)

(Total 12 marks)

9   **a**   Show that $(\alpha + \beta)(\alpha^2 - \alpha\beta + \beta^2) = \alpha^3 + \beta^3$

                        $(\alpha - \beta)(\alpha^2 + \alpha\beta + \beta^2) = \alpha^3 - \beta^3$ (3)

                        $f(x) = x^2 + 7x + 3, \, x \in \mathbb{R}$

The equation $f(x) = 0$ has roots α and β where $\alpha > \beta$.

Without solving the equation, calculate the value of

   b $\alpha^3 + \beta^3$,   (3)

   c $(\alpha - \beta)^2$.   (2)

Hence

   d   calculate the exact value of $\alpha^3 - \beta^3$,   (3)

   e   form a quadratic equation, with integer coefficients, with roots $\dfrac{\alpha}{\beta^2}$ and $\dfrac{\beta}{\alpha^2}$.   (4)

(Total 15 marks)

10 $\sin(A + B) \equiv \sin A \cos B + \cos A \sin B$,

        $\cos(A + B) \equiv \cos A \cos B - \sin A \sin B$.

   a   By writing $\tan(A + B) \equiv \dfrac{\sin(A + B)}{\cos(A + B)}$, prove that $\tan(A + B) \equiv \dfrac{\tan A + \tan B}{1 - \tan A \tan B}$.   (3)

Practice examination papers

b Hence or otherwise, find the exact value of
   i tan 75°.   **ii** tan 15°.
   simplifying your answers as far as possible.   (5)

c Use the result in **a** to write down an expression for $\tan 2\theta$ in terms of $\tan \theta$.   (1)

d Hence find the exact value of $\tan 22.5°$.   (4)

Given that $\tan \theta = \frac{2}{5}$ and θ is an acute angle,

e find the exact value of $\sin 2\theta$.   (4)
                     (Total 17 marks)

TOTAL FOR PAPER: 100 MARKS

(All questions © Edexcel Limited)

Appendix : Formulae, notation and symbols

This appendix gives formulae that students are expected to remember and will not be included on the examination paper.

Logarithmic functions and indices

$$\log_a xy = \log_a x + \log_a y$$

$$\log_a \frac{x}{y} = \log_a x - \log_a y$$

$$\log_a x^k = k \log_a x$$

$$\log_a \frac{1}{x} = -\log_a x$$

$$\log_a a = 1$$

$$\log_a x = \frac{\log_b x}{\log_b a}$$

$$\log_a 1 = 0$$

$$\log_a b = \frac{1}{\log_b a}$$

Quadratic equations

$ax^2 + bx + c = 0$ has roots given by $x = \dfrac{-b \pm \sqrt{b^2 - 4ac}}{2a}$

When the roots of $ax^2 + bx + c = 0$ are α and β then $\alpha + \beta = -\dfrac{b}{a}$ and $\alpha\beta = \dfrac{c}{a}$

and the equation can be written $x^2 - (\alpha + \beta)x + \alpha\beta = 0$

Series

Arithmetic series: nth term $= a + (n - 1)d$

Sum to n terms $= \dfrac{n}{2}\{2a + (n - 1)d\}$

Geometric series: nth term $= ar^{n-1}$

Sum to n terms $= \dfrac{a(r^n - 1)}{r - 1}$

Sum to infinity $= \dfrac{a}{1 - r} \quad |r| < 1$

Binomial series

For $|x| < 1, n \in \mathbb{Q}$

$$(1 + x)^n = 1 + nx + \frac{n(n - 1)}{2!}x^2 + \ldots + \frac{n(n - 1) \ldots (n - r + 1)}{r!}x^r + \ldots$$

Coordinate geometry

The gradient of the line joining two points (x_1, y_1) and (x_2, y_2) is $\dfrac{y_2 - y_1}{x_2 - x_1}$

The distance d between two points (x_1, y_1) and (x_2, y_2) is given by

$$d^2 = (x_1 - y_1)^2 + (x_2 - y_2)^2$$

The coordinates of the point dividing the line joining (x_1, y_1) and (x_2, y_2) in the ratio

$m:n$ are $\left(\dfrac{nx_1 + mx_2}{m + n}, \dfrac{ny_1 + my_2}{m + n} \right)$

Calculus

Differentiation:

function	derivative
x^n	nx^{n-1}
$\sin ax$	$a \cos ax$
$\cos ax$	$-a \sin ax$
e^{ax}	ae^{ax}
$f(x)g(x)$	$f'(x)g(x) + f(x)g'(x)$
$\dfrac{f(x)}{g(x)}$	$\dfrac{f'(x)g(x) - f(x)g'(x)}{(g(x))^2}$
$f(g(x))$	$f'(g(x))g'(x)$

Integration:

function	integral
x^n	$\dfrac{1}{n+1}x^{n+1} + c \quad n \neq -1$
$\sin ax$	$-\dfrac{1}{a}\cos ax + c$
$\cos ax$	$\dfrac{1}{a}\sin ax + c$
e^{ax}	$\dfrac{1}{a}e^{ax} + c$

Area and volume:

Area between a curve and the x axis $= \displaystyle\int_a^b y\,dx, \; y \geqslant 0$

$\left| \displaystyle\int_a^b y\,dx \right|, \; y < 0$

Area between a curve and the y-axis $= \displaystyle\int_c^d x\,dy, \; x \geqslant 0$

$\left| \displaystyle\int_c^d x\,dy \right|, \; x < 0$

Area between $g(x)$ and $f(x) = \displaystyle\int_a^b |g(x) - f(x)|\,dx$

Volume of revolution $= \displaystyle\int_a^b \pi y^2\,dx \; $ or $ \; \displaystyle\int_c^d \pi x^2\,dy$

Trigonometry

Radian measure: length of arc $= r\theta$

$$\text{area of sector} = \tfrac{1}{2}r^2\theta$$

In triangle ABC: $\dfrac{a}{\sin A} = \dfrac{b}{\sin B} = \dfrac{c}{\sin C}$

$$a^2 = b^2 + c^2 - 2bc\cos A$$

$$\cos^2\theta + \sin^2\theta = 1$$

$$\text{area of a triangle} = \tfrac{1}{2}ab\sin C$$

Notation

$\mathbb{N}$	the set of positive integers and zero, $\{0, 1, 2, 3, ...\}$
$\mathbb{Z}$	the set of integers, $\{0, \pm 1, \pm 2, \pm 3, ...\}$
$\mathbb{Z}^+$	the set of positive integers, $\{1, 2, 3, ...\}$
$\mathbb{Q}$	the set of rational numbers
$\mathbb{Q}^+$	the set of positive rational numbers $\{x : x \in \mathbb{Q}, x > 0\}$
$\mathbb{R}$	the set of real numbers
$\mathbb{R}^+$	the set of positive real numbers $\{x : x \in \mathbb{R}, x > 0\}$
$\mathbb{R}_0^+$	the set of positive real numbers and zero $\{x : x \in \mathbb{R}, x \geqslant 0\}$
$\lvert x \rvert$	the modulus of x, $\lvert x \rvert = \begin{cases} x & \text{for } x \geqslant 0 \\ -x & \text{for } x < 0 \end{cases}$
$\approx$	is approximately equal to
$\displaystyle\sum_{r=1}^{n} f(r)$	$f(1) + f(2) + ... + f(n)$
$\dbinom{n}{r}$	the binomial coefficient $\dfrac{n!}{r!(n-r)!}$ for $n \in \mathbb{Z}^+$
	$\dfrac{n(n-1)...(n-r+1)}{r!}$ for $n \in \mathbb{R}$
$\ln x$	the natural logarithm of x, $\log_e x$
$\lg x$	the common logarithm of x, $\log_{10} x$
$f'(x), f''(x), f'''(x)$	the first, second and third derivatives of $f(x)$ with respect to x
$\lvert \mathbf{a} \rvert$	the magnitude of $\mathbf{a}$
$\lvert \overrightarrow{AB} \rvert$	the magnitude of $\overrightarrow{AB}$

Chapter 1

1.1
Exercise 1A

1 **a** x^7 **b** $6x^5$ **c** $2p^2$ **d** $3x^{-2}$
   e k^5 **f** y^{10} **g** $5x^8$ **h** p^2
   i $2a^3$ **j** $2p^{-7}$ **k** $6a^{-9}$ **l** $3a^2b^{-2}$
   m $27x^8$ **n** $24x^{11}$ **o** $63a^{12}$ **p** $32y^6$
   q $4a^6$ **r** $6a^{12}$

3 **a** ± 5 **b** ± 9 **c** 3 **d** $\frac{1}{16}$
   e $\pm\frac{1}{3}$ **f** $\frac{1}{125}$ **g** 1 **h** ± 6
   i $\pm\frac{125}{64}$ **j** $\frac{9}{4}$ **k** $\frac{5}{6}$ **l** $\frac{64}{49}$

1.2
Exercise 1B

1 $2\sqrt{7}$ **3** $5\sqrt{2}$ **5** $3\sqrt{10}$
7 $\sqrt{3}$ **9** $7\sqrt{2}$ **11** $-3\sqrt{7}$
13 $23\sqrt{5}$ **15** $19\sqrt{3}$ **17** $\frac{\sqrt{11}}{11}$
19 $\frac{\sqrt{5}}{5}$ **21** $\frac{1}{4}$ **23** $\frac{1}{3}$

1.3
Exercise 1C

1 **a** $\log_4 256 = 4$ **b** $\log_3\left(\frac{1}{9}\right) = -2$
   c $\log_{10} 1\,000\,000 = 6$ **d** $\log_{11} 11 = 1$
3 **a** 3 **b** 2 **c** 7 **d** 1
   e 6 **f** $\frac{1}{2}$ **g** -1 **h** 10
5 **a** 1.30 **b** 0.602 **c** 3.85 **d** -0.105

1.4
Exercise 1D

1 **a** $\log_2 21$ **b** $\log_2 9$ **c** $\log_5 80$
   d $\log_6\left(\frac{68}{81}\right)$ **e** $\log_{10} 120$
3 **a** $3\log_a x + 4\log_a y + \log_a z$
   b $5\log_a x - 2\log_a y$
   c $2 + 2\log_a x$
   d $\log_a x + \frac{1}{2}\log_a y - \log_a z$
   e $\frac{1}{2} + \frac{1}{2}\log_a$

1.5
Exercise 1E

1 **a** 2.460 **b** 3.465 **c** 4.248
   d 0.458 **e** 0.774
3 **a** 6.23 **b** 2.10 **c** 0.431 **d** 1.66

1.6
Exercise 1F

1 For graphs, please see online PDF
3 For graphs, please see online PDF

Exercise 1G

1 **a** y^8 **b** $6x^7$ **c** 32^x **d** $12b^9$
3 **a** $\frac{4}{9}$ **b** $\frac{3375}{4913}$
5 **a** $\frac{\sqrt{3}}{3}$ **b** $\frac{15}{\sqrt{5}}$
7 **a** 2.72 **b** 2.47
9 $\frac{1}{3}, 9$

Chapter 2

2.1
Exercise 2A

1 $x(x+4)$ **3** $(x+8)(x+3)$
5 $(x+8)(x-5)$ **7** $(x+2)(x+3)$
9 $(x-5)(x+2)$ **11** $(2x+1)(x+2)$
13 $(5x-1)(x-3)$ **15** $(2x-3)(x+5)$
17 $(x+2)(x-2)$ **19** $(2x+5)(2x-5)$
21 $4(3x+1)(3x-1)$ **23** $2(3x-2)(x-1)$

2.2
Exercise 2B

1 $(x+2)^2 - 4$ **3** $(x-8)^2 - 64$
5 $(x-7)^2 - 49$ **7** $3(x-4)^2 - 48$
9 $5(x+2)^2 - 20$ **11** $3\left(x+\frac{3}{2}\right)^2 - \frac{27}{4}$

2.3

Exercise 2C

1 $x = 0$ or $x = 4$ **3** $x = 0$ or $x = 2$

5 $x = -1$ or $x = -2$ **7** $x = -5$ or $x = -2$

9 $x = 3$ or $x = 5$ **11** $x = 6$ or $x = -1$

13 $x = -\frac{1}{2}$ or $x = -3$ **15** $x = -\frac{2}{3}$ or $x = \frac{3}{2}$

17 $x = \frac{1}{3}$ or $x = -2$ **19** $x = 13$ or $x = 1$

21 $x = \pm\frac{\sqrt{5}}{3}$ **23** $x = 1 \pm \frac{\sqrt{11}}{3}$

25 $x = -\frac{1}{2}$ or $x = \frac{7}{3}$ **27** $x = -3 \pm 2\sqrt{2}$

29 $x = 5 \pm \sqrt{30}$ **31** $x = \frac{3}{2} \pm \frac{\sqrt{29}}{2}$

33 $x = \frac{1}{8} \pm \frac{\sqrt{129}}{8}$ **35** $x = -\frac{3}{2} \pm \frac{\sqrt{39}}{2}$

2.4

Exercise 2D

1 $x = 1$

3 $x = 3.56$ or -0.562

5 $x = 0.781$ or -1.28

7 $x = 1.37$ or -1.70

9 $-3 \pm \frac{\sqrt{5}}{2}$, -0.38 or -2.62

11 $-3 \pm \sqrt{3}$, -1.27 or -4.73

13 $5 \pm \frac{\sqrt{31}}{3}$, -3.52 or 0.19

15 $9 \pm \frac{\sqrt{53}}{14}$, -0.12 or -1.16

17 2 or $-\frac{1}{4}$

2.5

Exercise 2E

1 **a** $x^2 + 8x - 1 = 0$
    b $x^2 - 6x + 8 = 0$

3 **a** $x^2 - 5x + 9 = 0$
    b $x^2 + 5x + 1 = 0$

Mixed Exercise 2F

1 **a** $x(3x + 4)$ **b** $2y(2y + 5)$
    c $x(x + y + y^2)$ **d** $2xy(4y + 5x)$

3 **a** $y = -1$ or -2 **b** $x = \frac{2}{3}$ or -5

    c $x = -\frac{1}{5}$ or 3 **d** $5 \pm \frac{\sqrt{7}}{2}$

5 **a** $p = 3, q = 2, r = -7$ **b** $-2 \pm \frac{\sqrt{7}}{3}$

7 ± 4

9 **a** $\alpha\beta = t, \alpha^2 + \beta^2 = 2t(2t - 1)$

    b $t = 1 + \frac{\sqrt{577}}{2}$

    c $x^2 - 2\sqrt{577}x + 1 = 0$

Chapter 3

3.1

Exercise 3A

1 **a** $x^2 + 5x + 3$ **b** $x^2 + x - 9$
    c $x^2 - 3x + 7$ **d** $x^2 - 3x + 2$
    e $x^2 - 3x - 2$

3 **a** $x^2 + 3x - 1$ **b** $x^2 - 1$
    c $2x^2 + x - 2$ **d** $2x^2 - x + 4$
    e $x^2 + 3x + 2$

3.2

Exercise 3B

1 $(x - 1)(x + 3)(x + 4)$

3 $(x - 5)(x - 4)(x + 2)$

5 **a** $(x + 1)(x - 5)(x - 6)$
    b $(x - 2)(x + 1)(x + 2)$
    c $(x - 5)(x + 3)(x - 2)$

7 2

9 $p = 3, q = 7$

3.3

Exercise 3C

1 -1 **3** 30

5 $8\frac{8}{27}$ **7** $p = 8, q = 3$

3.4

Exercise 3D

1 **a** $x = 5, y = 6$ or $x = 6, y = 5$

    b $x = 0, y = 1$ or $x = \frac{4}{5}, y = \frac{3}{5}$

    c $x = -1, y = -3$ or $x = 1, y = 3$

    d $x = 4\frac{1}{2}, y = 4\frac{1}{2}$ or $x = 6, y = 3$

    e $a = 1, b = 5$ or $a = 3, b = -1$

    f $u = 1\frac{1}{2}, v = 4$ or $u = 2, v = 3$

3 $(-1\frac{1}{6}, -4\frac{1}{2})$ and $(2, 5)$

5 a $x = 3 + \sqrt{13}, y = -3 + \sqrt{13}$ or $x = 3 - \sqrt{13},$
$y = -3 - \sqrt{13}$

b $x = 2 - 3\sqrt{5}, y = 3 + 2\sqrt{5}$ or $x = 2 + 3\sqrt{5},$
$y = 3 - 2\sqrt{5}$

3.5
Exercise 3E

1 a $x < 4$ **b** $x \geqslant 7$ **c** $x > 2\frac{1}{2}$

d $x \leqslant -3$ **e** $x < 11$ **f** $x < 2\frac{3}{5}$

g $x > -12$ **h** $x < 1$ **i** $x \leqslant ??$

j 8 **k** $x > 1\frac{1}{7}$

3 a $x > 2\frac{1}{2}$ **b** $2 < x < 4$ **c** $2\frac{1}{2} < x < 3$

d No values   **e** $x = 4$

3.6
Exercise 3F

1 a $3 < x < 8$ **b** $-4 < x < 3$

c $x < -2, x > 5$ **d** $x \leqslant -4, x \geqslant -3$

e $-\frac{1}{2} < x < 7$ **f** $x < -2, x > 2\frac{1}{2}$

g $\frac{1}{2} \leqslant ??$ **h** $x \leqslant ??$

i $1\frac{1}{2}$ **j** $x < \frac{1}{3}, x > 2$

k $-3 < x < 3$ **l** $x < -2\frac{1}{2}, x > \frac{2}{3}$

m $x < 0, x > 5$ **n** $-1\frac{1}{2} < ??$

o $x \leqslant ??$ **p** 0

3.7
Exercise 3G

1 $-3 \leqslant x < 4$

3 $2y + x \geqslant 10$ or $2y + x \leqslant 4$

5 $4x + 3y \leqslant 12, y \geqslant 0$ and $y < 2x + 4$

7 $x \geqslant 0, y \geqslant 0, y < -\dfrac{3x}{2+9}$ and $y \leqslant -\dfrac{2x}{3+6}$

9 For graph, please see online PDF

11 For graph, please see online PDF

13 £64 from 6 adults and 8 children

15 £282 from making 6 of ornament A and 14 of ornament B

Mixed Exercise 3H

1 $x = 4, y = 3\frac{1}{2}$

3 $x = -1\frac{1}{2}, y - 2\frac{1}{4}$ and $x = 4, y = -\frac{1}{2}$

5 $3 < x < 4$

7 $x < 0, x > 1$

9 $p = 1, q = 3$

11 7

13 a $p = 1, q = -15$ **b** $(x + 3)(2x - 5)$

15 a $(x - 1)(x + 5)(2x + 1)$ **b** $-5, -\frac{1}{2}, 1$

17 -18

19 $\frac{1}{2}, 3$

21 $\{y \geqslant 3$ and $2x + y \leqslant 6\}$

Chapter 4
4.1
Exercise 4A

1 For graph, please see online PDF

3 For graph, please see online PDF

4.2
Exercise 4B

1 For graph, please see online PDF

4.3
Exercise 4C

1 For graph, please see online PDF

3 For graph, please see online PDF

5 For graph, please see online PDF

4.4
Exercise 4D

1 a i For graph, please see online PDF

    ii 3

    iii $x^2 = x(x^2 - 1)$

b i For graph, please see online PDF

    ii 1

    iii $x(x + 2) = -\dfrac{3}{x}$

c i For graph, please see online PDF

    ii 3

    iii $x^2 = (x + 1)(x - 1)^2$

d i For graph, please see online PDF

    ii 2

    iii $x^2(1 - x) = -\dfrac{2}{x}$

e **i** For graph, please see online PDF

    ii 1

    iii $x(x-4) = \dfrac{1}{x}$

f **i** For graph, please see online PDF

    ii 3

    iii $x(x-4) = -\dfrac{1}{x}$

g **i** For graph, please see online PDF

    ii 1

    iii $x(x-4) = (x-2)^3$

h **i** For graph, please see online PDF

    ii 2

    iii $-x^3 = -\dfrac{2}{x}$

i **i** For graph, please see online PDF

    ii 2

    iii $-x^3 = x^2$

j **i** For graph, please see online PDF

    ii 3

    iii $-x^3 = -x(x+2)$

3 a For graph, please see online PDF

  b $(0,0); (2,18); (-2,-2)$

5 a For graph, please see online PDF

  b $(-3,9)$

7 a For graph, please see online PDF

  b Only 2 intersections

9 a For graph, please see online PDF

  b Graphs do not intersect.

11 a For graph, please see online PDF

   b $(0,0); (-2,-12); (5,30)$

13 a For graph, please see online PDF

   b $(0,-8); (1,-9); (-4,-24)$

4.5
Exercise 4E

1 $y = 4x - 4$

3 $y = 2x + 4$

5 $y = x - 4$

7 Asymptotes $x = -1$ and $y = 3$

9 Asymptotes $x = 1$ and $y = 2$

11 Asymptotes $x = 1, y = 2$

13 Asymptotes $x = 2, y = -4$

4.6
Exercise 4F

1 For graphs, please see online PDF

4.7
Exercise 4G

1 a $x = 1, y = 4.21; x = 5, y = 3.16$

  b Graph

  c (Draw $y = 4$) and $x \approx 1.35$

  d (Draw $y = x + 1$) intersection at $x \approx 2.55$

3 a $x = 1, y = 2 + \ln 1 = 2; x = 4, y = 3.39$

  b Graph

  c (Draw $y = 2.5$) and $x \approx 1.60$

  d (Draw $y = x$) intersection $x \approx 3.1$

Mixed Exercise 4H

1 a For graph, please see online PDF

  b $x = 0, -1, 2$; points $(0,0), (2,0), (-1,-3)$

3 a Graph

  b Graph

5 a Graph $(x = 0, y = 4.5)$

  b Graph $(x = 0, y = 2$ and $x \approx -0.86, y = 0)$

Chapter 5

5.1
Exercise 5A

1 Arithmetic sequences are **a, b, c, h, l**

3 a £5800   **b** £$(3800 + 200m)$

5.2
Exercise 5B

1 a $78, 4n - 2$ **b** $42, 2n + 2$

  c $23, 83 - 3n$ **d** $39, 2n - 1$

  e $-27, 33 - 3n$ **f** $59, 3n - 1$

  g $39p, (2n - 1)p$ **h** $-71x, (9 - 4n)x$

3 $d = 6$

5 24

7 $7 \times \frac{1}{2}, x = 8$

5.3
Exercise 5C

1 a 820   **b** 450   **c** -1140

  d -294 **e** 1440   **f** 1425

  g -1155 **h** $21(11x + 1)$

3 2550

5 1683, 32674

7 $d = -\frac{1}{2}, -5.5$

5.4

Exercise 5D

1 a $(3r + 1)$ **b** $(3r - 1)$
   c $4(11 - r)$ **d** $6r$

For epsilon pictures, please see online PDF

3 19

5.5

Exercise 5E

1 a Geometric $r = 2$ **b** Not geometric
   c Not geometric   **d** Geometric $r = 3$
   e Geometric $r = \frac{1}{2}$ **f** Geometric $r = -1$
   g Geometric $r = 1$ **h** Geometric $r = \frac{1}{4}$

3 a $3\sqrt{3}$ **b** $9\sqrt{3}$

5.6

Exercise 5F

1 a $486, 39\,366, 2 \times 3^{n-1}$
   b $\frac{25}{8}, \frac{25}{128}, \frac{100}{2^{n-1}}$
   c $-32, -512, (-2)^{n-1}$
   d $1.610\,51, 2.357\,95, (1.1)^{n-1}$

3 $a = 1, r = 2$

5 -6 (from $x = 0$), 4 (from $x = 10$)

5.7

Exercise 5G

1 a 255   **b** 63.938 (3 dp)
   c -728 **d** $546\frac{2}{3}$
   e 5460   **f** 19 680
   g 5.994 (3 dp)   **h** 44.938 (3 dp)

3 $2^{64} - 1 = 1.84\, x\, 10^{19}$

5 a 2.401   **b** 48.8234

7 22 terms

9 25 years

5.8

Exercise 5H

1 a $\frac{10}{9}$ **b** Doesn't exist
   c $6\frac{2}{3}$ **d** Doesn't exist
   e Doesn't exist   **f** $4\frac{1}{2}$
   g Doesn't exist   **h** 90
   i $\frac{1}{1} - r$ if $|r| < |$ **j** $\frac{1}{1} + 2x$ if $|x| < \frac{1}{2}$

---

3 $-\frac{2}{3}$

5 $\frac{40}{3} = 13\frac{1}{3}$

7 4

9 $r < 0$ because $S\infty < S_3, a = 12, r = -\frac{1}{2}$

Mixed Exercise 5I

1 a Add 6 to the previous term, i.e. $U_{n+1} = U_n + 6$
(or $U_n = 6n - 1$)
   b Add 3 to the previous term, i.e. $U_{n+1} = U_n + 3$
(or $U_n = 3n$)
   c Multiply the previous term by 3, i.e. $U_{n+1} = 3U_n$
(or $U_n = 3^{n-1}$)
   d Subtract 5 from the previous term,
i.e. $U_{n+1} = U_n - 5$ (or $U_n = 15 - 5n$)
   e The square numbers ($U_n = n^2$)
   f Multiply the previous term by 1.2, i.e. $U_{n+1} = 1.2U_n$
(or $U_n = (1.2)^{n-1}$)

Arithmetic sequences are:
a $a = 5, d = 6$
b $a = 3, d = 3$
c $a = 10, d = -5$

3 32

5 a $a = 25, d = -3$ **b** -3810

7 a 5   **b** 45

9 b $11k - \frac{9}{3}$ **c** 1.5   **d** 415

11 a 0.8235 (4 dp), $10x\,(0.7)^{n-1}$
   b $640, 5 \times 2^{n-1}$
   c $-4, 4 \times (-1)^{n-1}$
   d $\frac{3}{128}, 3 \times (-\frac{1}{2})^{n-1}$

13 a 9   **b** $\frac{8}{3}$
   c Doesn't converge   **d** $\frac{16}{3}$

15 b 200   **c** $333\frac{1}{3}$ **d** 8.95×10^{-4}

17 a $1, \frac{1}{3}, -\frac{1}{9}$

19 a $-\frac{1}{2}$ **b** $\frac{3}{4}, -2$ **c** 14

Chapter 6

6.1

Exercise 6A

1 $1 + 8x + 28x^2 + 56x^3$

3 $1 + 5x + \frac{45}{4}x^2 + 15x^3$

5 a $p = 5$ **b** -10 **c** -80

7 a $-20x^3$ **b** $120x^3$ **c** $1140x^3$

6.2

Exercise 6B

1. a $1 + 6x + 12x^2 + 8x3$, valid for all x
   b $1 + x + x^2 + x^3$, $|x| < 1$
   c $1 + \frac{1}{2}x - \frac{1}{8}x^2 + \frac{1}{16}x^3$, $|x| < 1$
   d $1 - 6x + 24x^2 - 80x^3$, $|x| < \frac{1}{2}$
   e $1 - x - x^2 - \frac{5}{3}x^3$, $|x| < \frac{1}{3}$
   f $1 - 15x + \frac{75}{2}x^2 + \frac{125}{2}x^3$, $|x| < \frac{1}{10}$
   g $1 - x + \frac{5}{8}x^2 - \frac{5}{16}x^3$, $|x| < 4$
   h $1 - 2x^2 + \dots$, $|x| < \frac{\sqrt{2}}{2}$

3. $1 + \frac{3x}{2} - \frac{9}{8}x^2 + \frac{27}{16}x^3$, $10.148\,891\,88$, accurate to 6 d.p.

5. N\A – you need to show the answer is in the question

Mixed Exercise 6C

1. a $p = 16$ b 270 c -1890
3. a $n = 8$ b $\frac{35}{8}$
5. a $1 - 12x + 48x^2 - 64x^3$, all x
   b $1 + 2x + 4x^2 + 8x^3$, $|x| < \frac{1}{2}$
   c $1 - 2x + 6x^2 - 18x^3$, $|x| < \frac{1}{3}$
7. $1 - \frac{3}{2}x^2 + \frac{27}{8}x^4 - \frac{135}{16}x^6$
9. a $n = -2, a = 3$
   b -108
   c $|x| < \frac{1}{3}$

Chapter 7

7.1

Exercise 7A

1. For graph, please see online PDF
3. $\sqrt{569} \approx 23.9$

7.2

Exercise 7B

1. a $2a + 2b$ b $a + b$ c $b - a$
3. a Yes ($\lambda\,2$) b Yes ($\lambda\,4$) c No
   d Yes ($\lambda\,-1$) e Yes ($\lambda\,-3$) f No
5. a $b - a, \frac{5}{6}(b - a), \frac{1}{6}a + \frac{5}{6}b$
   b $-\frac{1}{6}a + (\lambda - \frac{5}{6})b$
   c $-\mu a + (\mu - \lambda)b$
   d $\lambda = \frac{1}{2}, \mu = \frac{1}{6}$

7. a $-a + b$ b $\frac{1}{2}a + \frac{1}{2}b$
   c $\frac{3}{8}a\,\frac{3}{8}b$ d $-\frac{5}{8}a + \frac{3}{8}b$
   e $-a + kb$ f $5 : 3, k = 35$

7.3

Exercise 7C

1. $\frac{5}{6}a + \frac{1}{6}b$
3. $\overrightarrow{OC} = -2a + 2b$, $\overrightarrow{OD} = 3a + 2b$, $\overrightarrow{OE} = -2a + b$

7.4

Exercise 7D

1. a $\begin{pmatrix} 12 \\ 3 \end{pmatrix}$ b $\begin{pmatrix} -1 \\ 16 \end{pmatrix}$ c $\begin{pmatrix} -21 \\ -29 \end{pmatrix}$
3. a $\frac{1}{5}\begin{pmatrix} 4 \\ 3 \end{pmatrix}$ b $\frac{1}{13}\begin{pmatrix} 5 \\ -12 \end{pmatrix}$
   c $\frac{1}{25}\begin{pmatrix} -7 \\ 24 \end{pmatrix}$ d $\frac{1}{\sqrt{10}}\begin{pmatrix} 1 \\ -3 \end{pmatrix}$

Mixed Exercise 7E

1. $m = 3, n = 1$
3. a $\overrightarrow{XM}\begin{pmatrix} -1 \\ 3 \end{pmatrix}$
   $\overrightarrow{XZ} = \begin{pmatrix} -10 \\ 6 \end{pmatrix}$
   b $v\begin{pmatrix} 7 \\ 3 \end{pmatrix}$
   c $\begin{pmatrix} 8 \\ 0 \end{pmatrix} + w\begin{pmatrix} -10 \\ 6 \end{pmatrix}$
   d $v = \frac{2}{3}, w = \frac{1}{3}$
5. $v + w = \begin{pmatrix} 4 \\ 5 \end{pmatrix}, \sqrt{41}$
   $2v - w = \begin{pmatrix} 5 \\ -2 \end{pmatrix}, \sqrt{29}$
   $v - 2w = \begin{pmatrix} 1 \\ -7 \end{pmatrix}, \sqrt{50}$
7. a Chloe $\begin{pmatrix} 5 \\ 7 \end{pmatrix}$; Leo $\begin{pmatrix} 4 \\ 5 \end{pmatrix}$; Max $\begin{pmatrix} 3 \\ 2 \end{pmatrix}$
   b Chloe: 74 km, 2.9 km\h
   Leo: 41 km, 2.1 km\h
   Max: 13 km, 1.2 km\h

Chapter 8

8.1
Exercise 8A

1 a -2 b -1 c 3 d $\frac{1}{3}$
   e $\frac{2}{3}$ f $\frac{5}{4}$ g $\frac{1}{2}$ h 2
   i $\frac{1}{2}$ j $\frac{1}{2}$ k -2 l $\frac{3}{2}$

3 a $4x - y + 3 = 0$ b $3x - y - 2 = 0$
   c $6x + y - 7 = 0$ d $4x - 5y - 30 = 0$
   e $5x - 3y + 6 = 0$ f $7x - 3y = 0$
   g $14x - 7y - 4 = 0$ h $27x + 9y - 2 = 0$
   i $18x + 3y + 2 = 0$ j $2x + 6y - 3 = 0$
   k $4x - 6y + 5 = 0$ l $6x - 10y + 5 = 0$

5 $2x + 5y + 20 = 0$

7 $y = \frac{2}{3}x$

9 $(\frac{5}{3}, 0)$

8.2
Exercise 8B

1 a $\frac{1}{2}$ b $\frac{1}{6}$ c $\frac{3}{5}$ d 2
   e -1 f $\frac{1}{2}$ g $\frac{1}{2}$ h 8
   i $\frac{2}{3}$ j -4 k $\frac{1}{3}$ l $\frac{1}{2}$
   m 1 n $\dfrac{q^2 - p^2}{q - p} = q + p$

3 12

5 $2\frac{1}{4}$

7 26

8.3
Exercise 8C

1 a $y = 2x + 1$ b $y = 3x + 7$
   c $y = -x - 3$ d $y = -4x - 11$
   e $y = \frac{1}{2}x + 12$ f $y = \frac{2}{3}x - 5$
   g $y = 2x$ h $y = -\frac{1}{2}x + 2b$

3 $y = 2x + 8$

5 $-\frac{1}{5}$

7 $2x + 3y - 12 = 0$

9 $y = \frac{4}{3}x - 4$

8.4
Exercise 8D

1 a Perpendicular   b Parallel
   c Neither   d Perpendicular
   e Perpendicular   f Parallel
   g Parallel   h Perpendicular
   i Perpendicular   j Parallel
   k Neither   l Perpendicular

3 $4x - y + 15 = 0$

5 a $y = 3x + 11$ b $y = -\frac{1}{3}x + \frac{13}{3}$
   c $y = \frac{2}{3}x + 2$ d $y = -\frac{3}{2}x + \frac{17}{2}$

7 $7x - 4y + 2 = 0$

8.5
Exercise 8E

1 10 2 13 3 5
4 $\sqrt{5}$ 5 $2\sqrt{10}$ 6 $\sqrt{106}$
7 $\sqrt{113}$ 8 $a\sqrt{53}$ 9 $3b\sqrt{5}$
10 $5c$ 11 $d\sqrt{61}$ 12 $2e\sqrt{5}$

8.6
Exercise 8F

1 a $(3, 9)$ b $(0, 6)$ c $(0, 2)$ d $(2, 3\frac{2}{7})$

Mixed Exercise 8G

1 a $y = -3x + 14$ b $(0, 14)$
3 a $y = \frac{1}{7}x + \frac{12}{7}, y = -x + 12$ b $(9, 3)$
5 a $y = \frac{3}{2}x - \frac{3}{2}$ b $(3, 3)$
7 a $y = -\frac{1}{2}x = 3$ b $y = \frac{1}{4}x + \frac{9}{4}$
9 a $2x + y = 20$ b $y = \frac{1}{3}x + \frac{4}{3}$
11 a $(2, 7)$ b $x + 2y - 16 = 0$
    c $(0, 8)$
    d Area of triangle $ABD = 12.5$

Chapter 9

9.1
Exercise 9A

1 $7x^6$ 3 $4x^3$ 5 $\frac{1}{4}x^{-\frac{4}{3}}$
7 $-3x^{-4}$ 9 $-2x^{-3}$ 11 $-\frac{1}{3}x^{-\frac{4}{3}}$
13 $-2x^{-3}$ 15 $3x^2$ 17 $5x^4$

9.2

Exercise 9B

1 a $4x^3 - x^{-2}$ **b** $-x^{-3}$ **c** $-x^{-\frac{3}{2}}$

3 a $(2\frac{1}{2}, -6\frac{1}{4})$ **b** $(4, -4)$ and $(2, 0)$

   c $(16, -31)$ **d** $(\frac{1}{2}, 4), (-\frac{1}{2}, -4)$

5 a 1 **b** $\frac{2}{9}$ **c** -4 **d** 4

9.3

Exercise 9C

1 a $2e^{2x}$ **b** $-6e^{-6x}$

   c $e^x + 6x$ **d** $2\cos 2x$

   e $-3\sin 3x$ **f** $12\cos 4x - 12\sin 3x$

3 -2

5 -8

9.4

Exercise 9D

1 a $8(1 + 2x)^3$ **b** $6x(1 + x^2)^2$

   c $\dfrac{2}{\sqrt{3 + 4x}}$ **d** $6(x + 1)(x^2 + 2x)^2$

3 a $2\cos(2x + 1)$ **b** $-4x\sin(2x^2 + 4)$

   c $3\sin^2 x \cos x$ **d** $-4\sin 2x \cos 2x$

5 a $e^{2x}(1 + 2x)$ **b** $e^{-x}(2x - x^2 - 3)$

   c $e^{x^2}(6x^2 - 10x + 3)$

7 a $\dfrac{5}{(x + 1)^2}$ **b** $\dfrac{-4}{(3x - 2)^2}$

   c $\dfrac{-6x}{(2x - 1)^3}$

9 a $\dfrac{x\cos x - \sin x}{x^2}$ **b** $\dfrac{e^x(\sin x + \cos x)}{\cos^2 x}$

   c $\dfrac{2\sin x(\cos x - \sin x)}{e^{2x}}$

9.5

Exercise 9E

1 a $y + 3x - 6 = 0$

   b $4y - 3x - 4 = 0$

   c $y = x$

3 $y = -8x + 10, 8y - x - 145 = 0$

5 $y = \frac{1}{3}e$

7 $8y - 4x = 8 - \pi$

9.6

Exercise 9F

1 $\frac{1}{4}x^4 + x^2 + c$

3 $2x^{\frac{5}{2}} - x^3 + c$

5 $x^4 + x^{-3} + rx + c$

7 $\frac{2}{3}t^3 + 6t^{-\frac{1}{2}} + t + c$

9 $\dfrac{p}{5x^5} + 2tx - 3x^{-1} + c$

11 a $\frac{1}{2}x^4 + x3 + c$

   b $2x - \dfrac{3}{x} + c$

   c $\frac{4}{3}x^3 + 6x^2 + 9x + c$

   d $\frac{2}{3}x^3 + \frac{1}{2}x^2 - 3x + c$

   e $\frac{4}{5}x^{\frac{5}{2}} + 2x^{\frac{3}{2}} + c$

13 a $5e^x + 4\cos x + \dfrac{x^4}{2} + c$

   b $-2\cos x - 2\sin x + x^2 + C$

   c $5e^x + 4\sin x + \dfrac{2}{x} + c$

   d $e^x - \cos x + \sin x + C$

9.7

Exercise 9G

1 $10t$

3 a $40 + 10t$ **b** $70\,\text{m\textbackslash s}$

5 a $a = 32$ **b** $s = 16t^2 + 100t$

7 a $3t^2 + 8t - 5$ **b** $6t + 8$

   c $v = 6\,\text{m\textbackslash s}, a = 14\,\text{m\textbackslash s}^2$

9 a $a = 2t + 10$ **b** $a = 14\,\text{m\textbackslash s}^2$

   c $s = 32\frac{2}{3}$

9.8

Exercise 9H

1 a -28 **b** -17 **c** $-\frac{1}{5}$

3 a $(-\frac{3}{4}, -\frac{9}{4})$ **b** $(\frac{1}{2}, 9\frac{1}{4})$

   c $(-\frac{1}{3}, 1\frac{5}{27}), (1, 0)$ **d** $(3, -18), (-\frac{1}{3}, \frac{14}{27})$

   e $(1, 2), (-1, -2)$ **f** $(3, 27)$

5 $\left(\dfrac{3\pi}{8}, \dfrac{1}{\sqrt{2}}e^{\frac{3\pi}{4}}\right)$ maximum, $\left(\dfrac{7\pi}{8}, -\dfrac{1}{\sqrt{2}}e^{\frac{7\pi}{4}}\right)$ minimum

9.9

Exercise 9I

1 a 8 **b** $9\frac{3}{4}$ **c** $19\frac{2}{3}$

   d 21 **e** $8\frac{5}{12}$

3 a A(1, 3), B(3, 3)   **b** $1\frac{1}{3}$

5 a (2, 12)   **b** $13\frac{1}{3}$

9.10
Exercise 9J

1 $\frac{8}{9}\pi$

3 $15e^2$

5 2%

Exercise 9K

1 a $x = 4, y = 20$

b $\dfrac{d^2y}{dx^2} = \dfrac{15}{8} > 0 \therefore$ minimum

3 a $7\frac{31}{32}$

b $\dfrac{x^3}{3} - 2x - \dfrac{1}{x} - 2\frac{2}{3}$

c $f'(x) = \left(\dfrac{x-1}{x}\right)^2 > 0$ for all values of x.

5 a $y = 1 - \dfrac{x}{2} - \dfrac{\pi x}{4}$

c $\dfrac{2}{4+\pi}$ m^2 (0.280 m^2)

7 b $\dfrac{10}{3}$ **c** $\dfrac{d^2v}{dx^2} < 0 \therefore$ maximum

d $\dfrac{2300\pi}{27}$ **e** $22\frac{2}{9}\%$

9 b $x = \pm 2\sqrt{2}$, or $x = 0$

c $OP = 3$; $f''(x) > 0$ so minimum when $x = \pm 2\sqrt{2}$ (maximum when $x = 0$)

11 $3x^2 \cos 3x + 2x \sin 3x$

13 $x \cos x - \dfrac{\sin x}{x^2}$

15 $-(x^3 - 2x)e^{-x} + (3x^2 - 2)e^{-x}$

17 i $\frac{1}{2}x \sin 2x + \frac{1}{4}\cos 2x + c$

    ii $\pi\left(\dfrac{\pi^2}{4} + 1\right)$

Chapter 10

10.1
Exercise 10A

1 a 9°   **b** 12°   **c** 75°

d 90°   **e** 140°   **f** 210°

g 225°   **h** 270°   **i** 540°

3 a 0.479   **b** 0.156   **c** 1.74

d 0.909   **e** −0.897

5 a 0.873   **b** 1.31   **c** 1.75

d 2.79   **e** 4.01   **f** 5.59

10.2
Exercise 10B

1 a i 2.7   **ii** 2.025   **iii** 7.5π (23.6)

b i $16\frac{2}{3}$ **ii** 1.8   **iii** 3.6

c i $1\frac{1}{3}$ **ii** 0.8   **iii** 2

3 2π

5 a 10.4 cm   **b** $1\frac{1}{4}$

7 0.8

9 6.8 cm

10.3
Exercise 10C

1 a 19.2 cm^2 **b** 6.75π cm^2

c 1.296π cm^2 **d** 38.3 cm^2

e $5\frac{1}{3}\pi$ cm^2 **f** 5 cm^2

3 12 cm^2

5 $40\frac{2}{3}$ cm

7 8.88 cm^2

9 4.5 cm^2

11 78.4 cm

10.4
Exercise 10D

1 a $\dfrac{\sqrt{2}}{2}$ **b** $-\dfrac{\sqrt{3}}{2}$ **c** $-\dfrac{1}{2}$

d $\dfrac{\sqrt{3}}{2}$ **e** $\dfrac{\sqrt{3}}{2}$ **f** $-1\backslash 2$

g $\dfrac{1}{2}$ **h** $-\dfrac{\sqrt{2}}{2}$ **i** $\dfrac{-\sqrt{3}}{2}$

j $-\dfrac{\sqrt{2}}{2}$ **k** -1 **l** -1

m $\dfrac{\sqrt{3}}{3}$ **n** $-\sqrt{3}$ **o** $\sqrt{3}$

10.5
Exercise 10E

1 a $x = 84, y = 6.32$

b $x = 13.5, y = 16.6$

c $x = 85, y = 13.9$

d $x = 80, y = 6.22$ (Isosceles $\triangle$)

e $x = 6.27, y = 7.16$

f $x = 4.49, y = 7.49$ (right-angled

3 a $x = 74.6, y = 65.4$
  $x = 105, y = 34.6$
 b $x = 59.8, y = 48.4$
  $x = 120, y = 27.3$
 c $x = 56.8, y = 4.37$
  $x = 23.2, y = 2.06$

5 a $108(.2)°$ **b** $90°$ **c** $60°$
 d $52.6°$ **e** $137°$ **f** $72.2°$

7 a $155°$ **b** $13.7\,\text{cm}$

9 $6.50\,\text{cm}^2$

d L.H.S. $= \dfrac{\cos x \cos y - \sin x \sin y}{\sin x \sin y} + 1$
  $= \cot x \cot y - 1 + 1 = \cot x \cot y =$ R.H.S.

e L.H.S. $= \cos\theta \cos\dfrac{\pi}{3} - \sin\theta \sin\dfrac{\pi}{3} + \sqrt{3}\sin\theta$
  $= \dfrac{1}{2}\cos\theta - \dfrac{\sqrt{3}}{2}\sin\theta + \sqrt{3}\sin\theta$
  $= \dfrac{1}{2}\cos\theta - \dfrac{\sqrt{3}}{2}\sin\theta$
  $= \sin\dfrac{\pi}{6}\cos\theta + \cos\dfrac{\pi}{6}\sin\theta$
  $= \sin\left(\dfrac{\pi}{6} + \theta\right) =$ R.H.S.

10.6

Exercise 10F

1 a $11.7\,\text{cm}$ **b** $14.2\,\text{cm}$ **c** $34.4°$
 d $63.4°$

3 a $14.1\,\text{cm}$ **b** $17.3\,\text{cm}$ **c** $35.4°$

5 a $4.47\,\text{m}$ **b** $4.58\,\text{m}$ **c** $29.2°$
 d $12.6°$ **e** $26.6°$

7 a $43.3\,\text{cm}$ **b** $68.7\,\text{cm}$ **c** $81.2\,\text{cm}$

9 a $16.2\,\text{cm}$ **b** $67.9°$ **c** $55.3\,\text{cm}^2$
 d $71.6°$

11 a $30.3°$ **b** $31.6°$ **c** $68.9°$

13 a $15\,\text{m}$ **b** $47.7°$ **c** €91 300

15 $46.5\,\text{m}$

10.7

Exercise 10G

1 a $\dfrac{\sin^2\theta}{2}$ **b** 5 **c** $-\cos^2 A$
 d $\cos\theta$ **e** $\tan x^0$ **f** $\tan 3A$
 g 4 **h** $\sin^2\theta$ **i** 1

3 a $\sin 35°$ **b** $\sin 35°$ **c** $\cos 210°$
 d $\tan 31°$ **e** $\cos\theta$ **f** $\cos 7\theta$
 g $\sin 3\theta$ **h** $\tan 5\theta$ **i** $\sin A$
 j $\cos 3x$

5 a L.H.S. $= \sin A \cos 60° + \cos A \sin 60°$
  $+ \sin A \cos 60° - \cos A \sin 60°$
  $= 2\sin A \cos 60°$
  $= 2\sin A \left(\tfrac{1}{2}\right) = \sin A =$ R.H.S.

 b L.H.S. $= \dfrac{\cos A \cos B - \sin A \sin B}{\sin B \cos B} = \dfrac{\cos (A + B)}{\sin B \cos B}$
  $=$ R.H.S.

 c L.H.S. $= \dfrac{\sin x \cos y + \cos x \sin y}{\cos x \cos y}$
  $= \dfrac{\sin x \, \cancel{\cos y}}{\cos x \, \cancel{\cos y}} + \dfrac{\cancel{\cos x} \sin y}{\cancel{\cos x} \cos y}$
  $= \tan x + \tan y =$ R.H.S.

10.8

Exercise 10H

1 a $270°$ **b** $60°, 240°$
 c $60°, 300°$ **d** $15°, 165°$
 e $140°, 220°$ **f** $135°, 315°$
 g $90°, 270°$ **h** $230°, 310°$
 i $45.6°, 134.4°$ **j** $135°, 225°$

3 a $-\pi, 0, \pi, 2\pi$ **b** $-\dfrac{4\pi}{3}, -\dfrac{2\pi}{3}, \dfrac{2\pi}{3}$
 c $-\dfrac{7\pi}{4}, -\dfrac{5\pi}{4}, \dfrac{\pi}{4}, \dfrac{3\pi}{4}$ **d** $-0.14, 3.00, 6.14$

5 a $-\dfrac{7\pi}{12}, -\dfrac{\pi}{12}$ **b** $1.48, 5.85$

10.9

Exercise 10I

1 a $30°, 210°$
 b $135°, 315°$

3 a $60°, 120°, 240°, 300°$
 b $0°, 180°, 199°, 341°, 360°$
 c $60°, 300°$
 d $30°, 60°, 120°, 150°, 210°, 240°, 300°, 330°$
 e $270°$
 f $0°, 18.4°, 180°, 198°, 360°$
 g $194°, 270°, 346°$

Mixed Exercise 10I

1 a $\cos^2\theta \sin^2\theta$
 b $\sin^4 3\theta$
 c 1

3 a $2\sin 2\theta = \cos 2\theta \Rightarrow 2\sin 2\theta \setminus \cos 2\theta = 1$
  $\Rightarrow 2\tan 2\theta = 1 \Rightarrow \tan 2\theta = 0.5$
 b $13.3, 103.3, 193.3, 283.3$

5 a $\dfrac{11\pi}{12}, \dfrac{23\pi}{12}$ **b** $\dfrac{2\pi}{3}, \dfrac{5\pi}{6}, \dfrac{5\pi}{3}, \dfrac{11\pi}{6}$

7 $0, \pi, 2\pi$

9 a i $\dfrac{1}{2}$ **ii** $\dfrac{1}{2}$ **iii** $\sqrt{3}\backslash 3$

  b $23.8°, 203.8°$

Review exercise

1 a $A = 5, B = -\dfrac{5}{2}, C = -28\dfrac{1}{4}$

  b $f_{min} = -\dfrac{113}{4}, x = \dfrac{5}{2}$

2

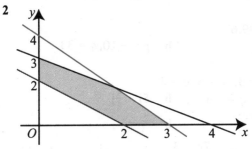

3 a 3 **b** $2\dfrac{1}{2}$ **c** $125\dfrac{1}{2}$

4 814

5 a – **b** $P = 126.8°, Q = R = 26.6°$

6 a i $\dfrac{1}{4}\mathbf{b} - \mathbf{a}$ **ii** $\dfrac{1}{3}\mathbf{a} + \dfrac{1}{6}\mathbf{b}$ **iii** $\dfrac{1}{3}\mathbf{a} - \dfrac{5}{6}\mathbf{b}$

  b $\dfrac{2}{5}$ **c** $\dfrac{2}{3}$

7 a – **b** $54.5°, 234.5°$

8 $4\dfrac{1}{2}$ m

9 $21.8°, 38.2°, 120°$

10 a $3.18, 6.69, 13.04$ **b** –

  c 2.3 **d** 0.6 (0.5 acceptable)

11 $x^6 - 18x^4 + 135x^2$

12 $-3 < p < 2$

13 –

14 a $(3.14), (5, 24)$ **b** $1\dfrac{1}{3}$

15 a – **b** 12 cm **c** $6\sqrt{3}$

  d $54.7°$ **e** $109.5°$

16 $\dfrac{1}{2}x\%$

17 a–b $(-3, -\dfrac{5}{3}), (2, \dfrac{5}{2})$ **c** $y = -\dfrac{6}{5}(x - 1)$

  d –

18 a $0.253, 2.89$ **b** $1.11, 2.68$

  c $1.91, 2.30$

19 a 625 **b** 2.64

  c $x = 2, y = 3$

20 –

21 $82.8°$

22 a $8\mathbf{i} - \mathbf{j}$ **b** –

23 $449\dfrac{2}{5}\pi$

24 a $\cos 2\theta = 2\cos^2\theta - 1$ **b** $\sin 2\theta = 2\sin\theta\cos\theta$

  c – **d** $0.767, 1.33, 2.86$ **e** 4

25 a -6 **b** 50 **c** 17

26 a $(2, 4), (5, 16)$ **b** $x \leqslant 2, x \geqslant 5$

27 a $-\mathbf{i} - 11\mathbf{j}$ **b** $\dfrac{13}{5}\mathbf{i} - \dfrac{2}{5}\mathbf{j}$

28 $73.9°$

29 a – **b** $12\,791$

30 $15\,200$

31 a $r = \dfrac{1}{2}, r = -3$ **b** 10

32 $46.5°, 133.5°$

33 $\dfrac{1}{2}$

34 a $2y + x = 25$ **b** $(25, 0)$ **c** $(10, 0)$

35 a 4 m/s^2 **b** $25\dfrac{1}{3}$ m

36 a $4y = x + 23$ **b** $y = -4x + 26$

  c $(-3, 38)$ **d** $6\dfrac{16}{17}$

  e $12\dfrac{28}{51}$

37 a $-2p + q = 28, 3p + q = 18$

  b $-2, 24$

  c $(x + 2)(x - 3)(x - 4)$

  d –

  e $-\dfrac{12}{5}, 2$

  f $7\dfrac{7}{12}$

38 –

39 a $2y = 3x - 18$ **b** $3y = -2x + 51$

  c 156 **d** 216π

40 a $1 + \dfrac{x}{2p} - \dfrac{x^2}{8p^2} + \dfrac{x^3}{16p^3}$

  b $p = \pm\dfrac{1}{2}$

41 a – **b** – **c** 4.76

  d – **e** 408

42 a – **b** 4000

43 a $1 - 2x - 4x^2$ **b** 2.76132

  c 0.087% **d** $a = 1, b = -5, c = 8$

  e $|x| < \dfrac{1}{6}$

44 $2y = x - 2$

45 $\pi[\dfrac{1}{4}e^8 + 4e^4 + 27\dfrac{3}{4}]$

46 a – **b** –

  c $15, 75, 105, 165$ **d** $\dfrac{3}{8}$

47 a i $y = 2$ **ii** $x = -1$

  b $(0, 3), (-\dfrac{3}{2}, 0)$

  c

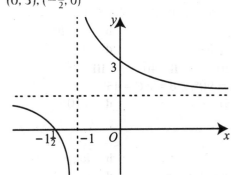

48 a $4\,\text{m/s}^2$ **b** $90\,\text{m}$

49 a $\frac{1}{2}\mathbf{b} - \frac{1}{3}\mathbf{a}$ **b** $2\mathbf{b} - \frac{4}{3}\mathbf{a}$ **c** –

50 a $\dfrac{dy}{dx} = 10x\cos 3x - 15x^2 \sin 3x$

   b $\dfrac{dy}{dx} = \dfrac{3e^{3x}(x^2 + 3) - 2x\,e^{3x}}{(x^2 + 3)^2}$

51 $0.212\,\text{m/s}$

52 a 1.39 **b** $28.7°$

53 $p < -5,\ p > 2$

54 a $1,\ 3.75,\ 5.89,\ 6.92$ **b**   –
   c 0.79 **d** 2.1

55 a $A = -\frac{7}{2},\ B = -\frac{9}{4}$ **b** $-\frac{9}{4},\ x = \frac{7}{2}$
   c $(1, 4),\ (7,10)$ **d** $(2, 0),\ (5, 0)$
   e –   **f** 24

56 $(-2, 1),\ (-1, 3)$

57 a **i** $\frac{p^2}{4} + 6$ **ii** 9 **b** $p = \pm 4$
   c $x^2 - 10x + 9 = 0$

58 a $-\frac{9}{11},\ 5$ **b** 2
   c 4 **d** $16\,380$

59 a $\dfrac{dy}{dx} = 10xe^{2x} + 2(5x^2 - 2)e^{2x}$

   b $\dfrac{dy}{dx} = \dfrac{2x^3 - x^4 + 4x - 2}{(x - x^2)^2}$

60 $\ln 4$

61 $91.1°$

62 $23\frac{2}{5}$

63 a $1 + \dfrac{x}{12} - \dfrac{x^2}{144}$ **b** $1 + \dfrac{x}{12} - \dfrac{x^2}{72}$

   c $|x| < 4$ **d** $1 + \dfrac{x}{6} - \dfrac{x^2}{72}$

   e 0.308

64 a $\cos 2A = 2\cos^2 A - 1$
   b $\sin 2A = 2\sin A \cos A$
   c –
   d $17.7°,\ 102.3°,\ 137.7°$
   e $\dfrac{3\sqrt{3}}{8}$

65 $(6, -1),\ (1, 4)$

66 a $p^5 + 5p^4qx + 10p^3q^2x + 10p^2q^3x + 5pq^4x^4 + q^5x^5$
   b $p = \frac{6}{5},\ q = \frac{12}{5}$ or $p = -2,\ q = 4$

67 a 3 **b** $q = 20$
   c $a = 2,\ b = 1$ **d** 9

68 a **i** $\sqrt{20}$ **ii** $\sqrt{40}$ **iii** $\sqrt{20}$
   b $\angle A = 90°,\ \angle B = \angle C = 45°$
   c $(5, 5)$ **d** $\sqrt{10}$

69 $\pm 60°$

70 $67.4°$

71 a 2 **b** $\log p$
   c $r = n - 1,\ s = n$ **d**   –

72 a $2x^2 - 5x + 2 = 0$ **b** $x^2 - \dfrac{12}{p}x + \dfrac{12}{p} = 0$
   c $\frac{8}{3}$ **d** $\frac{3}{2}$

73 $-4 < p < 3$

Practice examination papers

Paper 1

1 $80.4°$ or $99.6°$

2 a –   **b** $p = -10,\ q = 33$

3 $20\,\text{cm}^2/\text{s}$

4 $x = 2\ y = 3,\ x = 3\ y = 2$

5 a $p = 6,\ q = -4$ **b** $5\mathbf{i} + \frac{4}{3}\mathbf{j}$

6 a $\left(\frac{1}{3},\ 2\sqrt{\frac{5}{3}}\right)$ **b** $\frac{25}{3}\pi$

7 a 5 **b** $\dfrac{7r}{2} + \dfrac{3}{2}$ **c** $3\frac{1}{2}$ **d** 11

8 a $a^6 + 6a^5bx + 15a^4b^2x^2 + 20a^3b^3x^3 + 15a^2b^4x^4$
     $+\ 6ab^5x^5 + b^6x^6$
   b $a = 2\ b = \frac{4}{3},\ a = -2\ b = -\frac{4}{3}$

9 a 5 **b** 28 **c** $9, 3$

10 a $(2, 4)$ **b** $y = 4x - 4$
   c $y = 4$ **b** $8\,\text{units}^2$

11 a $11.0\,\text{cm}$ **b** $11.9\,\text{cm}$ **c** $40.1°$
   d $101.4°$ **e** $61.9°$

Paper 2

1 $2e^{2x}\sin 3x + 3e^{2x}\cos 3x$

2 a $37.0°$ **b** $17.2\,\text{cm}^2$

3 a **i** $y = 3$ **ii** $x = 2$ **b** **i** $\left(2\frac{2}{3}, 0\right)$ **ii** $(0, 4)$
   c

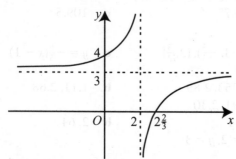

4 a

x	0	0.5	1.0	1.5	2.0	2.5	3.0	3.5	4.0
y	1	0.649	-1.28	-4.52	-8.61	-12.8	-15.9	-15.9	-9.40

  b graph drawn   **c** **i** 1.9   **ii** 1.3

5 a 0, 3, 4   **b** –   **c** 11.8 m

6 a $\pm\frac{1}{2}$ **b** $a = 120x$ **c** 4

7 a $(\ln 3, 36), (0, 4)$ **b** 32.02   **c** 82.2 units^2

8 a –   **b** 2.71   **c** –   **d** 138

9 a –   **b** -280 **c** 37

  d $46\sqrt{37}$ **e** $9x^2 + 280 + 3 = 0$

10 a –   **b** **i** $\dfrac{\sqrt{3} + 1}{\sqrt{3} - 1}$ **ii** $\dfrac{\sqrt{3} - 1}{\sqrt{3} + 1}$ Fully simplified form: **i** $2 + \sqrt{3}$ **ii** $2 - \sqrt{3}$

  c $\tan 2\theta = \dfrac{2 \tan \theta}{1 - \tan^2 \theta}$

  d $\sqrt{2} - 1$

  e $\frac{20}{29}$

6009